Chemically Modified Surfaces in Catalysis and Electrocatalysis

Chemically Modified Surfaces in Catalysis and Electrocatalysis

Joel S. Miller, EDITOR

Occidental Research Corporation

Based on a symposium jointly
sponsored by the Divisions of
Inorganic, Analytical, and
Petroleum Chemistry at the
182nd ACS National Meeting,
New York, New York,
August 23–25, 1981

ACS SYMPOSIUM SERIES 192

AMERICAN CHEMICAL SOCIETY
WASHINGTON, D. C.   1982

Library of Congress Cataloging in Publication Data

Chemically modified surfaces in catalysis and electrocatalysis.
(ACS symposium series, ISSN 0097–6156; 192)

Includes bibliographies and index.

1. Materials—Surfaces—Congresses. 2. Electrodes—
Congresses. 3. Catalysis—Congresses.
I. Miller, Joel S. II. Series.

TA418.7.C48 1982   600.2'9453   82–8731
ISBN 0–8412–0727–5 AACR2 ACSMC8 192 1–292
                                                      1982

ACS Symposium Series

M. Joan Comstock, *Series Editor*

FOREWORD

The ACS SYMPOSIUM SERIES was founded in 1974 to provide a medium for publishing symposia quickly in book form. The format of the Series parallels that of the continuing ADVANCES IN CHEMISTRY SERIES except that in order to save time the papers are not typeset but are reproduced as they are submitted by the authors in camera-ready form. Papers are reviewed under the supervision of the Editors with the assistance of the Series Advisory Board and are selected to maintain the integrity of the symposia; however, verbatim reproductions of previously published papers are not accepted. Both reviews and reports of research are acceptable since symposia may embrace both types of presentation.

CONTENTS

PREFACE

A T MANY ACADEMIC AND INDUSTRIAL RESEARCH LABORATORIES, surface scientists as well as inorganic, organic, polymer, and analytical chemists have focused on the chemical modification of surfaces to alter the bulk properties of materials. Chemical bonding of substituent groups to surfaces has been used to achieve catalytic, electron transfer, surface wetting, corrosion resistance, photochemical, and polymer binding properties that bulk materials inherently do not possess. Rapid advances have been made in these areas as synthetic and analytical methodology has been successfully developed and exploited. The types of materials that have been chemically modified range from inorganic solids (such as semiconducting titanium dioxide and tin dioxide) through alumina, silica, and silicates (such as clays) as well as ordered material such as zirconium phosphates. In contrast, organic materials ranging from the semimetal graphite to polymers, such as insulating polystyrene and the unusual conductor polypyrrole, have been of major concern in numerous research laboratories throughout the world.

Major concerns are the availability and limitations of the analytical techniques necessary to determine that surface modification has occurred, and the extent to which it has occurred. Herein, the state-of-the-art of the chemical modification of surfaces is presented by 17 chapters that also discuss the nature of the binding of the pendant groups to the surface and their frequency and spatial distributions. The principal focus in these chapters is on modification of materials for catalytic purposes and the modification of organic and inorganic electrode materials for electrocatalytic and photoelectrochemical applications.

JOEL S. MILLER
Occidental Research Corporation
Irvine, California

February 1982

Chemically Modified Surfaces in Catalysis

DAVID E. BERGBREITER

Texas A&M University, Department of Chemistry, College Station, TX 77843

In recent years, considerable attention has been given to methods in which organic and inorganic surfaces are chemically modified in order to increase their usefulness in catalytic processes. The materials resulting from such chemical modifications have considerable potential as alternatives to conventional homogeneous and heterogeneous catalysts. For example, homogeneous catalysts immobilized on an organic or inorganic support can in principle possess both the experimental advantages of typical heterogeneous catalysts and the reactivity and selectivity of their homogeneous analogs. Immobilized metal clusters can be used as catalysts themselves or as precursors to highly dispersed metal crystallites or as precursors to metal oxide particles. Immobilization of transition metal complexes and metal clusters both provides reliable routes to a type of heterogeneous catalyst whose nature and mechanism may be more readily understood and, potentially, offers ways to manipulate metal particle and crystallite size to achieve new types of catalytic reactions. Surface modification of electrodes is another example of this type of chemistry. Chemical modification of electrode surfaces either by adsorption of specific molecules or by binding a polymer or molecule to the electrode covalently provides opportunities to modify the stability and reactivity of electrodes to facilitate more useful electrocatalysis. This introduction discusses some of the general problems encountered in this rapidly developing field of chemistry and some of the advantages of these approaches to developing new types of catalysts. More specific examples of ways in which chemically modified surfaces have been used in studying or developing new catalysts are discussed in the accompanying papers in this volume and in recent reviews (1-5).

Modification of organic surfaces or more generally of organic polymers for the preparation of new types of catalysts illustrates the potential and many of the problems common to this type of chemistry. Modification of organic polymers may entail several different approaches. Typically organic polymers are modified either by chemical modification of an existing polymer or by poly-

0097-6156/82/0192-0001 $6.00/0

merization of appropriately derivatized monomers. In many cases, the resulting chemically modified polymers contain a ligand suitable for immobilization or "heterogenization" of a catalyst derived from a transition metal complex or metal cluster (1,2). Alternatively, the polymer may contain a non-metallic catalyst (3-5). Although various types of organic polymers can or have been chemically modified for use as catalysts or catalyst precursors, divinylbenzene (DVB) crosslinked polystyrene has been the most widely used polymer. This particular polymer is easily derivatized either before or after polymerization by unexceptional electrophilic aromatic substitution reactions. Furthermore, the physical restraints imposed by the polymer backbone on chemical reactivity of the attached catalysts are also readily controllable by varying the percentage of divinylbenzene crosslinking reagent and the polymerization method. For example, rigid macroporous DVB-crosslinked polystyrene possessing relatively large pores whose size is not very solvent dependent or gel-type microporous DVB-crosslinked polystyrene for which access to interior catalyst sites is very solvent dependent are both readily available or can be readily prepared.

One of the earliest examples of the use of chemically modified polymers as catalysts is the use as a catalyst of sulfonated DVB-crosslinked polystyrene which is commonly available in the form of ion exchange resins (4). This strongly acidic polymer has found application in a number of industrially important processes catalyzed by acids including dehydration reactions, esterifications, and olefin isomerizations. This heterogeneous polymeric acid is useful as a general substitute for mineral acids such as sulfuric acid in these processes. The primary advantage of this modified polymer as a catalyst in these reactions is its heterogeneity and the resulting ease with which this strong acid can be handled and reused.

More recent work with chemically modified organic polymers containing non-metallic catalysts has tended to emphasize the use of polymers to bind more exotic catalysts or ligands to facilitate the separation of catalysts and products after reaction. Phase transfer catalytic reactions are one example of this more recent chemistry. Phase transfer catalysts such as tetraalkylammonium or tetraalkylphosphonium salts or macrocyclic ethers have been successfully attached to polymers such as DVB-crosslinked polystyrene to produce heterogeneous organic catalysts or so called "triphase" catalysts (3,5). These catalysts are used to facilitate common organic reactions such as nucleophilic substitution reactions in which a polar reagent more soluble in water than the usual nonpolar organic solvents is required. Again, the primary advantage of immobilization of these catalysts is their facile recovery and the ease with which the reaction products can be separated from the catalysts.

Immobilization of otherwise homogeneous transition metal catalysts represents the second broad area in which chemically modi-

fied organic polymeric surfaces are of increased utility in catalysis (1,2). In this case, the objective is to transfer the experimental advantages usually associated with heterogeneous catalysts
to homogeneous catalysts while retaining the reactivity, selectivity and mechanistic understanding usually associated with homogeneous systems. The immobilization procedures by which common
homogeneous catalysts are attached to organic polymers typically
involve chemically modifying the organic polymer so that it contains a suitable ligand that can bind the transition metal. In
many cases, this ligand is a relatively simple triaryl- or alkyl-
diarylphosphine. However, inclusion of more complex phosphine
ligands including chelating and optically active phosphine ligands
has also been successfully accomplished (6). In fact, virtually
every imaginable type of ligand has been incorporated into organic
polymers or could be incorporated into an organic polymer to bind
a catalyst. Some common examples include cyclopentadienyl ligands,
bipyridyl ligands, ionic ligands including carboxylates, sulfonates and diketonates, and π-complexes in which the pendant aryl
groups of a polymer like polystyrene serve as the liganding group
(7). The diversity of types of ligands attached to organic polymeric surfaces has led to a corresponding diversity in terms of
the types of catalysts which can be bound to polymers. The only
limitations to binding a catalyst to a polymer such as polystyrene
are the possible reactivity of the polymer backbone to a particularly reactive catalyst, the physical diffusional restraints which
complicate catalyst immobilization, or the hydrophobicity of the
interior of organic polymers like polystyrene which could impose
chemical restraints on the type of species which could exist within the interior of a polystyrene matrix. All types of catalysts
including catalysts for typical homogeneously catalyzed hydrogenations, asymmetric hydrogenations and hydroformylations, olefin
dimerizations, olefin isomerizations, hydroformylation, and hydro-
metallation have been successfully attached to organic polymers.
Polymer bound versions of homogeneous catalysts usually function
as catalysts for the same reactions as their homogeneous counterparts although some recent reactions have shown that this condition is not always true (8,9).

Chemically modified polymers may also be used to support
transition metal carbonyl clusters which may in turn either be
used as "heterogenized" analogs of homogeneous clusters in catalysis in subsequent reactions or which may be decomposed to form
small metal crystallites. Transition metal carbonyls are most
commonly bound to organic polymers such as polystyrene using
phosphine ligands although other ligands such as bipyridyl ligands
have also been used. Mixed metal clusters can also be immobilized
(10).

Immobilization of homogeneous catalysts on organic polymers
has many real advantages and considerable potential for catalysis.
The most obvious advantage is the experimental advantage of heterogeneity. This permits recovery of both catalyst and ligand along

with ready separation of catalyst from the reaction product. In
suitable cases, a polymer bound catalyst can be used in continuous
processes in which the polymeric catalyst is used as part of a
fixed bed into which reactants enter and products exit. In certain cases where the catalyst ligand has a particularly unique
property such as optical activity, ligand recovery could be of
special significance. Other advantages of immobilized homogeneous
catalysts over their analogs in solution include the possibility
of not requiring solvent and the potential of increased catalyst
stability. Another potential advantage would be the possibility
of altering catalytic activity and selectivity. Although there
are already examples of immobilized catalysts which do indeed
achieve this latter objective, general approaches to achieving
this result are presently hampered by the analytical difficulties
associated with identification and characterization of the actual
catalytically active species present within a crosslinked polymer
support.

        Organic polymers can also be designed with certain other
properties which could be and in some cases have been used to substantially improve the utility of a homogeneous catalyst after immobilization. For example, the flexibility of a crosslinked polymer and, in turn, the extent of interaction between reactive sites
on such a polymer can be controlled either by varying the extent
of crosslinking in the polymer backbone or by changing the loading
of catalyst species on the polymer. A good example of this concept applied to a problem in catalysis is the use of a relatively
rigid polymer support such as 20% DVB-crosslinked polystyrene to
support a reactive titanocene hydrogenation catalyst (11). In
this particular instance, the known propensity of reactive titanocene moieties in solution to dimerize to form a less active catalyst was diminished by immobilization of titanocene on this rigid
polymer. The result was a more reactive hydrogenation catalyst.
Another example of how polymer structure can influence the catalytic behavior of a bound catalyst would be examples in which diffusional limitations resulting from the polymer structure have
been used to alter catalyst selectivity. Diffusion of reactants
into a DVB-crosslinked polystyrene bead containing a catalyst is
dependent on the polymer's pore size which depends partly on the
extent of crosslinking and the nature of the solvent swelling the
polymer. The result in one example involving a polystyrene bound
rhodium(I) complex catalyzed alkene hydrogenation was a physical
discrimination between diffenent sized substrates by the polymer
analogous to the shape selectivity seen with zeolite catalysts
(12).

        In addition to the advantages associated with immobilizing
homogeneous transition metal complexes on polymers for catalytic
reactions, there are certain disadvantages and unresolved problems. One problem characteristic of all the chemistry associated
with surface modified materials is the difficulty in determining
what the actual chemical structures present on the heterogeneous

material are or what the distribution of reactive species is in
the solid polymer or on the surface.   In the case of catalysts
attached to either organic or inorganic materials, characterization of the actual catalyst is a non-trivial problem.   Infrared
spectroscopy is the most commonly used analytical procedure used
to characterize these heterogeneous materials and is particularly
useful in certain cases. For example, immobilized metal carbonyl
clusters can be advantageously studied by this technique because
of the intensity and variability of the carbonyl absorption.
Other more qualitative techniques such as ESCA, elemental analysis, characterization on the basis of reactivity or chemical procedures or less readily available techniques such as X-ray absorption using synchrotron radiation are also useful in cases.   The
rapidly developing area of solid state NMR will be particularly
suited to these analytical problems and may contribute to solving
the problems which are presently unresolved because of these analytical difficulties.

Catalysts attached to organic polymers also have certain disadvantages that are the result of either polymer structure or the
immobilization process. Specifically, while gel-type polymers have
been used to achieve shape selective catalytic hydrogenations, the
variability of swelling phenomena poses certain restrictions. For
example, polar solvents which are desirable in some reactions such
as asymmetric hydrogenations are not useful with gel-type DVB-
crosslinked polystyrene and alternative polymeric supports had to
be prepared to permit the use of such polar solvents. If solvent
properties change significantly during a reaction because of product formation, the possible swelling changes which might result
must also be considered when using a catalyst attached to an organic polymer. Catalysts immobilized in an organic polymer network
also necessarily differ from their homogeneous counterparts because of the altered microenvironment within a polymer network
relative to bulk solution. In cases where preexisting polymers
are chemically modified to facilitate attachment of catalysts,
the success of the reaction used to modify the polymer and the
success of the reaction step in which the catalyst is bound to
the polymer can also be problematic. Specific problems which are
not uncommon include the presence of undesirable but unavoidable
impurities as a result of side reactions, incomplete reactions,
or the formation of insoluble by-products. Further potential experimental problems which often have to be considered include the
mechanical fragility of some organic polymer systems and the low
thermal stability associated with organic polymers relative to
inorganic refractory materials such as silica or alumina. This
latter property of organic polymers can pose serious experimental
problems in very exothermic reactions in which heat transport from
an organic polymer is not very efficient.

Modification of the surface of inorganic materials such as
silica or alumina in order to transform such surfaces into catalyst ligands is an alternative to modifying organic polymer sur-

faces (1,2). Inorganic materials also offer certain advantages
over organic materials in some cases as a result of the properties
of inorganic polymers. For example, inorganic materials are typically very thermally stable, these materials often possess highly
ordered structures, and these materials can be obtained with
both good mechanical stability and with high surface areas.

One common approach taken to modification of inorganic
materials is to first introduce more versatile functional groups
by the use of an appropriate silylating reagent. Equation 1 illustrates this approach. The inorganic surfaces resulting from

$$\begin{array}{c} \text{—OH} \\ \text{—OH} \\ \text{—OH} \end{array} + (EtO)_3Si\text{✺}PPh_2 \longrightarrow \begin{array}{c} \text{—O} \\ \text{—O—Si}\text{✺}PPh_2 \\ \text{—O} \end{array} \quad (1)$$

this type of chemical modification closely resemble those discussed above for organic polymers. This type of chemical modification procedure retains many of the desirable properties of
the inorganic support. The principle advantage of using this
approach rather than the direct reaction of a metal complex with
whatever functional groups are present at an inorganic surface is
that there is a greater likelihood of retaining the molecular
integrity of the catalyst complex when ligands are first introduced using functionalized silylating reagents. The most commonly
used ligands are again phosphine ligands but other types of ligands such as amino, pyridyl, and cyclopentadienyl groups have also
been used (2).

The alternative to first modifying an inorganic support in
order to attach a phosphine ligand and then a metal complex is to
directly react a metal complex with the inorganic support using
oxygen, hydroxyl, or oxide groups typically present at the surface
of inorganic materials like silica or alumina. This approach has
been widely used, especially in reactions in which metal carbonyl
cluster compounds have been attached to silica and alumina. In
these reactions, physical adsorption is followed by reaction of
the surface hydroxyl groups with the metal carbonyl complex.
These reactions may involve either decarbonylation and coordination of a surface oxide to the metal to produce a new metal carbonyl complex attached to the inorganic surface through nonionic
bonds or modification of the original carbonyl complex to form
an ionic species which attached to the inorganic surface electrostatically. Further reaction at higher temperatures typically
leads to further decarbonylation which may be accompanied by
hydrogen evolution and oxidation of the metal. Eventually metal
oxide particles or dispersed metal crystallites are formed after
extended reaction.

Chemical modification of highly ordered inorganic materials
such as clays and inorganic ion exchangers like zirconium phos-

phates provides another approach for catalyst immobilization on inorganic materials which is under active investigation. This approach potentially could combine the shape selectivity often associated with ordered inorganic systems like zeolites with the advantages cited above for immobilization of molecular complexes of metals on organic supports since organic ligands can be included into or onto these inorganic materials. Such systems potentially could have a significant advantage over examples in which ligands or catalysts are only attached to the outside of an inorganic material since chemical modifications throughout an inorganic ion exchange matrix will result in a higher level of functionalization of the inorganic matrix.

Surface modification of electrodes to facilitate electrocatalysis parallels in many respects the chemistry discussed above for immobilization of catalysts on organic and inorganic materials. However, the objectives are somewhat different in electrode modification. Specifically, the principle objectives in electrode modification are usually to alter electrode stability, to alter the kinetics of reactions at electrode surfaces, or to alter an electrodes electrochemical properties. Electrode modification may involve covalent attachment of electroactive compounds or coating of the electrode surface with a polymeric phase.

The modification of surfaces in order to develop new catalysts and new types of catalysts has great promise. Although many problems remain unresolved, the potential of this area of chemistry has continued to attract attention from both industrial and academic laboratories. It is expected that future developments in this area will continue and that the combination of organic, inorganic and surface chemistry will produce new types of catalysts whose capabilities differ from those of conventional catalysts. Electrochemical processes, depending necessarily on interfacial phenomena, are especially likely candidates for study. Indeed, the rapid advances in this particular area over the last few years attest to the potential of surface modification for dealing with unsolved problems in this area. Advances in analytical characterization of surfaces and solid materials will be particularly important in advancing this technology and in understanding these types of catalysts and their reactions.

Literature Cited

1. Bailey, D. C.; Langer, S. H. Chem. Rev. 1981, 81, 109–148.
2. Whitehurst, D. D. CHEMTECH 1980, 44–49.
3. Regen, S. L. Angew. Chem., Int. Ed. Eng. 1979, 18, 421–429.
4. Hodge, P.; Sherrington, D. C. "Polymer Supported Reactions in Organic Synthesis"; J. Wiley and Sons, Ltd.: London; 1980.
5. Mathur, N. K.; Narang, C. K.; Williams, D. R. "Polymers as Aids in Organic Chemistry"; Academic Press: New York; 1980
6. Takaishi, N.; Imai, H.; Bertelo, C. A.; Stille, J. K. J. Am. Chem. Soc. 1978, 100, 264–268. Masuda, T.; Stille, J. K.

Ibid. 1978, 100, 268–272.   Dumont, W.; Poulin, J. C.; Dang, T. P.; Kagan, H. B. Ibid. 1973, 95, 8295–8299.

7. Chauvin, Y.; Commereuc, D.; Dawans, F. Prog. Polym. Sci. 1977, 5, 95–226.
8. Perkins, P.; Vollhardt, K. P. C. J. Am. Chem. Soc. 1979, 101, 3985–3986.
9. Bergbreiter, D. E.; Parsons, G. L. J. Organomet. Chem. 1981, 208, 47–53.
10. Pierantozzi, R.; McQuade, K. J.; Gates, B. C.; Wolf, M.; Knozinger, H.; Ruhmann, W. J. Am. Chem. Soc. 1979, 101, 5436–5438.
11. Bonds, W. D. Jr.; Brubaker, C. H. Jr.; Chandrasekaran, E. S.; Gibbons, C.; Grubbs, R. H.; Kroll, L. C. J. Am. Chem. Soc. 1975, 97, 2128–2134.
12. Grubbs, R. H.; Kroll, L. C. J. Am. Chem. Soc. 1971, 93, 3062–3064.
13. Reed, J.; Eisenberger, P.; Teo, B.-K.; Kincaid, B. M. J. Am. Chem. Soc. 1977, 99, 5217–5218.

RECEIVED April 5, 1982.

Preparation and Characterization of Poly(styrene–divinylbenzene)-Supported Catalysts

J. V. MINKIEWICZ, D. MILSTEIN, J. LIETO, and B. C. GATES
University of Delaware, Center for Catalytic Science and Technology, Department of Chemical Engineering, Newark, DE 19711

R. L. ALBRIGHT
Rohm and Haas Company, Philadelphia, PA 19137

Crosslinked polystyrene is a valuable catalyst support, since it is easily functionalized and available with a wide range of physical properties. Synthesis routes are reviewed for preparation of polymers from styrene, divinylbenzene (and possibly functionalized monomers) to give membranes, gel-form beads, and macroporous beads. Methods are summarized for functionalization of these polymers to give pendent groups such as $-Br$ and $-CH_2Cl$, which can be converted into ligands such as $-PPh_2$, $-NR_2$, $-SH$, and $-OH$. The ligands are useful for attachment of catalytically active organometallic complexes, by processes such as ligand exchange, ligand association, and in situ synthesis. Characterization of the supported catalytic groups has been most successful with infrared spectroscopy of metal carbonyls and with EXAFS, which provides structural data.

Polymers, especially poly(styrene–divinylbenzene), have been applied often as catalyst supports, providing the means for using well-defined catalytic groups in a phase separate from that holding the reactants and thereby minimizing the difficulties of product purification and corrosion associated with homogeneous catalysis. Polymers offer several advantages as catalyst supports: (1) they are easily functionalized, especially when they incorporate aryl groups; (2) unlike surfaces of metal oxides, the most common catalyst supports, polymeric hydrocarbons are nearly inert and are not expected to interfere in catalysis, which may therefore be associated with a single kind of catalytic group and occur selectively; (3) the polymers can be prepared with a wide range of physical properties--this is especially true of poly(styrene–divinylbenzene). There are also disadvantages of polymers, including their lack of stability at high temperatures

and their fragility--many polymers cannot be used in stirred
reactors without being pulverized.

Most of the reported research with polymer-supported catalysts
has been done with commercially available polymers. Many of these
have been prepared by poorly described techniques and contain
impurities such as surfactants used in the polymerization to
impart the desired physical properties to the polymers. The
nature of the impurities in commercial polymers is usually unknown
to the user; structural data, such as the crosslinking, are also
usually lacking, typically varying significantly from batch to
batch.

It is our thesis that it is advantageous in research with
polymer-supported catalysts to use well-characterized materials
having high purities. Consequently, we have prepared
poly(styrene-divinylbenzene)-supported catalysts to meet these
standards. In the following pages, we review techniques for
synthesis, functionalization, and characterization of crosslinked
polystyrene supports and supported catalysts. The information
presented here is primarily drawn from literature sources. All
the cited methods have been tested in our laboratories, and
only the recommended ones are presented, some modified slightly
from the original, cited methods. Our objective is to provide
a detailed guide that will be useful to those preparing and
testing crosslinked polystyrene-supported catalysts. A thorough
review of functionalized polymers used in catalysis was published
in 1977 (1). Reviews of the chemistry and the properties of
crosslinked polymers (2) and of polymer-supported catalysts (3,4)
were also published recently.

Preparation of Poly(styrene-DVB) Supports

Membranes

Two types of membrane supports were prepared because of their
suitability for characterization by transmission infrared spectroscopy. One type is made by copolymerization of styrene and
divinylbenzene (DVB, the crosslinking agent) and requires further
functionalization prior to incorporation of the catalytic species.

The second type includes a functionalized monomer copolymer-
ized with styrene and DVB. For example, p-bromostyrene may be
included in the reaction mixture to provide the desired concentration of functional groups in the support. These groups may
eventually be converted into phosphines by reaction with lithium
diphenylphosphide. Such resins with low phosphine concentrations
are the supports of choice for attachment of monophosphine-
substituted metal clusters because the ligands are sparsely and
almost randomly distributed in the polymers (5).

Another type of support can be prepared from styrene, DVB,
and the phosphine-functionalized monomer, p-styryldiphenylphosphine. This preparation, because of the differences in reactivity

of the monomers, leads to the formation of a block copolymer
even at low concentrations of p-styryldiphenylphosphine (1 mol%).
This type of support has been useful in the preparation of
multi-phosphine substituted metal clusters (5) (Figure 1).

Similar supports can be prepared from styrene, DVB, and
p-aminostyrene. This preparation, like that involving
p-styryldiphenylphosphine, leads to the formation of a block
copolymer (6).

The membrane syntheses were carried out as follows (5): The
commercial reagent-grade monomers were vacuum distilled shortly
before use to remove polymerization inhibitors. A typical
membrane synthesis employed 3 ml of styrene for each individual
sample, with the amounts of DVB and other monomer(s) chosen to
regulate the degree of crosslinking and functionalization. The
most widely used membrane formulation included 2 mol% DVB, since
with this crosslinking the flexibility of the polymer matrix
allowed the greatest success in subsequent functionalization
reactions and attachment of metal complexes. The functionalized
monomers   comprised 5 to 15 mol% of the monomer mixture. The
monomers were thoroughly mixed just prior to use, and 0.1 wt%
azobisisobutyronitrile (AIBN) was added to initiate the free-
radical copolymerization. Benzoyl peroxide could not be used with
phosphine groups because of their possible oxidation.

The membranes were formed from the monomers in a specially
designed apparatus (7). An aluminum template was placed on a
scrupulously clean, dry, and almost perfectly flat glass plate.
This template was cut from foil of uniform thickness (11 μm) and
had a window area of 5x6 cm. The monomer mixture was carefully
pipetted into the space inside the confines of the aluminum frame.
A second glass plate of similar quality was carefully mounted onto
the first, with care taken to exclude air bubbles from the
entrapped solution, and the pair was then sandwiched between a set
of rubber spacers and brass plates which completely covered the
glass. The entire unit was compressed with screws in a brass press
and submerged in a thermostated water bath held for 3 days at
70°C followed by 5 days at 90°C. The presses were then removed
from the bath and allowed to cool to room temperature before
removal of the glass plates. The plates were placed in water and
carefully pried apart. Once free, the membrane floated to the
surface of the water. A razor blade was useful in separating the
glass plates and disengaging the membrane from the aluminum
template. A piece of filter paper was then slipped beneath the
membrane and used to extract and support it for drying. The
membrane was dried in an oven at 80°C for several hours. Since it
was delicate, it was protected from physical damage in subsequent
operations by encasement in stainless steel mesh or Teflon mesh.

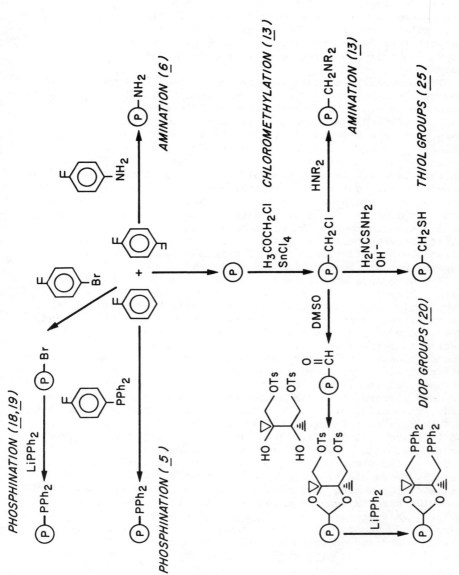

Figure 1. Summary of synthetic routes for functionalization of poly(styrene–DVB): incorporation of pendent $-Br$, $-PPh_3$, $-NH_2$, $-CH_2NR_3$, $-CH_2SH$, and DIOP groups.

Gel-form Beads

Gel-form ("microporous") beads are the supports which have most commonly been used for larger-scale investigations of polymer-supported catalysts. Uniformity of bead production can be achieved by the inclusion of a water-soluble surfactant to stabilize the emulsion of organic monomers in an aqueous reaction medium.

A three-neck round-bottom flask, equipped with a mechanical stirrer, an addition funnel, and a thermometer, was charged with 110 ml of water, 0.11 g of polyvinyl alcohol (surfactant), and 0.02 g of $CaCO_3$. This solution was heated to 50°C with stirring. The addition funnel was charged with 16 ml of xylene solvent, 8.32 g (80 mmole) of styrene, 2.60 g (20 mmole) of DVB (this amount produced 20% crosslinking in the resin), and 0.2 g of benzoyl peroxide initiator. Many preparations also included p-bromostyrene, which resulted in the formation of brominated polymer similar to that formed in the membrane synthesis.

When the temperature of the aqueous solution reached 50°C, the contents of the addition funnel were emptied into the reaction flask, and the temperature of the mixture was raised to 95°C. The addition funnel was replaced with a reflux condenser and the mixture was stirred vigorously for 24 hr. Then an additional 150 ml of water was added to the flask and the contents were steam distilled to remove the xylene.

When the reaction mixture had cooled, the polymer beads were transferred to a Büchner funnel mounted on a suction flask. The beads were initially washed with 200 ml of water, followed in sequence by 50 ml each of 50:50 water:methanol, methanol, 50:50 methanol:methylene chloride, and methylene chloride. A large enough funnel was used to allow sufficient space for expansion of the beads, which swell markedly in the presence of methylene chloride. The beads were then dried under vacuum.

Macroporous Beads

A series of porous, crosslinked polymers composed of DVB (8.0%), ethylvinylbenzene (EVB) (6.1%), and styrene (85.9%) were prepared with a range of physical properties. The beads were made porous by carrying out the polymerization at 70°C in the presence of varying concentrations of methylisobutylcarbinol (MIBC). The beads had diameters in the range of about 0.25 to 1.0 mm. When sulfonated (as described below), the polymers had the following ranges of properties: The porosity varied from 0.13 to 0.70; the specific surface area from about 0 to 24 m^2/g, and the average pore diameter from 235 to 278 nm.

Porous polymer preparations have been described in the literature (8,9) and in patent art (10,11). A modified preparation is described here.

The porous polymer was made in spherical bead form by a two-phase, dispersion polymerization. The desired range of bead diameters within the limits of 0.250 to 1.19 mm was provided by the procedure given below. Further details are to be presented elsewhere (12).

The polymerization was carried out by making up the aqueous phase and the monomer phase separately. The aqueous phase was made up in the flask used to carry out the polymerization. The monomer phase was prepared in another vessel and added later to the reaction flask. The weight ratio of aqueous phase to monomer phase for these syntheses was 1:12. The aqueous phase consisted of 1.645 kg of tap water, 2.0 g of 50% aqueous NaOH, 4.35 g of boric acid, 38.12 g of poly(diallydimethylammonium chloride) aqueous solution (made from 12.5% solids), and 4.10 g of gelatin. The monomer phase consisted of 129.5 g of commercial DVB (measured by GLC to be 55.6% DVB), 42.3% EVB (97.9% polymerizable monomers), 773.2 g of styrene (99.8% pure), 600.0 g of MIBC, and 9.0 g of AIBN.

To a five-liter, three-necked, standard-tapered flask were charged the aqueous-phase ingredients except for 150 g of the water, the boric acid, and the gelatin. The boric acid and the gelatin were separately dissolved in water and then introduced into the flask; if these were added as solids, a turbid medium would result. All the ingredients for the aqueous phase were introduced with agitation. The flask was equipped with a polished metal-shafted stirrer carrying a single metal blade having the contour of the round bottom of the flask. Power for the stirrer was provided by a Contorque constant-speed motor. (It is important that the stirring speed be constant during the setting of the dispersion, since otherwise the size distribution of the polymer particles will be much broader than desired.) After the aqueous phase was thoroughly mixed and the liquid clear, the pH was measured. The pH should be within the range 8.3 to 8.7. If the pH is too high, small increments of boric acid are to be added; if the pH is too low, small increments of 50% aqueous sodium hydroxide are to be added.

The monomer mixture was prepared in a hood with a two-liter beaker stirred manually with a glass rod. The AIBN initiator was added to the monomers at 15 ± 2°C. The mixture was stirred manually until the AIBN was dissolved. With the agitation turned off, the clear monomer mixture was introduced into the reactor; the agitation was started and adjusted to 140 ± 2 rpm.

After the stirring rate had been established, the mixture, which should be an oil-in-water dispersion (not the reverse) was heated to 70 ± 1°C under an atmosphere of nitrogen over a period of one hour. Before heat-up, the flask was fitted with a water-cooled condenser, a heating mantle, and a Jack-O-Matic from I^2R or a comparable device to provide heating and cooling as demanded by the polymerization reaction. The temperature of 70 ± 1°C was maintained for four hours at the set stirring rate. During this time, the monomer droplets changed from transparent to opaque. After four hours at 70 ± 1°C, the flask was arranged for distillation and the introduction of additional water to replace the distillate to be removed. Heat flow to the reactor was increased, and distillate began to come over when the contents of the flask reached about 95-97°C. The water-MIBC azeotrope was allowed to distill out until no more MIBC was observed. (The cooled (20°C) distillate is a single phase.) Water was added as needed during the distillate to maintain fluidity. After the distillate became a single component--water--the flask temperature reached about 103°C, and the vapor temperature was 100°C. The distillation was continued for an additional 30 minutes to remove most of the MIBC.

The reactor was cooled to 70°C, siphoned free of the bulk liquid, washed twice with water, and washed three times with methanol. The water washing sequence was addition of 1.5 liters of water, agitation for 10 minutes, and siphoning free of bulk liquid. The methanol washing sequence was addition of 1.0 liter of methanol, stirring for 15 minutes, and siphoning free of bulk liquid. After the third methanol washing, the methanol-bead slurry was poured onto a Büchner funnel, drained free of liquid, transferred to a pyrex dish, and dried at 70-75°C for 16 hours in a convection oven.

The porous dried polymer was opaque-white or translucent. (If nonporous, the beads are transparent.) Physical properties of the macroporous beads are reported in Table I.

Table I

Macroporous Beads: Physical Properties as a Function
of the Concentration of Phase Extender

MIBC Content, wt%	Specific Surface Area, m^2/g	Porosity, vol%	Average Pore Diameter, Å	Crosslinking, wt% DVB
30.0	0	13.0	--	8.0
35.0	0	1.0	--	8.0
40.0	0	13.0	--	8.0
45.0	10.8	51.0	2586	8.0
50.0	11.0	65.0	4776	8.0
55.0	12.5	52.0	2347	8.0
60.0	24.0	68.0	2350	8.0
65.0	0	70.0	--	8.0
Sulfonated Polymer				
33.0	23	67.7	2571	16.0

Functionalization

The functionalization reactions are represented schematically in Figures 1 and 2. Almost all the reactions described in this section were carried out using standard methods for air-sensitive reagents.

Sulfonation

The porous polymers were sulfonated with concentrated (99+%) H_2SO_4 as both the reactant and the fluidizing agent. The sulfonation was performed upon the polymer in a partially swollen state with ethylene dichloride as the swelling agent. The reactants were 1.2 kg of conc. H_2SO_4 (technical grade 99+%), 124.8 g of ethylene dichloride, and 107.2 g of porous polymer.

A three-liter, three-necked, standard-taper flask was fitted with a thermometer, adapter, downward-sloping distillation condenser with a receiver attached, and a heating mantle. The sulfuric acid and ethylene dichloride were introduced into the flask and agitation begun. The agitator was a ground-glass shaft fitted through the proper glass bearing into the center opening atop the flask. The Teflon paddle was single-bladed. The agitation rate was adjusted to ensure adequate mixing. The porous polymer was charged and the slurry heated to 122°C over a two-hour period. At a temperature of 82°C the ethylene dichloride began to distill off and was collected in the receiver. Ethylene dichloride distillation was spent and ceased at about 92-94°C. The temperature was held at 121 ± 1°C for 4 hr, after which an addition funnel was inserted into one neck of the flask for the introduction of water. Hydration of the sulfonated beads was conducted by way of an increasing rate profile of water addition within the temperature limits of 90 to 100°C. The first 136.52 g of water were added at a rate of 3.413 ml/min (40 minutes duration); the next 341.3 g at a rate of 6.826 ml/min (50 minutes duration); the next 341.3 g at a rate of 13.65 ml/min (25 minutes duration); and the fourth 1228.0 g at a rate of 27.30 ml/min (45 minutes duration); and the final 2048 g at a rate of 54.6 ml/min (37.5 minutes duration). As the reaction flask filled with liquids, siphoning was started and carried on continuously with a rate of liquid removal equivalent to the rate of water introduction so that the slurry volume remained constant. The temperature was allowed to drop as the exothermic hydration slowed down. By the end of the hydration, the slurry temperature had reached about 60-70°C. The beads were transferred to a Büchner funnel, drained free of bulk water by aspiration, and dried in a pyrex dish in a convection oven at 106°C for 8 hr. For measurement of the internal physical properties, the sulfonated polymer must be completely free of water. The atmospherically dried product was washed three times with one bed-volume of methanol for each washing. The methanol-wet beads were dried in a vacuum oven at 50-70°C at full vacuum (760 mm Hg) for 4 hr. The completely dried beads were hygroscopic and had to be handled without exposure to moisture.

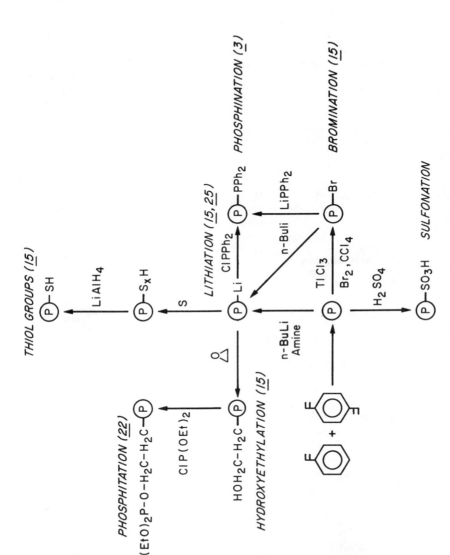

Figure 2. Summary of synthetic routes for functionalization of poly(styrene–DVB): incorporation of -CH₂OH, -CH₂CH₂OP(OEt)₂, -SH, -Br, -Li, -PPh₂, -SO₃H groups.

Chloromethylation

The polymers were chloromethylated according to the following procedure (13). A two-liter glass kettle reactor with a four-neck head equipped with a stirrer, condenser, dropping funnel, and thermometer was charged with 400 ml of propylene dichloride and 2.2 g of polymer beads. If membranes were to be functionalized instead of beads, unfunctionalized beads were added so that the total mass of polymer to be reacted was 2 g, which was considered optimal for this highly hazardous procedure. The mixture was allowed to stand at 20°C for one hour, after which 3.8 g of chloromethylmethyl ether was added in one step; the mixture was kept at room temperature with slow stirring. $SnCl_4$ catalyst (4.1 g) was then added dropwise over a period of 30 minutes. The temperature was maintained less than 25°C with an ice-water bath. After the complete addition of the catalyst, the reaction was stopped by addition of 250 ml of methanol. Two washings with methanol (250 ml) and three washings with a 5% aqueous HCl solution (250 ml) followed. Several washings with deionized water were done before drying the polymer at 60°C for 8 hours.

The chloromethylation was performed at Rohm and Haas Co., Philadelphia, where specially designed ventilation and gas scrubbing equipment allowed safe handling of the carcinogenic chloromethylmethyl ether (14).

Bromination

The bromination of 1% cross-linked polystyrene was done in the presence of $Tl(OAc)_3$ or $TlCl_3$, which are preferable to the inefficient $FeCl_3$ and the inconvenient BF_3 (15). The resin (2 g) was swollen in CCl_4 (30 ml) and contacted with $TlCl_3$ (0.2 g). The reactants were stirred in the dark for 30 min, then 1.36 g of Br_2 in 2 ml of CCl_4 were added slowly. After stirring for 1 hr at room temperature in the dark, the mixture was heated to reflux for 1.5 hr. The reaction mixture was filtered, and the beads were washed in sequence with CCl_4, acetone, water, benzene, and methanol. The beads were then dried in vacuum.

Lithiation

The lithiation of poly(styrene-DVB) can be carried out according to two reaction routes. The first involves the transformation of -Br groups into -Li groups by reaction of a brominated polystyrene with an excess of n-butyllithium (15,16). The second involves the direct lithiation of poly(styrene-DVB) by reacting the resin with n-butyllithium and N,N,N',N'-tetramethyl-ethylenediamine (TMEDA) (15,17).

In the two-step lithiation, 2 g of 3% crosslinked brominated macroporous poly(styrene-DVB-EVB) beads containing 4.36 mmol of Br/g in 40 ml of dry toluene under N_2 were brought in contact with 14.8 ml of 1.6 $\underline{M}$ n-BuLi, and the mixture was heated at 60°C with stirring for 3 hr. After cooling to 25°C, the beads were separated by filtration under N_2, washed with dry toluene and then THF, and kept in THF suspension under N_2 for further reaction.

In the direct lithiation, a dry cyclohexane suspension of poly(styrene-DVB-EVB) (3 g) was stirred with 4 ml of TMEDA and 15 ml of 2.5 $\underline{M}$ n-BuLi under N_2 for 5 hr at 65°C. During this time, the reaction mixture gradually turned red. The liquid was then removed by filtration under N_2, and the resin was washed in sequence with dry cyclohexane, THF, and cyclohexane and kept in THF suspension under N_2 until further reaction.

Hydroxyethylation

Hydroxyethyl functionalities can be anchored to poly(styrene-DVB) by reacting lithiated resin with ethylene oxide (15). A THF suspension of lithiated resin (2 g in 50 ml) was cooled to -80°C, and 15 ml of ethylene oxide at -80°C were added with a transfer pipet. The mixture was brought to room temperature (in about 3 hr) and the beads were separated by filtration, washed successively with THF:H_2O (3:1), 10% HCl, H_2O, THF, and ether, and then vacuum dried at 70°C. The infrared spectrum showed an OH absorption.

Phosphination

The phosphination procedure (18) was applied for functionalization of brominated beads and membranes. This same procedure was also the final step in the sequence for the attachment of the asymmetric phosphorus-containing ligand DIOP to the polymeric support. The phosphination involved the reaction of lithium diphenylphosphide prepared by a literature route (19) with the -Br groups.

Into a 500-ml three-neck round-bottom flask, equipped with a nitrogen inlet, mechanical Teflon stirrer, and addition funnel, was charged 250 ml of dry and deoxygenated tetrahydrofuran (THF) (freshly distilled under nitrogen over Na-benzophenone) under a nitrogen atmosphere. Redistilled chlorodiphenylphosphine (26.7 ml) was introduced into the addition funnel and carefully added under a nitrogen atmosphere to the THF solvent to minimize any temperature increase. With the addition funnel removed (but with the nitrogen still flowing), excess lithium metal, cleaned of residual packing oil with dry THF and subsequently sliced to expose surface, was then added to the solution to produce lithium diphenylphosphide. A reflux condenser was inserted into the vacant neck of the flask and the mixture vigorously stirred for 1 hr. The mixture turned a deep red color, and completion of

the reaction was achieved by heating the mixture to reflux for an
additional 6 hr. The mixture was allowed to cool to room
temperature and maintained under a nitrogen atmosphere.

To convert the brominated or chloromethylated polymers into
their corresponding phosphinated derivatives, the beads (or the
membranes in protective stainless steel mesh) were placed in a
second, similarly equipped round-bottom flask. The lithium
diphenylphosphide (mentioned above) was transferred into this
second flask using standard handling techniques for air-sensitive
reagents, e.g., transfer pipets and serum caps. Enough lithium
diphenylphosphide was transferred so that the phosphine:halide
molar ratio was 4:1. Additional dry and deoxygenated THF was
added as required to completely cover the enmeshed swollen
membranes. The phosphination reaction was allowed to proceed for
48 hr at reflux under a nitrogen atmosphere. During this period
the color of the reaction mixture changed from red to orange.
When the mixture had cooled to room temperature, the polymers were
separated from the solution and washed consecutively with THF,
water, toluene, hexane, THF, acetone, and petroleum ether. Again,
in work with polymer beads, care was taken to provide sufficient
room for expansion of the gel upon swelling with the various
organic solvents. The phosphinated polymers were dried under
vacuum for 24 hr and stored under nitrogen.

When highly functionalized supports are used, the transformation of $-CH_2Cl$ groups into $-CH_2PPh_2$ groups by reaction of the
$-CH_2Cl$ groups with lithium diphenylphosphide is accompanied by
quarterization of some of the phosphine groups, which react with
nearby unconverted $-CH_2Cl$ groups (3).

Phosphinated polymers can also be prepared by reaction of
lithiated polymers with chlorodiphenylphosphine (3).

DIOP

The asymmetric phosphorus-containing ligand DIOP, 2,2-0-
isopropylidene-2,3-dihydroxy-1,4-bis(diphenylphosphino)butane,
was incorporated into the chloromethylated polymers according to
a literature procedure (20). The chloromethyl function was
initially converted into the aldehyde, which was subsequently
condensed with a tosylated diol, and the tosyl groups were
ultimately converted into diphenylphosphine groups.

Into a 500-ml three-neck round-bottom flask, equipped with a
thermometer, reflux condenser and mechanical stirrer, were placed
the chloromethylated crosslinked polystyrene beads or membranes.
DMSO (300 ml--this amount should be sufficient to cover the
enmeshed membranes) and 15 g of sodium bicarbonate were added to
the flask, and the entire system was heated and stirred at 150°C
for 6 hr. When the mixture had cooled, the newly formed
aldehydic polymers were washed with water, THF, toluene, ethanol,
and acetone. The supports were then dried for 4 hr at
120°C under vacuum.

The next step consisted of the condensation of the aldehyde with the diol, 1,4-ditosylthreitol. This compound was previously prepared by refluxing one gram of L-(+)-0-isopropylidene-2,3-dihydroxy-1,4-bis(p-tosyl)butane in 20 ml of absolute ethanol in the presence of 5.5 mg of p-toluenesulfonic acid. The solution was allowed to reflux for 24 hr, after which the solvent was removed on a rotary evaporator. The oily residue which remained was redissolved in chloroform, and evaporation of this solvent then produced a grayish solid. The solid was recrystallized from 1:1 chloroform:hexane to yield white needles of 1,4-ditosyl-threitol (0.86 g, 98% yield).

The condensation reaction was likewise performed in the presence of p-toluenesulfonic acid as catalyst. The aldehydic polymer was refluxed with 1,4-ditosylthreitol in dry benzene solvent. In a typical preparation, one gram of polymer, 0.2 g of diol, and 3.2 mg of acid catalyst were refluxed for 24 hr, and the water which formed was continuously extracted and measured with a distillation water trap. Upon completion of reaction, the functionalized supports were filtered, washed, and dried as were the aldehydic materials.

The final step in the DIOP ligand attachment was the conversion of the tosyl groups into diphenylphosphine groups by reaction with lithium diphenylphosphide. The phosphination procedure was executed in the manner described above, i.e., with dry and deoxygenated THF as solvent and with the identical reaction time, temperature, and final wash sequence. A 3:1 molar excess of diphenylphosphine groups to tosyl groups was employed. The fully phosphinated polymeric reagents were dried under vacuum and stored under nitrogen.

Polymers containing DIOP functionalities can also be prepared by copolymerization with a monomer incorporating a DIOP precursor and methylvinylketone, the latter chosen to make the resulting polymer swellable in alcohol (21).

Phosphitation

Whereas phosphine-functionalized polymer supports are generally prone to oxidation, especially after attachment of a metal complex, polymers containing phosphite ligands are oxidatively stable. A disadvantage of the latter supports, however, is their greater susceptibility to hydrolysis.

Phosphite-functionalized polymers were prepared by lithiation of brominated poly(styrene-DVB) membranes or beads followed by hydroxyethylation with ethylene oxide and phosphitation with chlorodialkylphosphite and a base; dimethylaniline was found to be most suitable (22). Dimethylaniline hydrochloride, which is formed in the reaction, is highly soluble in chloroform and thus can be conveniently removed without the need for a more polar solvent which may cause solvolysis of the attached

phosphite ligand. Use of chlorodiphenylphosphite provides for
mixed phosphine/phosphite functionalities (Figure 2).

A hydroxyethylated polymer (0.6 g) was stirred at room
temperature with 0.37 ml of chlorodiethylphosphite and 0.33 ml
of dimethylaniline in 10 ml of toluene for 20 hr, during which a
white precipitate of dimethylaniline hydrochloride appeared. The
solution was removed by decantation, and the polymer was washed
with 3x20 ml of toluene and 2x30 ml of chloroform (alcohol free)
and vacuum dried. Elemental analysis showed that the polymer
contained 4.48% P. Reactions with other phosphites and with
chlorodiphenylphosphine were carried out similarly.

The procedures were similar when membranes were used: To two
hydroxyethylated membranes in 35 ml of dry toluene in a Schlenk
tube were added 0.45 ml of dimethylaniline followed by 0.5 ml of
chlorodiethylphosphite. After stirring at room temperature under
N_2 overnight, the solution was removed by decantation and the
membranes were washed with benzene.

Amination

The procedure recommended for amination is that of Pepper
et al. (13). Polymers containing quarternary, tertiary, secondary,
and primary amines were prepared. In all cases, the dried polymer
had to be swelled with a solvent such as THF or dioxane. The amine
was then added, which reacted with the chloromethyl groups to produce polymer-bound amine groups. All the steps were carried out
under an inert atmosphere. Quaternary ammonium salt groups
were obtained by reacting 20 g of polymer swollen in dioxane and
100 ml of cold anhydrous trimethylamine at 0°C. The mixture was
kept at 0°C for 2 days with stirring under N_2. The polymer was
then washed sequentially with 2N HCl, 0.1N NaOH, 2N HCl, 2N NaCl,
and finally deionized water until the effluent was chloride free.

Tertiary amine groups were incorporated in the polymer by
adding 100 ml of cold diethyl amine to 15 g of swollen polymer.
The mixture was stirred at 0°C under N_2 for four days. The
polymer was then washed with deoxygenated dioxane followed by 50
vol% solution of acetone in water. The polymer was then
equilibrated with a solution containing 150 ml of 0.1N NaOH and
150 ml of acetone for several hours, decanted, and equilibrated
again. Next, the polymer was repeatedly washed with 50 vol%
solution of acetone in deionized water until the rises tested
neutral. The polymer was rinsed twice with acetone and vacuum
dried in the flask.

Secondary amine groups were incorporated in the polymer by
adding 70 ml of ethylamine solution (33 vol% in H_2O) to the
swollen polymer (8 g). The mixture was stirred under N_2 at room
temperature for about 5 days. The washing and drying procedures
were identical to those used for the tertiary amine polymer.

Incorporation of primary amine groups in the polymer involved
reacting gaseous, anhydrous ammonia with the swollen polymer. The

procedure was developed from a similar process involving the
reaction of gaseous trimethylamine with swollen polymer reported
by Patterson (23). The polymer (8 g) was swollen in 200 ml of
dioxane, to which 5 ml of 6N NaOH (1:1 mole ratio to Cl groups)
was added to neutralize any HCl produced and to prevent ammonium
salt formation. The mixture was stirred at room temperature with
ammonia being continuously bubbled into the solution for a period
of five days. The washing and drying procedures were identical to
those used for the tertiary amine polymer.

Primary amines were also introduced into polymers by copolymerization of styrene, DVB, and p-aminostyrene. This last monomer
was prepared according to a literature procedure (24). Membranes
containing $-NH_2$ groups were prepared.

It is emphasized that amine groups can react with $-CH_2Cl$
groups to produce quarternary ammonium salts when the concentration of the functionality is high (3).

Thiol Groups

Thiol groups can be attached to the polymer supports by
reacting lithiated poly(styrene-DVB) with elemental sulfur and then
reducing the S-S group with $LiAlH_4$ (15).

Alternatively, we prefer to prepare polymers containing the
thiol functionally (15,25) by reacting chloromethylated resin with
thiourea (25). The reaction of (P)-CH_2Cl with thiourea gives a
supported isothiouromium chloride. The latter solid is reacted
with hydroxyl groups to produce a thiol-containing polymer.

$$(P)-CH_2-Cl + S=C(NH_2)_2 \longrightarrow$$

$$(P)-CH_2-S-C\overset{\diagup NH}{\underset{\diagdown NH_2}{}} \cdot HCl \overset{OH^-}{\longrightarrow}$$

$$(P)- CH_2-SH$$

If the second step is carried out in the presence of oxygen, S-S
groups are produced (25).

Chloromethylated polystyrene-DVB (2.5 g) (1.23 meq/g) and
2 g of thiourea were refluxed with a mixture of THF:ethanol (2:1)
for 48 hr. The resin was then washed with water, followed by THF
and benzene, to remove all excess soluble reagents and byproducts.
The resin was then suspended in a 50 ml of benzene and 0.1 g of
tetraheptylammonium chloride and 2 g of sodium hydroxyde in 10 ml
of deionized and degassed water were added. The three-phase
mixture was refluxed under N_2 for 48 hr. After filtration,
washings with THF, water, THF:6N HCl (3:1), water, THF, acetone,
methylene chloride, and finally methanol were carried out. The
resulting resin was dried under vacuum.

Attachment of Metal Complexes

Several methods for incorporating metal complexes into the functionalized supports are illustrated schematically in Figure 3.

The simplest methods involve contacting the functionalized support with the metal complex (catalyst) in solution. If the complex is coordinatively unsaturated, a ligand association may occur, binding the molecular species to the solid. This type of attachment is exemplified by the following:

$$H_2Os_3(CO)_{10} + \text{(P)}-PPh_2 \rightarrow H_2Os_3(CO)_{10}Ph_2P-\text{(P)} \qquad (1)$$

Mixtures of variously substituted Os clusters can be avoided by using functionalized poly(styrene-DVB) with different concentrations and distribution of ligands.

If the molecular catalyst contains a labile ligand, a ligand exchange may occur involving the anchored ligand and the ligands on the complex. This type of attachment is exemplified by the following:

$$H_2Os_3(CO)_{10}PPh_3 + \text{(P)}-PPh_2 \rightarrow H_2Os_3(CO)_{10}PPh_2-\text{(P)} \qquad (2)$$

These ligand exchange and association reactions require complexes (catalysts) that are stable during the synthesis. An alternative is the in situ formation of the supported species, illustrated by the formation of a supported tetrairidium cluster, as follows:

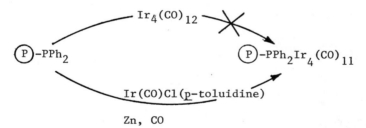

Zn, CO

In all these procedures for attachment, the solvent plays an important role. It must dissolve the catalyst to be attached; it should also swell the support sufficiently to eliminate the diffusional resistance in the polymer and thereby allow a uniform distribution of the metal in the support. The important role of the solvent is illustrated by the following example: Stuntz and Shapley (26) reported a direct synthesis of mono- and disubstituted phosphorus ligand derivatives of $Ir_4(CO)_{12}$. We attempted to apply their method using the attached ligand (P)-PPh$_2$ instead of PPh$_3$, keeping all the synthesis conditions constant. The desired formation of attached tetrairidium species did not occur. But when the methoxyethanol solvent was replaced by a mixture of

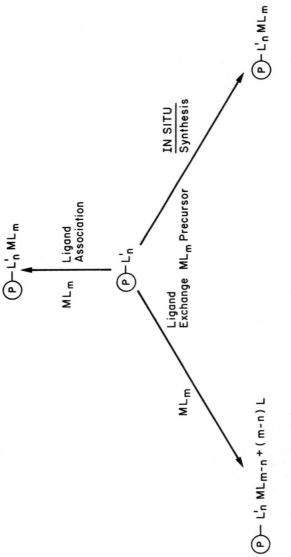

Figure 3. Schematic representation of the incorporation of metal complexes in functionalized polymers. Key: ML_m, metal complex; L, ligand; and Ⓟ, poly(styrene–DVB).

toluene–THF–water (a good swelling agent for the support), the formation of the attached cluster took place as shown in the preceding paragraph.

Characterization

A variety of spectroscopic techniques have been used to characterize the polymer–attached species. The identifications are based on comparisons between the spectra of known molecular compounds and those of the analogous attached species.

Infrared spectroscopy has been the most useful method, especially when the attached species incorporate carbonyl ligands. FT analysis is useful for substracting the background spectrum of the support and for allowing identification of species present in low concentrations. Membrane supports about 10 μm thick, described above, are optimal. Many examples are given in the literature (27), and the technique has been used to characterize working catalysts in the presence of vapor- and liquid-phase reactants.

Raman spectroscopy is useful for detecting metal–ligand and metal–metal bonds in molecular complexes, but it has not yet been successfully applied to polymer-supported catalysts. We believe that the low concentrations of the metal species and the fluorescence associated with the support are largely responsible for the lack of good spectra. Further work is expected to bring success with this method.

The EXAFS technique is potentially of great value for structural characterization of supported catalysts, even in the working state. An EXAFS study of a polymer-bound analog of Wilkinson's catalyst established the Rh–Cl and Rh–P interatomic distances, which are in agreement with those determined by x-ray crystallography of the molecular complex (28). A scheme for structural changes of the polymer-bound catalyst was inferred from the EXAFS data: when Wilkinson's complex $RhCl(PPh_3)_3$ was brought in contact with a polymer containing phosphine groups, a binuclear complex was attached to the polymer. This binuclear complex reacted with H_2 to form mononuclear hydride complexes.

^{31}P NMR was used to characterize polymer-supported rhodium species (29). The supports were made by homopolymerization of p-styryldiphenylphosphine or p-styryldicyclohexylphosphine. Each ring of the highly swollen polymer was functionalized with a phosphine group, giving a relatively high signal strength and relatively little variation in the environment of the phosphorus in the polymer. Complexes such as $RhCl(C_2H_4)_2$ were added stepwise to triphenylphosphine and to the analogous polymer. A series of complexes was formed, depending on the Rh/P ratio. The polymer ligands had ^{31}P signals at positions differing only slightly from those of their molecular analogs. This agreement strongly suggests a similarity in structure and, since the structures of the molecular complexes have been well determined, those of the

supported complexes are probably correct. The ^{31}P technique is
not expected to be successful with typical polymers used as
catalyst supports, since they are less uniform in the environments
around the phosphorus and have lower phosphorus loadings.

Polymers have been characterized by electron microprobe
analysis to determine profiles of metal and functional groups (30).
A catalyst particle (e.g., a spherical bead) is sectioned and
traversed with an electron beam in a vacuum system. The emitted
x-ray signals allow quantitative elemental analysis of a roughly
1 μm^3 volume of the catalyst. The results indicate the uniformity
of incorporation of functional groups and metal in the polymer.

Catalytic Kinetics Measurements

Polymers incorporating Rh complexes, among others, have been
tested as catalysts in flow systems with the reactant flow rates
measured individually (5,31,32). For example, H_2 and He flowed
through a bed of supported copper, held at 300°C to remove traces
of O_2, and through a bed of zeolite 5Å (Linde) to remove traces of
water. Liquid reactants (e.g., hexene-1) were introduced from a
variable-speed syringe pump into a vaporizer made of a 0.1-m
length of 6.4-mm stainless-steel tubing packed with glass beads.
The vaporized reactants flowed out the vaporizer with the H_2 and/
or He mixture. The reactor, giving differential conversions, was
connected to an on-line gas detector. This system allowed the
recording of differential conversions, and therefore, reaction
rates.

The reactor used in these experiments was also a thermostated, controlled-atmosphere infrared cell, allowing monitoring
of spectra of functioning membrane catalysts. An FTIR allows
monitoring of both transient and steady-state spectra. The
system is designed to provide reaction kinetics and spectra
indicating the predominant form of the functioning catalyst—not
necessarily the catalytically active species. This apparatus is
of value in the diagnosis of catalyst breakin and aging
phenomena (27) and under favorable circumstances may give some
indication of intermediates in the catalytic cycles. Such
information can also—in prospect—be determined by application
of other kinds of spectroscopy, especially Raman and EXAFS, to
functioning catalysts.

Conclusions

1. Poly(styrene-DVB) offers the advantages of high-purity
   catalyst supports which are easily prepared and functionalized.
2. Synthesis methods allow systematic variation of the physical
   form, crosslinking, the nature of the functional groups, the
   degree of functionalization, and the distribution of
   functional groups.

3. Incorporation of catalytic groups has been carried out by
    ligand exchange and ligand association reactions as well as
    by in situ syntheses modeled on syntheses of molecular
    analogs.
4. Characterization has been done most successfully by infrared
    spectroscopy and EXAFS, and both these techniques can be
    combined with measurements of catalytic kinetics to allow
    investigation of functioning catalysts.

Acknowledgments

The work at the University of Delaware was supported by the
National Science Foundation. We thank Rohm and Haas Company for
permission to publish work done there.

Literature Cited

1. Chauvin, Y.; Commereuc, D.; and Dawans, F. Prog. Polym. Sci.
    1977, 5, 95.
2. Fréchet, J. M. J.; and Farrall, M. J. in "Chemistry and
    Properties of Crosslinked Polymers," Labana, S. S., ed.,
    Academic Press, 1977, New York.
3. Whitehurst, D. D. Chemtech, 1980, 44.
4. Grubbs, R. H. Chemtech, 1977, 512.
5. Lieto, J.; Rafalko, J. J.; and Gates, B. C. J. Catal., 1980,
    62, 149.
6. N'Guini Effa, J. B.; Lieto, J.; and Aune, J.-P., to be
    published.
7. Zundel, G., in "Hydration and Intermolecular Interaction.
    Infrared Investigations with Polyelectrolyte Membranes,"
    1969, Academic Press, New York.
8. Kun, K. A.; and Kunin, R. J. Polym. Sci., 1967, C 16, 1457;
    1968, A-1, 6, 2684.
9. Heitz, W., in "Advances in Polymer Science," H.-J. Cantow,
    editor, 1977, Springer-Verlag, Berlin, Heidelberg, New York.
10. Albright, R. L. U.S. Patent, 1972, 3,663,467; 1973,
    3,767,600.
11. Meitzner, E. F.; and Olive, J. E. Union of South Africa
    Patent, 1959, 59-2393; British Patents, 1963, 932,125 and
    932,126.
12. Albright, R. L.; Dooley, K. B.; and Gates, B. C., to be
    published.
13. Pepper, K. W.; Paisley, H. M.; and Young, M. A. J. Chem.
    Soc., 1953, 4097.
14. Black, R. F.; Quertz, C. K.; and Pasek, R. J. U.S. Patent,
    1976, 3,980,755.
15. Farrall, M.-J.; and Fréchet, J. M. J. J. Org. Chem., 1976,
    41, 3877.
16. Braun, D. Makromol. Chem., 1959, 30, 85.
17. Chalk, A. J. J. Polym. Sci., 1968, B-6, 649.

18. Evans, D. C. J. Polym. Sci., 1974, 12, 247.
19. Tamborski, C.; Ford, F. E.; Lehn, W. L.; Moore, G. J.; and Soloski, E. J. J. Org. Chem., 1962, 27, 619.
20. Dumont, W.; Poulin, J. C.; Dang, T. P.; and Kagan, H. B. J. Am. Chem. Soc., 1973, 95, 8295.
21. Masuda, T.; and Stille, J. K. J. Am. Chem. Soc., 1978, 100, 268.
22. Tatarsky, D.; Milstein, D.; Dooley, K. M.; and Gates, B. C. to be published.
23. Patterson, J. A., in "Biochemical Aspects of Reactions on Solid Supports," G. E. Stark, ed., 1971, Academic Press, New York.
24. Sabetay, L.; and Mintson, G. Bull. Soc. Chim., 1929, 45, 842.
25. Fréchet, J. M. J.; de Smet, M. D.; and Farrall, M. J. Polymer, 1979, 20, 675.
26. Stuntz, G. F.; and Shapley, J. R. Inorg. Chem., 1976, 15, 1994.
27. Gates, B. C.; and Lieto, J. Chemtech, 1980, 195, 248.
28. Reed, J.; Eisenberger, P.; Teo, B.-K.; and Kincaid, B. M. J. Am. Chem. Soc., 1977, 99, 5217.
29. Naaktgeboren, A. A.; Nolte, R. J. M.; and Drenth, W. J. Am. Chem. Soc., 1980, 102, 3350.
30. Hanson, D. L.; Katzer, J. R.; Gates, B. C.; Schuit, G. C. A.; and Harnsberger, H. F. J. Catal. 1974, 32, 204.
31. Thornton, R.; and Gates, B. C. J. Catal., 1974, 34, 275.
32. Jarrell, M. S.; and Gates, B. C. J. Catal., 1975, 40, 255.

RECEIVED November 4, 1981.

Polymeric Cofactors for Homogeneous Rhodium(I) Catalyzed Alkene Hydrogenations

DAVID E. BERGBREITER, MARIAN S. BURSTEN, KAELYN COOK, and GREGORY L. PARSONS

Texas A&M University, Department of Chemistry, College Station, TX 77843

Polymeric reagents prepared by exchanging silver(I) for H$^+$ on a macroreticular polystyrene sulfonate ion exchange resin are shown to be capable of sel- ectively absorbing triphenylphosphine from solu- tions of RhCl(PPh$_3$)$_3$. Addition of this silver(I) polystyrene sulfonate to triphenylphosphine pois- oned hydrogenations selectively removes the tri- phenylphosphine and restores the original hydrogen- ation rate. Silver(I) polystyrene sulfonate did not accelerate normal alkene hydrogenations but ad- dition of ethylene as a temporary ligand in con- junction with addition of silver(I) polystyrene sulfonate to RhCl(PPh$_3$)$_3$ catalyzed hydrogenations of 1-hexene, cyclohexene, and ethylene led to rate increases of 196%, 135%, and 580% respectively. Both silver(I) and dimethylammonium polystyrene sulfonate polymers activated hydrogenations of nor- bornene and norbornadiene using this same catalyst. HCL absorption was a factor in these latter two activations.

Insoluble organic polymers have been used increasingly in re- cent years either to support homogeneous catalysts or as reagents in organic synthesis (1-5). These applications of insoluble poly- mers in organic reactions produce both experimental advantages over comparable homogeneous systems (product isolation, catalyst recovery) and, on occasion, different reaction rates and/or sel- ectivities (6,7). We have used this difference between polymeric reagents and their homogeneous counterparts in a novel but useful application in catalysis. Specifically, we have used soft acid containing polymers to selectively remove inhibitors or poisons from a homogeneous catalytic reaction. In effect, we have used the polymers described herein as cofactors in homogeneous rhodi- um(I) catalyzed alkene hydrogenation reactions.

0097-6156/82/0192-0031 $6.00/0

In many homogeneous transition metal catalytic systems the
more active form of the catalyst results from dissociation of a
ligand in an unfavorable equilibrium like eq 1. Active catalysts

$$ML_n \; \rightleftarrows \; ML_{n-1} \; + \; L \qquad (1)$$

are also often generated by oxidative addition of H_2 followed by
the reductive elimination of HX (X = halide, alkyl, aryl)

$$MX \; + \; H_2 \; \rightleftarrows \; MH_2X \; \rightleftarrows \; MH \; + \; HX \qquad (2)$$

(eq 2). Decreasing the concentration of either the ligand L (eq
1) or HX (eq 2) can increase the concentration of the active catalyst species ML_{n-1} or MH according to Le Chatelier's principle.
Thus, it might be possible to observe increased hydrogenation
rates if suitable procedures for removing L or HX from a catalytically active system could be devised. The relatively common ex-
pedient of adding a base to produce a metal hydride catalyst ex-
emplifies this idea. Out initial goal was to design a functionalized polymer to selectively absorb a nonvolatile ligand L such as
triphenylphosphine (PPh_3) from an active catalytic system in the
hope that the catalysis would then proceed more rapidly. The
metal containing polymers described below meet this objective and
do indeed accelerate certain alkene hydrogenations using
$RhCl(PPh_3)_3$.
      Other attempts to shift equilibria 1 and 2 have been made.
One of the reasons $RhCl(PPh_3)_3$ was first supported on a polymer
was in the hope of shifting equilibrium 1 (8). It was hoped that
the concentration of ML_{n-1} could be increased. Several methods
for removal of triorganophosphines from solution have also been
tried. For example, reverse osmosis was used by Knoth, Gosser,
and Parshall to separate PPh_3 and other low molecular weight compounds from transition metal catalysts (9,10). Selective reaction
of dissociated PPh_3 with a Lewis acid would also consume PPh_3 and
shift equilibrium 1 rightward (11,12,13). However, side reactions
such as halide exchange or metal hydride formation limit the utility of this approach. Our procedure combines advantages of both
of these previous procedures.

Results and Discussion

      We have prepared Lewis acid containing polymers which select-
ively absorb PPh_3 in the presence of a homogeneous transition
metal catalyst. This selectivity is the result of diffusional
limitations inherent in these crosslinked polymers which discrim-
inate in favor of the smaller PPh_3 molecules. These ligand absorbing polymers circumvent many of the side reactions encountered
in earlier attempts by Shriver to use soluble Lewis acids to selectively react with PPh_3 in solutions of transition metal catalysts (12,13). In addition, the polymeric reagents we have design-

ed meet several important criteria. Specifically, the polymers are not catalysts themselves, they are easily prepared, handled and they are air stable. Further, although these polymeric reagents do eventually absorb homogeneous catalysts, absorption of triphenylphosphine is sufficiently fast that the desired selectivity is achieved.

Preparation of the desired polymeric reagents was successfully accomplished using ion exchange resins which had been exchanged with various metal salts by conventional ion exchange techniques (14). The ion exchange resin chosen as a substrate for preparation of these reagents was Amberlyst 15, a sulfonated macroreticular polystyrene (PS-SO_3H) obtained from Rohm and Haas. This resin has pore sizes of ca. 250 Å and can easily accomodate a molecule of PPh_3. Exhaustive extraction of this polymer with DMF both removed any impurities left from the polymerization process and, inadvertently, generated PS-SO_3^-H$_2$NMe$^+$ which was used with PS-SO_3Na in various experiments as a comparison to metal sulfonates. Metals used included Co^{+2}, Ni^{+2}, Cu^{+2} and Ag^+. After these metals were exchanged onto this polymer, the resulting polymeric metal sulfonates were washed first with water, then ethanol, then ether, and dried first in air and then in vacuo until a constant weight was achieved. In some cases (Co^{+2} and Cu^{+2}), the hydrated metal sulfonates isolated before complete drying were also evaluated as PPh_3 absorbers. The efficacy of these reagents for PPh_3 absorption was determined by monitoring the disappearance of PPh_3 from a PPh solution which contained the solid PS-SO_3M by either GC or NMR spectroscopy. Fully dried metal sulfonates were more effective PPh_3 absorbers than hydrated metal sulfonates. The silver(I) exchanged polymer (PS-SO_3Ag) was the most effective at removing PPh_3 from solutions in THF, toluene and ethanol and was the metal sulfonate used in subsequent applications. The PS-SO_3Ag absorbed 0.3 mmol of PPh_3/mmol of PS-SO_3Ag and typically contained 2.5-3.0 mmol of Ag^+/g of polymer (this corresponds to roughly 50% exchange of silver for sodium in the exchange of silver onto the polymer). Control experiments showed that macroporous polystyrene without functional groups (PS-H), dimethylammonium polystyrene sulfonate (PS-SO_3^-H$_2$NMe$_2^+$), and sodium polystyrene sulfonate (PS-SO_3Na) (an impurity in the PS-SO_3Ag) were ineffective at absorbing PPh_3. All the sulfonate polymers were equally able to absorb HCl to reform the starting PS-SO_3H.

The ability of PS-SO_3Ag to selectively absorb PPh_3 was shown by UV-visible and NMR spectroscopy. In these experiments, a toluene solution of RhCl(PPh_3)$_3$ was allowed to react with PS-SO_3Ag and PS-SO_3^-H$_2$NMe$_2^+$. The relative rates of absorption of PPh_3 and RhCl(PPh_3)$_3$ by PS-SO_3Ag and PS-SO_3^-H$_2$NMe$_2^+$ were then determined spectroscopically. Concentrations in the UV-visible experiments were typical of catalytic conditions (e.g. 10^{-3}-10^{-4} M in rhodium(I). The PPh_3 absorption was monitored at 262 nm and the RhCl(PPh_3)$_3$ absorption was monitored at 417 nm. The absorbance at 417 nm was found to decrease in the presence of both PS-SO_3Ag and

PS-SO$_3^-$H$_2$NMe$_2^+$; a more rapid decrease was found with PS-SO$_3$Ag. To
an extent this decrease in absorbance reflects the differing ε for
RhCl(PPh$_3$)$_3$ and {RhCl(PPh$_3$)$_2$}$_2$ (15). The dimer is reported to
form slowly in nonpolar solvents at these concentrations (15-18).
It was expected that dimer formation would be accelerated by
PS-SO$_3$Ag if this polymer were removing PPh$_3$ from solution. The
UV-visible determination of relative rates for rhodium(I) absorption versus PPh$_3$ absorption was therefore complicated by this
dimerization reaction which had the effect of reducing the apparent selectivity of PPh$_3$ absorption since dimer formation was indistinguishable from RhCl(PPh$_3$)$_3$ absorption by UV-visible spectroscopy.
Nevertheless, it was possible to estimate that PPh$_3$ absorption was
10-100 times faster than Rh(I) absorption. The non-polymeric reagent, C$_6$H$_5$SO$_3$Ag, reacted rapidly with both RhCl(PPh$_3$)$_3$ and PPh$_3$.

The expectation that dimer formation would be accelerated by
PPh$_3$ absorption by PS-SO$_3$Ag was verified by ^{31}P NMR. When a 0.44
M solution of RhCl(PPh$_3$)$_3$ was prepared in CDCl$_3$/CH$_2$Cl$_2$ (10/90,
v/v) we obtained the expected ^{31}P NMR spectrum consisting of a
doublet of triplets at δ 47.3 due to the PPh$_3$ trans to Cl (J$_{Rh-P}$ =
191 Hz, J$_{P-P}$ = 38 Hz) and a doublet of doublets at δ 30.6 due to
the PPh$_3$'s cis to Cl (J$_{Rh-P}$ = 144 Hz, J$_{P-P}$ = 38 Hz) (17). A small
impurity of triphenylphosphine oxide was also present at δ 27.
After contact with PS-SO$_3$Ag for 1800 s, the ^{31}P NMR spectrum
changed. Specifically the absorptions assigned to the PPh$_3$'s of
RhCl(PPh$_3$)$_3$ decreased in intensity and a new doublet appeared at
δ 50.9 (J$_{Rh-P}$ = 196 Hz) which was assigned to {RhCl(PPh$_3$)$_2$}$_2$. Extended contact of RhCl(PPh$_3$)$_3$ with PS-SO$_3$Ag (2 h, vigorous shak-
ing) led to precipitation of crystals of the dimer as expected
based on the dimer's reported lower solubility (17,19). Similar
experiments on a same time scale with PS-SO$_3^-$H$_2$NMe$_2$ failed to
produce evidence for significant amounts of dimer formation.
Taken together with the UV-visible spectroscopy experiments, these
data support the conclusion that selective removal of PPh$_3$ by
PS-SO$_3$Ag from solutions of rhodium complexes does occur. Isolation of the polymeric reagent after these experiments and extraction with acidified methanol (vide infra) verified that these
resins did indeed contain PPh$_3$.

Having prepared the desired type of functionalized polymer,
we next set out to use it to accelerate catalytic reactions. However, reactions in which RhCl(PPh$_3$)$_3$ only, RhCl(PPh$_3$)$_3$ and
PS-SO$_3^-$H$_2$NMe$_2^+$, or RhCl(PPh$_3$)$_3$ and PS-SO$_3$Ag were used to hydrogen-
ate the alkenes 1-octene, 1-hexene, cyclohexene, styrene, ethyl-
acrylate, and 1,5-cyclooctadiene (1,5-cyclooctadiene was not
hydrogenated) all occurred at the same rate. Reaction rates were
obtained by monitoring the uptake of H$_2$ consumed/s at 25 °C and at
atmospheric pressure. The rate was determined by fitting a
straight line to this data and taking its slope. However,
PS-SO$_3$Ag was shown to be capable of selective PPh$_3$ absorption under hydrogenation conditions. This was shown by hydrogenation
reactions carried out in the presence of added PPh$_3$. When 0.01 to

0.02 M PPh$_3$ was present in hydrogenations of styrene, 1-octene, and cyclohexene, the rates of hydrogenation were from 1 to 13 % of their uninhibited rates (cf. Table I). Addition of PS-SO$_3$Ag produced a dramatic increase in the rate of hydrogenation after an induction period of 350-1500 s; most induction periods were about 700-800 s. The final hydrogenation rate achieved was comparable to the rate observed in the absence of any added PPh$_3$; when more alkene was injected into the hydrogenation apparatus after all the alkene initially present had been consumed (about 2000 s after the addition of PS-SO$_3$Ag), the hydrogenation rate was the same as that observed in the absence of any added PPh$_3$. Extraction of the polymeric reagent after such reactions showed that the polymer contained PPh$_3$ (vide infra).

Although PS-SO$_3$Ag does have a kinetically detectable effect when the PPh$_3$ concentration is > 0.01 M in that addition of this phosphine absorbing polymer restores the original catalytic hydrogenation rate in a PPh$_3$ poisoned hydrogenation reaction, the polymer is clearly ineffective as a cofactor in normal hydrogenation reactions. This could be the result of several factors. First, in normal hydrogenations without added PPh$_3$ when the initial RhCl(PPh$_3$)$_3$ concentration is on the order of 1 x 10^{-3} M or less there is only a very low concentration of free ligand present. For example, equilibria forming dimer and/or RhCl(PPh$_3$)$_3$ at these initial concentrations of RhCl(PPh$_3$)$_3$ would produce free ligand at a concentration about half of that of the starting RhCl(PPh$_3$)$_3$ concentration using the equilibrium constants reported by Tolman (17). It has been suggested that the hydrogenation rate of RhCl(PPh$_3$)$_3$ catalyzed alkene hydrogenation may reach a limiting value when the alkene concentration is ca. 1 M and the PPh$_3$ concentration is ca. 1 x 10^{-3} M (20). Thus, PPh$_3$ absorption might not be expected to have a dramatic effect. Second, even if this limiting hydrogenation rate is not obtained under these conditions, the kinetic effectiveness of PS-SO$_3$Ag as a phosphine absorber on a time scale appropriate to these facile hydrogenations must inevitably decrease as the concentration of phosphine ligand approaches smaller and smaller values.

We reasoned that if it were possible to increase the concentration of free ligand PPh$_3$ while avoiding formation of a precipitate of dimer that we would maximize the possibility of observing enhanced hydrogenation rates. Such a scheme is indeed possible. Tolman et. al. had previously shown that an ethylene complex of RhCl(PPh$_3$)$_3$ is formed reversibly on exposure of toluene solutions of RhCl(PPh$_3$)$_3$ to ethylene (eq 3) (17). Although the equilibrium

$$RhCl(PPh_3)_3 + C_2H_4 \; \rightleftharpoons \; RhCl(PPh_3)_2(C_2H_4) + PPh_3 \qquad (3)$$

constant for this reaction is not large (K = 0.4) (17), an excess of ethylene will drive this equilbrium completely to the right and produce a PPh$_3$ solution whose concentration will be approximately the same as the concentration of the starting RhCl(PPh$_3$)$_3$.

Table I. Activation of $RhCl(PPh_3)_3$ Catalyzed Alkene Hydrogenations Inhibited by Triphenylphosphine Using $PS-SO_3Ag$.[a]

$[RhCl(PPh_3)_3]$ x 10^3, $\underline{M}$	[Alkene, $\underline{M}$]	$[PPh_3]$ added, $\underline{M}$	Induction period, s	Rate x 10^3 mmol of H_2/s Initial	Final
Styrene					
2.19	0.11	0.010	850	0.02	1.3
2.24	0.48	0.014	800	0.11	2.7
2.19	0.11	-	-	3.0	3.0
1-Octene					
2.22	0.10	0.014	1500	0.02	0.10
2.27	0.38	0.016	700	0.07	0.55
Cyclohexene					
3.33	0.12	0.017	350[b]	0.048[c]	0.90
1.88	0.11	0.011	550	0.0075	0.036
1.80	0.11	-	-	0.76	0.76

[a] Reactions were run in 15 mL of toluene. At about 3000 s, 0.20 g of $PS-SO_3Ag$ was added. The hydrogenation rate measured before this addition was the initial rate. After the $PS-SO_3Ag$ was added there was an induction period after which the final rate was measured. [b] H_2 uptake stopped until 350 s after the addition of $PS-SO_3Ag$. [c] The initial rate decreased to 0 mmol H_2/s after 400 s and was 0 at the time the $PS-SO_3Ag$ was added.

Absorption of this PPh_3 by $PS-SO_3Ag$ could then occur and small changes in subsequent hydrogenation rates might be achieved. Indeed, when $RhCl(PPh_3)_3$ was dissolved in the presence of $PS-SO_3Ag$ under an ethylene atmosphere absorption of PPh_3 did occur. Subsequent addition of an alkene (after 900 s of mixing), removal of the ethylene after 100 s by degassing, addition of hydrogen, and stirring then initiated a hydrogenation reaction. This procedure had no effect on the rates of hydrogenation of styrene or ethyl acrylate; these alkenes were the most rapidly hydrogenated alkenes used in this study. However, 1-hexene, cyclohexene, and ethylene were observed to react faster after ethylene pretreatment. The rate increases seen were: 1-hexene (196 %); cyclohexene (135 %); and ethylene (580 %). Control experiments employing ethylene pretreatment in the absence of any cofactor, ethylene pretreatment in the presence of $PS-SO_3^-H_2NMe_2^+$, and no ethylene pretreatment or cofactor present all failed to produce activated hydrogenation rates.

After an ethylene pretreated hydrogenation of 1-hexene in the presence of $PS-SO_3Ag$, the $PS-SO_3Ag$ was rinsed three times with CH_2Cl_2 to remove any PPh_3 which might be clinging to the surface. The polymer was then extracted with acidified methanol. A λ_{max} at 262 nm was observed in the resulting extract by UV spectroscopy. This was the same as the maximum for PPh_3 in this solution. A spectrum of the acidified methanol extract from a sample of $PS-SO_3H$ or $PS-SO_3^-H_2NMe_2^+$ showed no absorbance in this region. Thus $PS-SO_3Ag$ does absorb PPh_3 when ethylene pretreatment is employed.

A typical hydrogenation procedure for the above experiments was as follows: The catalyst (10-60 μmol) was placed in a 100-mL 3-necked flask and the cofactor (0.2 g) was put in a solid addition tube attached to this flask. The apparatus was assembled, evacuated, flushed with H_2 three times, and then held under vacuum for 10 min. The apparatus was flushed with H_2 and evacuated three more times, then filled with H_2 and then the solvent (10 mL of toluene) was added. The solution was carefully degassed and filled with H_2 three times and stirred vigorously under H_2 until the catalyst fully dissolved. At this point, the stirring was stopped and the alkene (2-20 mmol) was injected. When the cofactor was to be added at the beginning of a hydrogenation, it was added at this point by turning the solid addition tube. Hydrogenation was initiated by resumption of stirring. Alternatively, the cofactor was added after the hydrogenation had been initiated. When hydrogenations were carried out utilizing an ethylene pretreatment, the catalyst and the cofactor were both placed in the hydrogenation vessel as the apparatus was set up. The third neck of the hydrogenation flask was fitted with a gas inlet valve connected to an ethylene source. The hydrogenation apparatus was evacuated and filled with ethylene three times. Toluene (10 mL) was added and the resulting suspension was flushed with ethylene (3x). The resulting mixture was allowed to stir under an ethylene atmosphere for 900 s at which time the alkene to be hydrogenated (2-20 mmol) was injected. After an additional 100 s, the apparatus was carefully evacuated and vigorously stirred for 15 s. During this time the catalyst solution turned from yellow (the color of the ethylene complex) to red. Once the ethylene had been removed the apparatus was filled with H_2. After two more cycles consisting solely of filling with H_2 and careful evacuation, the apparatus was filled with H_2 and the hydrogenation was initiated.

In order to determine whether any catalytic activity resided on the polymer beads, some hydrogenation experiments were stopped before alkene had been consumed. The polymer beads were allowed to settle and the supernatent was transferred via syringe to another H_2-filled hydrogenation apparatus and the hydrogenation was resumed. The polymeric cofactors were stirred two times with toluene (15 mL) which was then removed using a syringe. Fresh toluene (10 mL) and alkene (2-20 mmol) were injected and the stirring initiated. No catalytic activity was observed on the beads. Reactions for which catalytic activity was observed in the transferred solution but not on the polymer beads included hydrogenations of styrene, 1-hexene, and norbornene catalyzed by $RhCl(PPh_3)_3$ all using PS-SO$_3$Ag as a cofactor.

The rates of activated alkene hydrogenations seen in the above studies are comparable to those seen earlier by Wilkinson when $RhCl(PPh_3)$ was reportedly formed in situ from PPh_3 and $[RhCl(COD)]_2$ (21) supporting our conclusion that removal of phosphine was responsible for the activations seen in our procedures. However alternative explanations involving possible formation of a hydridorhodium catalyst (e.g. eq 4 and 5 must also be considered. The hydridorhodium catalysts formed in these equa-

$$RhH_2Cl(PPh_3)_2(C_2H_4) \; \rightleftharpoons \; RhH(PPh_3)_2(C_2H_4) \; + \; HCl \qquad (4)$$

$$RhCl(PPh_3)_3 \; + \; H_2 \; \rightleftharpoons \; RhH_2Cl(PPh_3)_3 \; \rightleftharpoons \; RhH(PPh_3)_3 + HCl \quad (5)$$

tions could be good hydrogenation catalysts; $RhH(PPh_3)_3$ has been reported to be especially active as a homogeneous alkene hydrogenation catalyst (22,23). Further, the polymeric cofactor we have employed is a good HCl absorber as a result of the affinity of silver(I) for chloride and because of the affinity of a polystyrene sulfonate resin for HCl.

Several observations suggest that HCl absorption to form a hydridorhodium catalyst is not the mode of activation seen in the 1-hexene, cyclohexene, and ethylene hydrogenations discussed above. First, PS-SO$_3^-$ $H_2NMe_2^+$, which is a good HCl absorber, does not activate any of these alkene hydrogenations with or without ethylene pretreatment. Second, addition of neutral alumina (another HCl absorber) or powdered KOH at KOH/Rh molar ratios of 20/1 was ineffective at producing a rate acceleration under our conditions. Larger ratios of KOH/Rh (e.g. 100/1) did accelerate 1-hexene hydrogenation by $RhCl(PPh_3)_3$ and under these conditions

RhH(PPh$_3$)$_3$ may have indeed been the species responsible for this greater rate of hydrogenation. In cases where additional 1-hexene had been added to such KOH-accelerated hydrogenation reactions and the products were analyzed by GC, some 2- and 3-hexenes were detected. These internal alkenes are presumably the result of isomerization of 1-hexene by RhH(PPh$_3$)$_3$ (24). Isomerization was not detected in PS-SO$_3$Ag accelerated hydrogenations. Finally, cyclohexene hydrogenation was accelerated under our conditions but RhH(PPh$_3$)$_3$ is reportedly not a good catalyst for hydrogenation of internal alkenes like cyclohexene.

Although we do not believe that HCl absorption by PS-SO$_3$Ag contributes significantly to the rate accelerations seen above, HCl absorption is apparently a factor in accelerating RhCl(PPh$_3$)$_3$ hydrogenations of norbornene and norbornadiene in the presence of PS-SO$_3$Ag or other polystyrene sulfonates. Both of these alkenes are hydrogenated more quickly by RhCl(PPh$_3$)$_3$ when PS-SO$_3$Ag is present; ethylene pretreatment is unnecessary. However, hydrogenations of both of these alkenes are also accelerated if PS-SO$_3^-$H$_2$NMe$_2^+$ is present as a cofactor. Since PS-SO$_3^-$H$_2$NMe$_2^+$ absorbs HCl but not PPh$_3$ this suggests elimination of HCl to form a hydridorhodium species may be occurring in these instances. We also observe an induction period after addition of PS-SO$_3$Ag which is shorter than that seen in other hydrogenations which also suggests that some different type of activation is occurring.

The activation of norbornene and norbornadiene hydrogenation varied depending on the cofactor which was added. For example, norbornene hydrogenations were 1.8X faster when PS-SO$_3^-$H$_2$NMe$_2^+$ was added and 3.7X faster when PS-SO$_3$Ag was added. This suggests that absorption of both HCl and PPh$_3$ may be important in this case. The hydrogenation rate of norbornadiene increased more dramatically, up to 550-fold following addition of PS-SO$_3$Ag or PS-SO$_3^-$H$_2$NMe$_2^+$ to a hydrogenation reaction. Neutral alumina also was effective at producing enhanced hydrogenation rates but the rate of the hydrogenation reaction slowly decreased with time. The most efficient cofactor found for inducing rate accelerations in norbornadiene hydrogenations was simply KOH at a KOH/Rh molar ratio of 160. The formation of a catalytically active species other than RhCl(PPh$_3$)(norbornadiene) is highly likely. Initially we did note an obvious color change on introduction of norbornadiene into a solution of RhCl(PPh$_3$)$_3$; the major species formed initially was probably RhCl(PPh$_3$)(norbornadiene).

Conclusions

Using a readily available ion exchange resin we have successfully prepared silver(I) containing ion exchange polymers which selectively remove PPh$_3$ from solutions of a transition metal complex such as RhCl(PPh$_3$)$_3$. In cases where excess PPh$_3$ inhibits alkene hydrogenation, addition of this polymer restores the original catalytic activity. In some cases involving representative alkenes (1-hexene, cyclohexene), modest rate accelerations of $RhCl(PPh_3)_3$ catalyzed hydrogenations could be achieved after ethylene pretreatment. In other cases such as $RhCl(PPh_3)_3$ catalyzed norbornene hydrogenations, $PS-SO_3Ag$ activated the hydrogenation by absorbing both HCl and PPh_3. Finally, in the case of norbornadiene, $PS-SO_3Ag$ led to both HCl and PPh_3 absorption but experiments with other heterogeneous cofactors suggest that only HCL absorption and the coordination ability of norbornadiene are important in this instance.

These results describe a distinctly different way of using polymers to modify homogeneous reactions. The results in these $RhCl(PPh_3)_3$ studies should be applicable to other phosphine complexed transition metal complexes. Extensions of these studies should be able to produce more selective and/or more efficient ligand absorbing polymers. Application of these procedures to other catalytic systems could also result in more practicable activations of conventional homogeneous alkene hydrogenation reactions and we are presently exploring these possibilities.

Acknowledgment

We thank the Office of Naval Research, the Department of Energy, and the Texas A&M Center for Energy and Mineral Resources for support of this research.

Literature Cited

1. Bailey, D. C.; Langer, S. H. Chem. Rev. 1981, 81, 109-148. James, B. R. Adv. Organometal. Chem. 1979, 17, 319-405.
2. Chauvin, Y.; Commereuc, D.; Dawans, F. Prog. Polym. Sci. 1977, 5, 95-226.
3. Manecke, G.; Storck, W. Angew. Chem., Int. Ed. Eng. 1978, 17, 657-668. Hodge, P. Chem. Br. 1978, 14, 237-243. Leznoff, C. C. Acc. Chem. Res. 1978, 11, 327-333.
4. Regen, S. L. Angew. Chem., Int. Ed. Eng. 1979, 18, 421-429.
5. Mathur, N. K.; Narang, C. K.; Williams, R. E. "Polymers as Aids in Organic Chemistry"; Academic Press: New York, 1980.
6. Bergbreiter, D. E.; Parsons, G. L. J. Organomet. Chem. 1981, 208, 47-53.
7. Pittman, Jr., C. U.; Wilemon, G. Ann. N. Y. Acad. Sci., 1980, 333, 67-73 and references therein.
8. Collman, J. P.; Hegedus, L. S.; Cooke, M. P.; Norton, J. R.; Dolcetti, G.; Marquardt, D. N. J. Am. Chem. Soc. 1972, 94, 1789-1790.
9. Gosser, L. W.; Knoth, W. H.; Parshall, G. W. J. Am. Chem. Soc. 1973, 95, 3436-3437.
10. Gosser, L. W.; Knoth, W. H.; Parshall, G. W. J. Mol. Catal. 1977, 2, 253-263.
11. Hidai, M.; Kuse, T.; Hikita. T.; Uchida, Y.; Misono, A. Tetrahedron Lett. 1970, 1715-1716.

12. Strauss, S. H.; Shriver, D. F. Inorg. Chem. 1978, 17, 3069-74.
13. Porter, R. A.; Shriver, D. F. J. Organomet. Chem.1975, 90, 41-47.
14. Dorfner, K. "Ion Exchangers: Properties and Applications;" Ann Arbor Science Publishers, Inc.: Ann Arbor, Michigan, 1973.
15. Arai, H.; Halpern, J. J. Chem. Soc., Chem. Commun. 1971, 1571-2.
16. Halpern, J.; Wong, C. S. J. Chem. Soc., Chem. Commun. 1973, 629-630.
17. Tolman, C. A.; Meakin, P.Z.; Lindner, D. L.; Jesson, J. P. J. Am. Chem. Soc. 1974, 96, 2762-2774; Meakin, P.; Jesson, J. P.; Tolman, C. A. J. Am. Chem. Soc. 1972, 94, 3240-3242.
18. Ohtani, Y.; Fujimoto, M.; Yamagishi, A. Bull. Chem. Soc. Jpn. 1976, 49, 1871-3.
19. Osborn, J. A.; Jardine, F. H.; Young, J. F.; Wilkinson, G. J. Chem. Soc. (A) 1966, 1711-32.
20. J. Halpern in "Organotransition-Metal Chemistry;" Ishii, Y.; Tsutsui, M.; Eds.; Plenum Press: New York, 1975; p 109-119.
21. Montelatici, S.; van der Ent, A.; Osborn, J. A.; Wilkinson, G. J. Chem. Soc. (A) 1968, 1054-8.
22. Ohtani, Y.; Yamagishi, A.; Fujimoto, M. Bull. Chem. Soc. Jpn. 1979, 52, 3747-8.
23. Strauss, S. H.; Diamond. S. E.; Mares, F.; Shriver, D. F. Inorg. Chem. 1978, 17, 3064-8.
24. Hjortkjaer, J. Adv. Chem. Ser. 1974, 132, 133-44.

RECEIVED January 22, 1982.

4

Reactive Organic Functional Groups Covalently Bound on Polymeric Supports and Solid Surfaces

S. MAZUR,[1] P. JAYALEKSHMY, J. T. ANDERSSON, and T. MATUSINOVIC

University of Chicago, Department of Chemistry, Chicago, IL 60637

Organic functional groups covalently bound to the surface of crystalline solids or insoluble polymers are subject to special constraints which may alter their reactivity in comparison with analogous small molecules. A summary is made of the general classes of phenomena which can influence the reactivity of functional groups at heterogeneous interfaces, and potential pitfalls are pointed out in the reliance upon molecular analogy. Experimental results are reviewed pertaining to the thermodynamic and kinetic encounter frequencies of reagents on crosslinked polystyrenes and the chemisorption of olefins on oxide-free surfaces of elemental carbon.

Interest in the chemistry of functional groups covalently bound at heterogeneous interfaces has intensified steadily over the past decade concurrent with the increasing importance of three broad areas of application: heterogeneous catalysis, polymeric reagents, and chemically derivatized electrodes. The focus of interest concerns the rates and mechanisms of reactions between molecules in a fluid phase and groups bound to a distinct, motionally restricted phase. Despite the important differences in these experimental systems, research efforts have been unified by a common goal of relating the chemistry of interfacial functionality to that of analogous small molecules in solution or the gas phase. To what extent can reactivity at a heterogeneous interface be usefully regarded as an extension of molecular reactivity?

In the following discussion we will first consider the general differences between molecular and interfacial functional groups and then review actual results for two illustrative experimental systems; reactive substituents on high molecular weight polymers and oxide-free carbon surfaces.

[1] Current address: E. I. du Pont de Nemours & Company, Central Research & Development Department, Wilmington, DE 19898.

0097-6156/82/0192-0043 $6.25/0

If we accept, for interfacial systems, the fundamental validity of the notion of a functional group; a structural sub-unit possessing intrinsic chemical characteristics largely independent of its nearest neighbors, then it is to be expected that those aspects of reactivity influenced by interfacial binding will be limited to certain classes of effects. These are conveniently subdivided into the catagories of composition, structure, and motion.

Composition. While the average environment of a molecule in solution is well represented by the bulk concentrations of the various constituents of a reaction mixture, the environment of a molecule bound to a heterogeneous interface may be strongly perturbed. The properties of the motionally restricted phase may dictate rather large deviations in the local concentrations of ions, reactants, and other mobile species from their respective bulk concentrations. The most important examples of this have been demonstrated for electrode-solution interfaces where, for example, the pH in the electrical double layer may differ significantly from its value in the bulk solution and can change with applied potential (1). A similar, though less extreme, example involves the interface between aqueous solutions and hydrophobic polymers.

Structure. The detailed interfacial topography in the immediate vicinity of a reactive group may create steric or conformational constraints which influence reactivity. The implications for controlling the selectivity of heterogeneous reagents have motivated much of the work in this area. The principle is central to considerations of enzyme selectivity. Another important consequence of structural detail is that there will generally be a spectrum of different local environments at each reactive site along an interface which may give rise to a distribution of reactivities and consequent complications in the kinetics. While molecules in solution undoubtedly experience similar inhomogeneities in their local environments, fluctuations occur much more rapidly than most reactions of interest, so that the kinetics reflect an ensemble average. The same may not be true for reagents at heterogeneous interfaces. Thus, static inhomogeneities in local environment are often a source of complex kinetic behavior.

Motion. As indicated by the name, the most important consequence of binding a reagent to a motionally restricted phase will be to limit its degrees of freedom. To whatever extent mass transport or large-scale conformational motions may be rate limiting in a given reaction, this factor can manifest itself. While alterations in such formally "physical" rate processes may not seem terribly interesting in themselves, they can have

dramatic chemical consequences. This will generally be the case
where mass transport distinguishes between two competitive pathways as with alternative bimolecular and unimolecular processes.

Experimental systems typically fall into two catagories. For
polymer-bound reagents it is often possible to know both the
identity and concentration of functional groups at the reaction
center. On the other hand, information regarding motional
properties is very difficult to obtain. By contrast, for reagents
covalently bound at the surface of a crystalline solid the situation with regard to translational degrees of freedom is well
defined, but structural or compositional data are often lacking
due to the comparative inadequacy of surface analysis techniques.
It should not, however, be overlooked that important
differences may also be caused by factors other than local structure or functionality. Of particular concern are intermediate
and long range forces of the sort generally encountered in solvation and interaction between pairs of charged or polar functional
groups. While solvation probably remains one of the least well
understood details of chemistry in homogeneous solutions, the
situation is considerably worse for heterogeneous systems. There
exists no measurable quantity analogous to dielectric strength
which characterizes the response of the reaction environment to
charge separation. The "reaction medium" is intrinsically anisotropic, nor can it be assumed that the polarity of a given phase
is the same at an interface as in the bulk. Does the low dielectric constant of a polymeric support destabilize ionic
functional groups on its surface? Can highly reactive species
such as carbonium ions be stabilized by proximal metallic surfaces
with effectively infinite polarizability? Finally, the interaction of the electric field of an ion pair, for example, with
the polarizable environment at a heterogeneous interface, will
depend strongly on the precise location and orientation of the
charge centers.
Mutual interactions between interfacial functionality raises
similar questions. The nature of interactions between different
groups on multifunctional organic molecules is reasonably well
understood. Good account can be given of the relative ionization
constants of polybasic acids, for example. Similar interactions
are undoubtedly important in heterogeneous systems as well. This
is commonly demonstrated by various kinds of coverage-dependent
adsorption equilibria. As a rule, direct information concerning
the proximity of neighboring reactive groups is difficult to
obtain. Moreover, those interactions which are electrostatic in
origin will be strongly influenced by the polarizability of the
environment. The greater the importance of factors such as these,
the less valuable will be information transferred from homogeneous molecular chemistry. In fact, the notion of a surface
functional group has never received universal acceptance among
surface physicists. The problem ultimately reduces to one of

defining the smallest structural subunit which chemically resembles the system as a whole for any given reaction. If this subunit must include a large, multicomponent replica of the actual system, then clearly the concept of a "surface functional group" is of limited value.

Reactive Functional Groups on Polystyrene

Because of their important application in peptide synthesis, considerable attention has been paid to polystyrene gels cross-linked with varying amounts of 1,4-divinylbenzene. Although the principal utility of polystyrene-bound reagents is associated with the efficiency and convenience of separating polymer-bound products from reaction mixtures, various mechanistic aspects have also been scrutinized with the objective of distinguishing any special and hopefully useful differences between these reagents and their simple molecular counterparts. Most work in the area has been carried out with rather low crosslink densities, less than 5%. These materials can be swollen in good solvents to several times their dry volume, and a large fraction of the aromatic residues are accessible to reagents in solution. It is actually somewhat misleading to classify such systems as heterogeneous since the majority of polymer repeat units probably experience an environment virtually identical to that of a linear polymer in solution. Indeed, in most respects, there is little evidence of behavior requiring a special heterogeneous interpretation. An interesting exception concerns the role of direct reactions between pairs of substituents on the same polymer gel.

A wide range of different experimental strategies have been designed to probe this question (2-9). In most cases, evidence has been sought for the occurrence of coupling reactions between pairs of polymer-bound substituents. Superficially, many of the results and conclusions appear to be mutually contradictory. However, they are all in fact compatible with a single model. Three different kinds of situations have been documented.

1. Coupling between pairs of polymer-bound functional groups can be driven to quite high conversions by reaction conditions which are essentially irreversible. This has been convincingly demonstrated by experiments (2, 3) in which carboxyl substituents are converted to anhydrides using irreversible dehydrating agents, even for resins with cross-link densities as high as 20%.

2. A different situation appears to prevail for the titanocene hydrogenation catalyst studied by Grubbs and coworkers (4, 5). The active monomeric form of the catalysts exists in equilibrium with inactive dimers and higher aggregates. The activity of the polymer-bound catalyst proved to be significantly higher than its solution-phase counterpart,

and the quantitative behavior was shown to be consistent
with a lower extent of aggregation for the polmer-bound species.

3. The rate of reaction between pairs of polymer-bound
   substituents has been investigated in several quite
   different systems. The entire spectrum of possible
   results have been reported, including examples where
   kinetics were indistinguishable from the analogous homogeneous process (6) and others where the heterogeneous
   system is several orders of magnitude slower (6-9).
   These variations are not simply correlated with the
   crosslink density or extent of functionalization. In
   some instances the observed behavior is best represented
   by a distribution of parallel reaction rates.

In order to correlate these observations and be able to
formulate some semiquantitative generalizations, it is useful to
review a few of the special thermodynamic features of a solvent
swollen polymer gel which govern its equilibrium conformation
and motion. First, consider the thermodynamics of dimerization
for a solute, m, in an ideal solution at initial mole fraction,
Xm. The system is governed by an entropy of mixing given by the
following expression:

$$S = - \sum_i X_i R \ln X_i$$

where the sum extends over all distinguishable components of the
solution. In Figure 1, the upper curve illustrates the variation
of S with the extent of dimerization, Fd (fraction of all m which
have dimerized), for Xm = 0.04. Neglecting molecular contributions to the entropy of reaction, the equilibrium extent of
dimerization may be viewed as a balance between dimerization
entropy (a function of Xm) and ΔHr, the enthalpy change for the
particular reaction involved, (see Figure 1).

Now imagine that these same molecules are bound as substituents, randomly distributed along a swollen polymer network at the
same overall mole fraction as above. The dimerization will be
governed by the same entropy of mixing effect as for the solution,
however, there will now be an additional term associated with
deformation of the polymer network, indicated schematically by the
lower curve of Figure 1. The functional form will depend upon
such factors as the initial crosslink density, extent of swelling,
and volume change attending the reaction. The important point is
that this conformational entropy function will always vary more
strongly with Fd than does the entropy of mixing. In certain
instances it may not be possible to achieve complete dimerization,
Fd = 1.0, without increasing the internal energy of the network
as well. This may involve creating strained chain conformations
or, in the limit, breaking primary bonds. It seems likely, however,
that for lightly crosslinked networks, the initial response to a

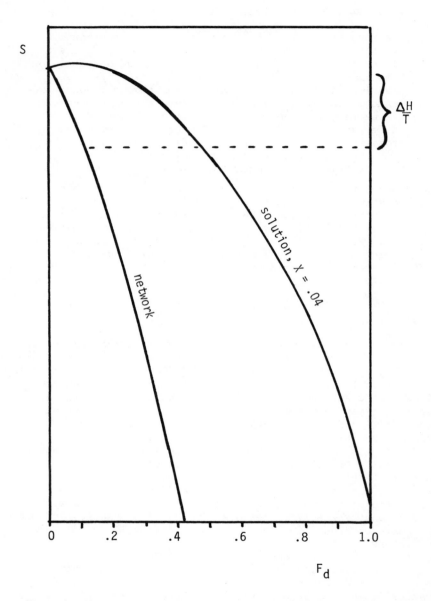

Figure 1. Variation in configurational entropy, S, with fraction of dimerized reagent, F_d, for dissolved and polymer-bound cases.

dimerization reaction will involve predominately entropy changes without significant changes in internal energy (see, for example, Flory's model of rubber elasticity (10)).

In the context of this broad thermodynamic picture, the concept of "site isolation" is seen to be highly misleading. Many of the conflicting conclusions which appear in the literature stem from the mistaken assumption that the number of mutually accessible sites is a discrete quantity, dictated by a particular cross-link density and extent of functionalization. In fact, the ultimate extent of coupling will represent a balance between the chemical driving force of the particular reaction involved and the conformational free energy of the polymer network. For sufficiently exothermic reaction conditions, coupling may be driven far toward completion and the polymer-bound substituents may act inconsequentially differently from their solution counterparts. However, with the identical functionalized polymer, when coupling is effected using a less exothermic reaction, as represented in Figure 1, the polymer-bound groups should undergo substantially less dimerization than an equal concentration of molecular reagent.

A convenient semiquantitative model for comparing the properties of dissolved and polymer-bound reagents would be to regard the latter as thermodynamically equivalent to a much more dilute solution of the former. Indeed, the lower curve of Figure 1 is roughly equivalent to that for an ideal solution of $X_m = 0.002$. In addition to providing a basis for understanding the response of the system to different reaction conditions, the idea of an equivalent concentration represents a means for quantitatively relating the polymer-bound reagent to its soluble counterpart in an experimentally useful way. "Pseudodilution" is especially useful in understanding kinetic behavior. Table I summarizes three different kinds of reactions which have been used to probe the kinetics of site-site interactions on crosslinked polystyrene. In our investigation of the chemistry of polymer-bound o-benzyne (7, 8), two different pieces of evidence were cited as indicative of the importance of motional restrictions on the fate of the reactive intermediate. (Results are summerized in Scheme 1.) First, when the 2-aminobenzotriazole precursor, I, was oxidized with lead tetraacetate (LTA), the characteristic Diels-Alder adduct with tetracyclone (TC) could be obtained even when the diene was added following completion of N_2 evolution, indicating that the polymer-bound intermediate had survived for tens of seconds. Secondly, while LTA oxidation of the monomeric aminotriazole I-a, affords the corresponding biphenylenes in high yield, the only products formed by I-b, in the absence of TC, were the aryl acetates II and III (combined yield of 80%). Monomeric o-benzyne is known to dimerize at the diffusion limited rate in the gas phase, therefore, formation of the Diels-Alder product following delayed addition of diene requires a substantially slower encounter process for the polymer-bound analog.

Table I

Encounter between Pairs of Reactive Sustituents on Crosslinked Polystyrenes

Reaction	Crosslink Density	Functionalization (mmole/gm)	Encounter Frequency (sec^{-1})
Benzyne dimerization	2%	0.89	$10^{-3} < \nu < 3 \times 10^{-2}$
Oligopeptide cyclization	4%	1.0	$10^{-2} \leq \nu$ first 50% $10^{-5} > \nu$ last 35%
Nucleophilic displacement	1%	1.18	$6 \times 10^{-5} \leq \nu$ first 70% $6 \times 10^{-5} > \nu$ last 30%

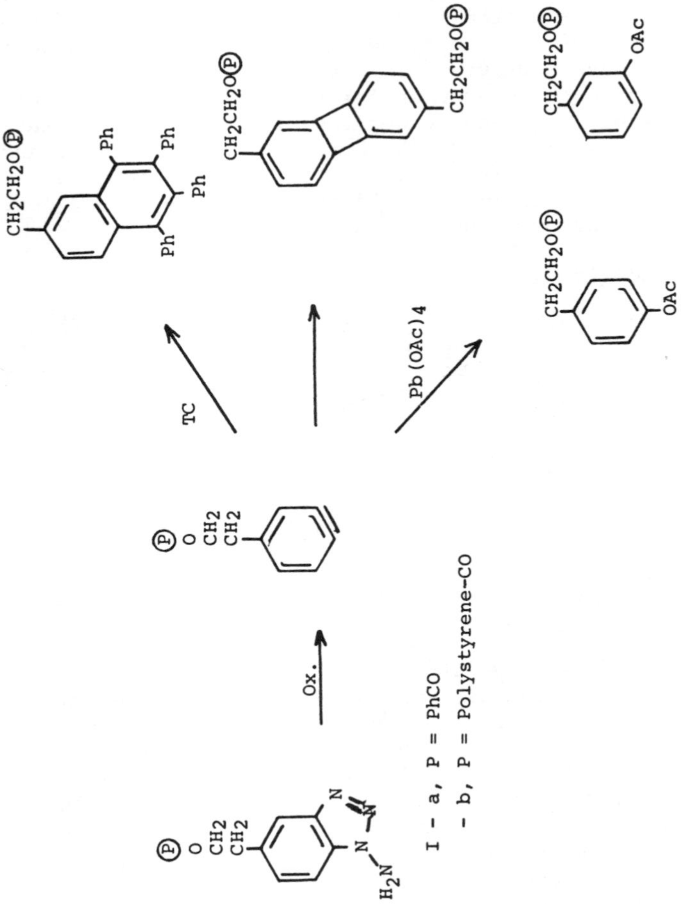

Scheme 1

Likewise, aryl acetate formation, the result of reaction between
o-benzyne and excess LTA and/or acetic acid, is unknown for the
monomeric aryne. Apparently, this acetoxylation reaction is
normally too slow to compete with dimerization for the molecular
case. Interestingly, when these experiments were repeated using
precursors bound to linear polystyrene molecules in solution, the
delayed trapping was unsuccessful, however, the aryl acetates
were formed in about 60% yield, corresponding to an intermediate
value of lifetime for the aryne. Finally, when o-benzyne was
generated from the same precursors using iodobenzene diacetate
(IBD) no aryl acetates were formed, and a small amount of coupling
product could be detected even for the crosslinked polymer
supported samples. Since, under the former conditions the lifetime of the aryne is limited by aryl acetate formation, and under
the latter conditions it is limited by dimerization, data from the
delayed trapping experiments (8) provides an upper and lower bound
for the frequency of encounter (see Table I).

Rebek & Trend (1979)

Regen & Bolikal (1981)

Rebek and Trend (9) studied the rate of acyl transfer between
glycine residues bound as p-nitrophenyl esters to a polystyrene
support. Once transfer had occurred the radio-labeled oligo-
peptides were released from the support via cyclization. This
experiment permitted a determination of the rate as a function of
conversion. Whereas the first 50% of reaction occurred smoothly
with a half-life on the order of a minute, the remaining label
was released at a progressively slower rate leaving approximately
35% ultimately unrecovered. A similar situation is apparently
represented by the nucleophilic displacement involving attack of
ion paired acetate on benzyl chloride substituents. Regen and
Bolikal (6) reported complete kinetic data for this reaction. Up
to 70% conversion pseudo-first-order kinetics were obeyed with a
rate constant essentially equal to that of the homogeneous
reaction. At higher conversions, the rate became progressively
slower and deviated from a simple second order law, indicative of
an encounter limited process. The latter two experimental systems

offer an advantage over studies of coupling reactions in that the crosslink density is unchanged during the course of the experiment. The complexity of the rate law at high conversions therefore clearly reflects an inhomogeneous distribution of encounter frequencies. Unfortunately, the actual reaction rates do not reflect purely encounter limited processes so they represent only a lower limit for the encounter frequency. The estimates derived from these different experimental systems are summarized in Table I.

Any model which is to be consistent with these results must include a broad spectrum of encounter frequencies for reaction partners at different relative locations in the network. The free energy of activation for these motions are related to the same factors previously discussed which govern the equilibrium properties. For the 4% crosslinked material there appears to be some fraction of substituents which are mutually inaccessible on any practical time scale. The majority of reactive pairs appear to be governed by encounter frequencies on the order of 10^{-3} sec^{-1}, more than ten orders of magnitude slower than for the molecular analogs in solution.

As in the case of equilibrium reactivity, the notion of pseudo-dilution provides a useful framework for predicting the practical consequences. The kinetics of intrapolymeric reactions will differ from that of the free molecules only when the pseudo-first order rate constant for the latter is less than the encounter frequency. This will obviously depend upon the intrinsic second order rate constant and the concentration. As a first order approximation, the polymer-bound reagents at about 1.0 mmole/gm on a 2% crosslinked polymer collide roughly as frequently as small molecules dissolved in a nonviscous, homogeneous solution at about ten picomolar concentration. It would be of interest to be able to quantitatively compare the pseudodilution factors determined independently from kinetically and thermodynamically controlled site-site reactions on the same sample. One might expect that the kinetic consequences would be more pronounced since the relatively slow conformational motions of the network are superimposed upon the entropic resistance to dimerization. To our knowledge, this question has not yet been investigated.

Reactions of Olefins with Oxide-Free Carbon Surfaces

In contrast with polymer-bound reagents, functional groups bound to the surface of a crystalline solid are truly immobilized, at least with regards to translation. Graphite is a particularly interesting substrate since its surface chemistry should in some sense relate to molecular organic chemistry. Considerable effort has been devoted to relating the reactivity and structure of graphite surfaces to small organic molecules. The surface chemistry of elemental carbon plays a key role in such diverse areas of its applications as electrodes, catalyst supports, high-modulus fibers, rubber modifiers, and electronic materials. The actual

materials involved vary tremendously in regards to physical state
and crystalline perfection but all are related to graphite in that
they feature extended two-dimensional networks of sp^2 carbon atoms
in fused six-membered rings. Most of the irreversible surface
chemistry (chemisorption) involves reactive groups at the edges of
the graphitic planes. Commonly these edge planes are populated by
surface oxides, a heterogeneous mixture of functionalities including carboxylic acids, phenols, quinones, lactones, etc. (11).
Direct spectroscopic methods remain largely inadequate for characterizing these groups and virtually all conclusions rest on the
evidence of chemical reactivity, a situation reminiscent of the
organic chemistry of the nineteenth century.

The situation is considerably simpler for an oxide-free surface since the number of different possible functional groups is
then much more limited. Figure 2 illustrates some of the alternative functional groups which may exist on the two structurally
distinct edge-oriented surfaces. The schematic representation
of sp hybrid orbitals are intended to point up the special bonding
problems which exist for the outermost atoms in these and all
other possible structures. The fact that all of the neighboring
atoms in the lattice lie in the same hemisphere means that these
atoms must either remain coordinatively unsaturated or form much
weaker, strained covalent bonds with their neighbors. The molecular analogs of these structures, dehydroaromatics and aryl radicals, are highly reactive. It is therefore not surprising that
such oxide-free   carbon surfaces can be maintained only under
high vacuum or inert atmosphere. Formation of surface oxides is
a very rapid and highly exothermic reaction at room temperature.

We undertook to investigate the reaction of olefins with
oxide-free carbon surfaces in the hopes that chemisorption would
occur in ways which could be related to the known chemistry of
aromatic free radicals and dehydroaromatics, and that suitable
manipulation might provide routes to homogeneously functionalized
surfaces. High surface-area carbon fibers were heated to approximately 1000°C under vacuum to remove the surface oxides (evolution
of H_2O, CO_2, and CO). The samples were cooled to room temperature and exposed to vapors of various different substrates. The
quantity of substrate adsorbed was determined and corrected for
the quantity of physisorbed material which could
be pumped off at room temperature. Some typical results are
reported in Table II. In certain cases the reactivity towards
oxygen was redetermined after exposure to the organic substrate.
In general, adsorption of the olefin competitively inhibited
adsorption of oxygen. However, only those olefins with some sort
of activating substituent were adsorbed in quantities comparable
to oxygen and were capable of fully supressing its subsequent
adsorption. Examples of intermediate reactivity, such as vinyl
bromide, appear to be indicative of a multiplicity of reactive
sites. That is, not all sites reactive towards oxygen are also

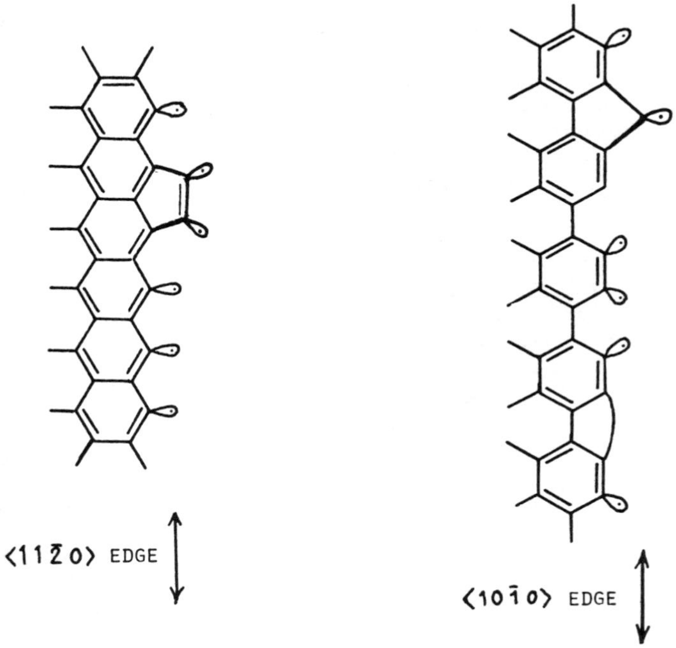

⟨11 2̄ 0⟩ EDGE

⟨10 1̄ 0⟩ EDGE

Figure 2.   Reactive functional groups at clean graphite surfaces.

Table II
Irreversible Adsorption on Oxide-Free Carbon Fiber[a]
(Union Carbide VYB fiber, surface area 240 m^2/g)

Substrate	Irreversible adsorption, mmol/g of fiber
Oxygen	0.62
Propane	0.00
Ethylene	0.02
Propylene	0.02
Isobutylene	0.25
followed by oxygen	0.43
Allene	0.63
followed by oxygen	0.09
Cyclopentadiene	0.35
followed by oxygen	0.30
Methyl acrylate	0.83
followed by oxygen	0.00
Acrylyl chloride	0.72
Vinyl bromide	0.48

[a] All values were measured at room temperature and were corrected for reversible adsorption at an ambient pressure of 20 Torr. Data from Ref. 12.

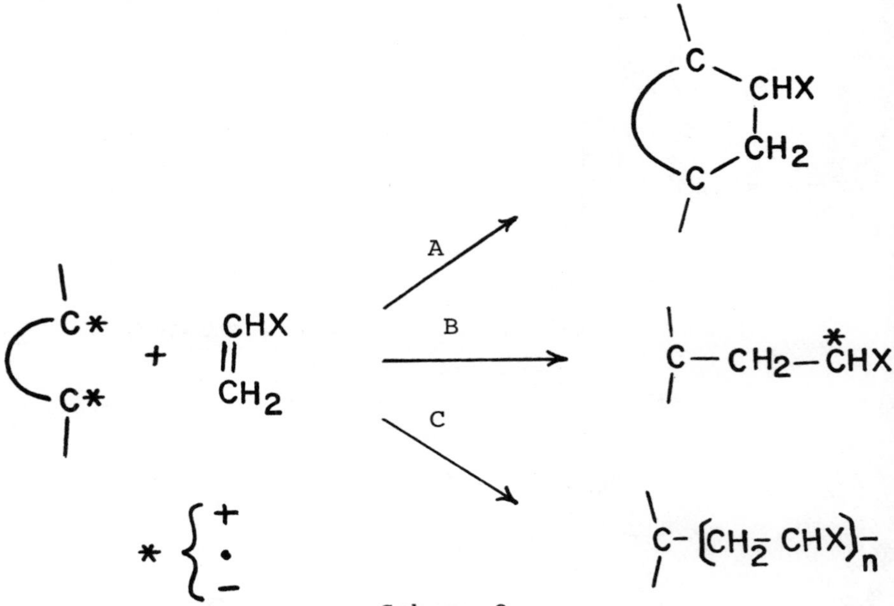

Scheme 2

reactive towards vinyl bromide. This conclusion is strengthed by
other data to be discussed below.

Scheme 2 illustrates three different kinds of reactions which
might account for adsorption of a suitably activated olefin. Even
within the optimistically limited bounds of this set of alternatives there remain several important points of ambiguity. Cycloaddition, 2-A,   may be expected to occur where pairs of
reactive C atoms occur separated by one, two or three bonds within
the lattice. But what about the possibility of pairs of reactive
centers in neighboring basal planes? Shoud we expect reactions
of this sort to be stereospecific? The electrical polarity of
the reactive centers is difficult to ascertain.   Ionic species
may seem unlikely, given the absence of solvent, but the pi-
electrons of the lattice are far more polarizable than any solvent
and may stabilize charge centers at the surface. The conjugate
addition, Scheme 2, might either be the first step in a polymerization process or may produce a metastable species whose lifetime
is limited only by the availability of other reagents in the gas
phase. The polymerization scheme raises questions about the
nature of the termination step. We attempted to answer some of
these questions by focusing on the chemistry of the surface-bound
olefins.

The strongest evidence in favor of cycloaddition was found in
the case of vinyl bromide (see Scheme 3), of 0.48 mmole/gm irreversibly adsorbed at room temperature, roughly 50% of the initial
adduct decomposed spontanteously releasing HBr. This observation
is consistent with cycloaddition to form a six-membered ring which
readily looses HBr with the formation of a new aromatic nucleus
continguous with the lattice. The remaining bromine was not
liberated even on heating to 200°C. However, when the sample was
soaked in dilute aqueous acid, all remaining Br^- was slowly released, obeying a simple first order rate law. It is less
apparent whether cycloadducts are also responsible for these more
robust functional groups, but the well behaved kinetics certainly
indicate that we are dealing with a single structural type and a
homogeneous environment. While the rate of solvolysis is too
large to be consistent with polyvinyl bromide under normal circumstances, it is not clear whether the polarizability of the surface
might not be an important mitigating influence.

A very different situation was represented by the behavior of
adsorbed vinyl acetate (13). The maximum quantity of this substrate which could be adsorbed at room temperature (1.28 mmole/gm),
is considerably greater than for the other olefins and for oxygen.
However, it turns out that most of this material could be recovered by desorption over the temperature range 100-200°C (see
Figure 3). While complete mass balance could not be achieved, the
only other products isolated on heating to as high as 340°C were
acetaldehyde and acetic acid. Control experiments verified that
these were not produced by secondary reaction of vinyl acetate at

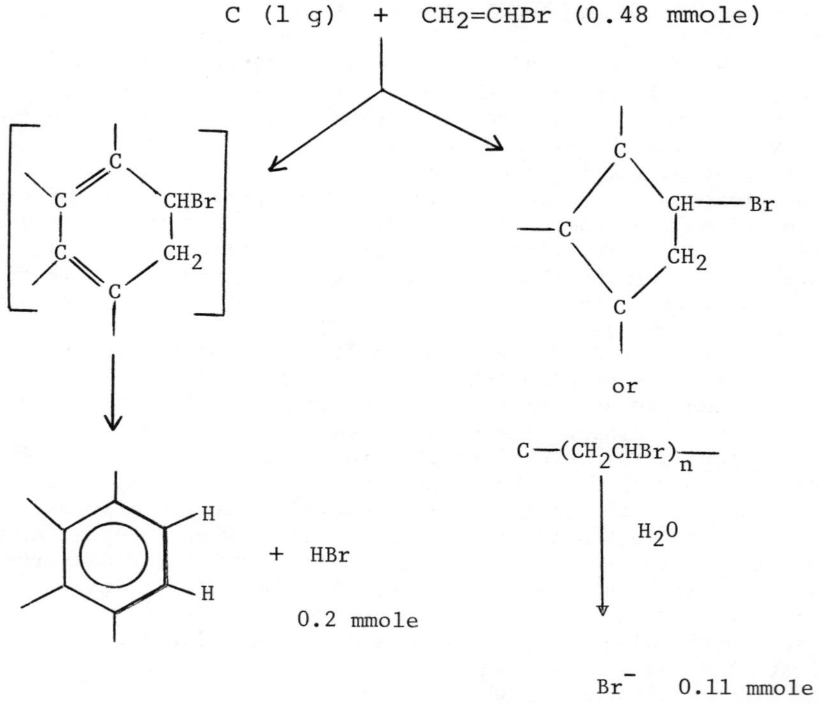
C (1 g) + CH2=CHBr (0.48 mmole)
CHBr
CH2
C
CH—Br
CH2
or
C—(CH2CHBr)n—
H2O
H
H
+ HBr
0.2 mmole
Br⁻ 0.11 mmole

Scheme 3

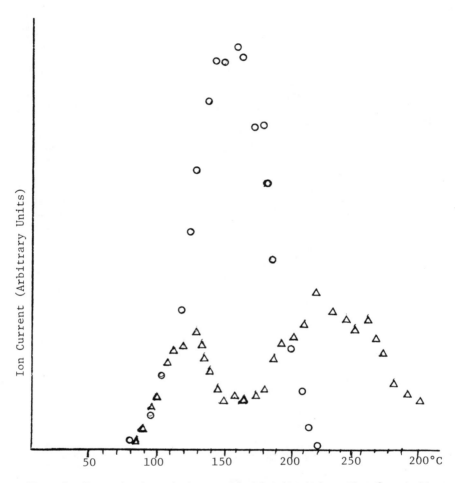

Figure 3. Desorption from vinyl acetate treated carbon surface. Key: ○, m/e 86; △, m/e 44.

the elevated temperatures. Typical results were as follows:

$$C + CH_2CHOAc \xrightarrow{22°} [C(CH_2CHOAc)] \xrightarrow{340°} CH_2CHOAc + CH_3CHO$$

    0.53 mmole/g   58%   15%

                                                                  (CH_3CO_2H)

                                                                  2%

Figure 3 shows a reaction profile obtained by bleeding the desorption products directly into the source of a mass spectrometer. (The detector signal is uncorrected for differential sensitivity, so the relative concentrations are not represented.)
    In order to find out more about the nature of the adsorbed intermediates and the source of acetaldehyde, these experiments were repeated using a stereospecifically labeled substrate, cis-2-deuterovinyl acetate which was prepared according to the sequence outlined in Scheme 4. In three different experiments the quantity of adsorbed substrate was varied between saturation and a very low coverage. The results are summarized in the following scheme:

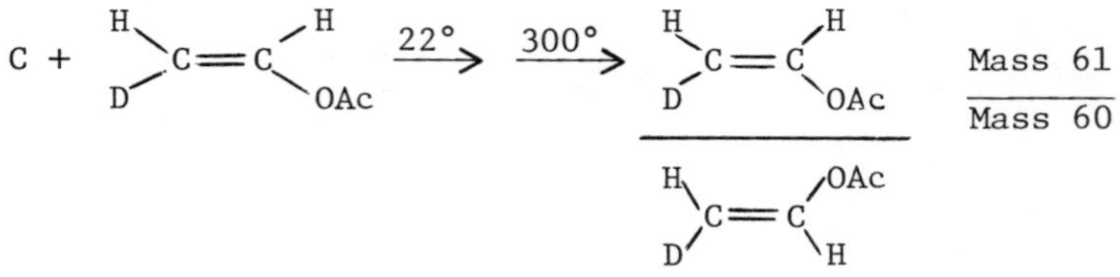

    1.28 mmole/g   2/1   1/2

    0.87 mmole/g   1/1
                                           (75%)

    0.05 mmole/g   –   2/1

The samples were gradually heated to 300°C while desorption products were pumped out through   a liquid nitrogen cooled trap. The ratio of isomers was evaluated by H^1-N.M.R. Mass spectra included very weak signals at m/e 60 and 61 which were tentatively identified with HOAc and DOAc, respectively. A control experiment established that no detectable amount of cis-trans isomerization occurred when vinyl acetate vapor was exposed to the same conditions in the absence of the carbon sample.
    The remarkable dependence of product composition upon the initial coverage is strong evidence for a multiplicity of different adsorption mechanisms. At high coverage, the last

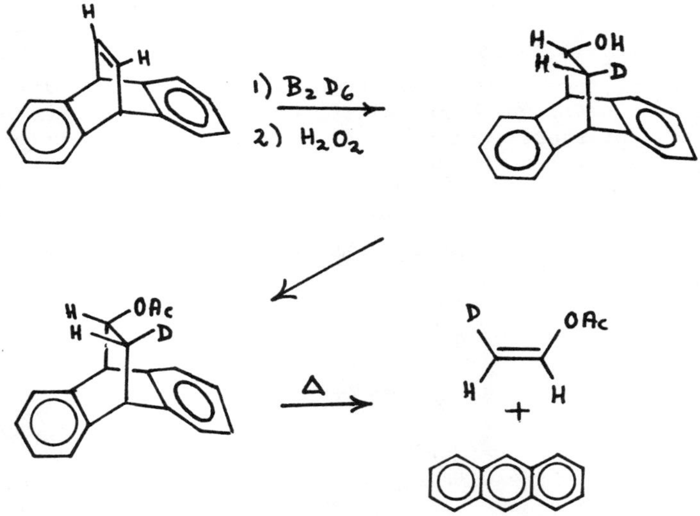

Scheme 4

material adsorbed is weakly bound to sites which apparently do not catalyze isomerization. A rather large number of sites, representing at least 0.65 mmole/gm, also reversibly bind the substrate but by a mechanism which erases the stereochemical memory of the precursor. Finally, the strongest adsorption gives rise to adducts which can no longer be decomposed reversibly but instead break down to give acetaldehyde and a small quantity of acetic acid. The deuterium content of the small amounts of acetic acid are also suggestive of some stereospecific elimination process.

   Reversible desorption with isomerization seems particularly consistent with a conjugate addition scheme. Also consistent is the observation that when the sample was exposed to air prior to desorption, the yield of acetic acid was considerably enhanced at the expense of recovered vinyl acetate. It is less obvious how acetaldehyde is formed, particularly under conditions which are rigorously anhydrous. One possibility might be the participation of anionic centers on the surface:

$$CH_2DCHO$$

   Interestingly, reversible adsorption with isomerization is not limited to olefins with electron donating substituents. Scheme 5 summarizes some preliminary results for 1,2-dichloroethylene. Here again, the extent of isomerization decreases with increasing coverage.

   By contrast with the polystyrene-bound reagents where the behavior may be understood and sometimes even predicted on the basis of measureable perturbations of molecular chemistry, the chemistry of carbon surfaces presents a far more formidable challenge. The lack of structure sensitive analytical tools combined with the much greater uncertainty of analogies with molecular systems severely restrict the effectiveness of many experiments and the generality of conclusions derived from them.

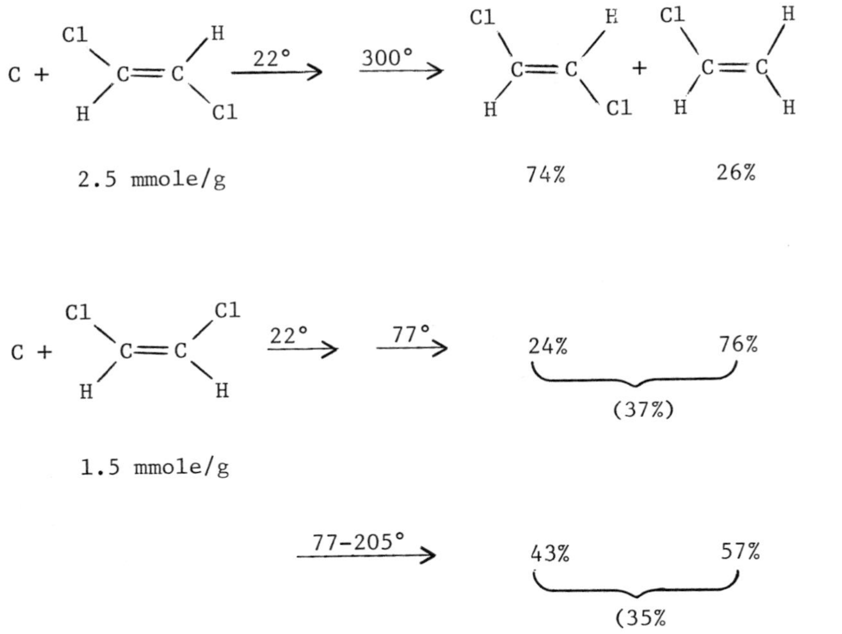

$$C + \quad \overset{Cl}{\underset{H}{>}} C = C \overset{H}{\underset{Cl}{<}} \quad \xrightarrow{22°} \quad \xrightarrow{300°} \quad \overset{Cl}{\underset{H}{>}} C = C \overset{H}{\underset{Cl}{<}} \quad + \quad \overset{Cl}{\underset{H}{>}} C = C \overset{H}{\underset{H}{<}}$$

2.5 mmole/g   74%   26%

$$C + \quad \overset{Cl}{\underset{H}{>}} C = C \overset{Cl}{\underset{H}{<}} \quad \xrightarrow{22°} \quad \xrightarrow{77°} \quad 24\% \qquad 76\%$$

$$\underbrace{}_{(37\%)}$$

1.5 mmole/g

$$\xrightarrow{77-205°} \quad 43\% \qquad 57\%$$

$$\underbrace{}_{(35\%}$$

Scheme 5

Literature Cited

1. Mazur, S.; Ohkubo, K.; J. Am. Chem. Soc. 1975, 97, 2911 and references therein.
2. Crowley, J. I.; Harvey, T. B.; Rapoport, A. H.; J. Macromol. Sci. Chem. 1973, 7, 1118.
3. Scott, L. T.; Rebek, J.; Ovsyanko, L.; Sims, C. L.; J. Am. Chem. Soc. 1977, 99, 625.
4. Bonds, W. D.; Brubaker, C. H.; Chandrasekaran, E. S.; Gibbons, C.; Grubbs, R. H.; Kroll, L. C.; Ibid. 1975, 2128.
5. Grubbs, R.; Lau, C. P.; Cukier, R.; Brubaker, C. H.; Ibid. 1977, 99, 4517.
6. Regen, S. L.; Bolikal, D.; Ibid., 1981, 103, 5248.
7. Jayalekshmy, P.; Mazur, S.; Ibid. 1976, 98, 6710.
8. Mazur, S.; Jayalekshmy, P.; Ibid. 1979, 101, 677.
9. Rebek, J.; Trend, J.; Ibid. 1979, 737.
10. Flory, P. J. "Principles of Polymer Chemistry"; Cornell Univ. Press, Ithaca, N.Y., 1953, Chapter XI.
11. Deviney, M. L.; Adv. Coll. Interfac. Sci. 1969, 2, 237
12. Mazur, S.; Matusinovic, T.; Cammann, K.; J. Am. Chem. Soc. 1977, 99, 3888.
13. Mazur, S.; Andersson, J.T.; unpublished results.

RECEIVED April 8, 1982.

Chemically Modified Conducting Polypyrrole Film Electrodes

M. SALMÓN, A. DIAZ, and J. GOITIA

IBM Research Laboratory, San Jose, CA 95193

Various para substituted poly-N-arylpyrrole polymer films were prepared and their electrochemical properties were measured. Of particular interest are the poly-N-p-nitrophenylpyrrole films which can be oxidized to produce the polypyrrole cation and reduced to produce the nitrophenyl anion. The polymer films can be repeatedly switched between the neutral, cationic and anionic forms with coulombic reversibility and with little π-interaction between the pyrrole and the aryl ring.

Recognizing that the conducting polypyrrole films can be chemically modified (1,2), the phenyl substituent assumes a particularly important role because it provides a means of introducing a wide selection of functional groups into the polymer. With this objective in mind, we have prepared a series of N-arylpyrrole polymers and find the thin poly-N-(p-nitrophenyl)pyrrole films of particular interest because they combine the electroactive properties of nitrobenzene and polypyrrole. With this combination, the polymer can be switched electrochemically between the cationic, neutral, and anionic form.

Thin films of the substituted polyphenylpyrrole were prepared on a platinum electrode by the electrooxidation of the corresponding monomer (3) in an acetonitrile solution containing 0.1M tetraethylammonium tetrafluoroborate using the procedure described for the N-phenyl analog (4). Good films were produced in every case except in the electrooxidation of N,N-dimethylaminophenylpyrrole, which instead produces soluble products. The films used in this study were prepared using 20 mC/cm^2. These films were analyzed by cyclic voltammetry in a one compartment cell containing 0.1M tetraethylammonium tetrafluoroborate in acetonitrile and a sodium chloride calomel reference electrode as before (4). The anodic region of the voltammograms show that peaks appear in the range 600-900 mV due to the redox reaction of the pyrrole units in the polymer backbone of each derivatized film (Table I). The reactions are coulombically reversible and the

0097-6156/82/0192-0065 $6.00/0
© 1982 American Chemical Society

TABLE I

Electrochemical Data for N-Substituted Pyrrole Polymer Films[a]

N-Substituent	Polymer		Monomer
	E_{pa},mV	E_{pc},mV	E_{pa},mV
phenyl	740	600	1800
p-tolyl	700	600	1500
p-anisyl	700	600	1360
p-dimethyl- aminophenyl			1290 (E^0) 720[b]
p-nitrophenyl	900 -900[b]	780 -1000[b]	1600 (E^0) -1110[b]
H	-100	-300	1200
methyl	500	400	1200
		nitrobenzene	-1140
		dimethylaniline	$(E_{1/2})$ 730[c]

[a] E_p versus SSCE measured in CH_3CN using a Pt electrode.
[b] Values for the aryl substituent.
[c] Reference 11. Measured with Pt versus SCE electrodes in CH_3CN containing Et_4NClO_4.

i_p values of the peaks scale linearly with sweep rate (v) in every case. Overall, the voltammograms resemble the one for the polyphenypyrrole (1), except that the peaks produced by the poly-N-nitrophenylpyrrole films are shifted anodically by 200 mV. This is not unreasonable, considering the inductive and resonance effects of the aryl group. With these films an additional small peak of unknown origin appears at 600 mV. The reactions are accompanied by a color change from light yellow (neutral film) to dark brown (oxidized film).

The poly-N-p-nitrophenylpyrrole films are of interest because the nitrophenyl group is independently electroactive. In the cathodic region of the voltammogram, the initial scans show double peaks for the reduction reaction of the pendent nitrophenyl group (Fig. (1)) at -1000 and -1150 mV (E_{pc}) plus the corresponding peak in the anodic scan at -900 mV (E_{pa}). The small peak at -1000 mV disappears after a few scans without changing the area under the peak. The reaction is coulombically reversible and the i_p values scale linearly with v, where i_{pc}/Av equals 11 mA·s/V·cm^2. For comparison, the corresponding value for the oxidation reaction at 920 mV is 4 mA·s/V·cm^2. The position of these signals are close to those for the reduction reaction of nitrobenzene ($E°$ at -1140 mV) and poly-p-nitrostyrene ($E°$ at -1500 mV versus a silver electrode) (5). Thus the negative charge in the polymer must be localized on the nitrophenyl group and is not extensively delocalized throughout the polymer π-electron structure. This result further suggests that the p-nitrophenyl and the pyrrole rings must remain orthogonal in this film and are poorly conjugated. The peak shapes and positions indicate that the reaction is not electrochemically reversible, which is not unexpected since the reaction of these films are known to involve slow ion diffusion (4,6,7).

The charge density ratio of the pyrrole oxidation to the nitrophenyl reduction reaction in the film is 0.2. This low value indicates that the oxidation reaction involves 0.2 charges/pyrrole ring, since the nitrophenyl reaction involves one electron/nitro group. A similar value was found with poly-N-phenylpyrrole (0.16) (4). This low sensitivity of the degree of oxidation of the pyrrole polymer to changes in the nature of the attached aryl group supports the idea that the aryl group is poorly conjugated to the rest of the polymer. The ESCA spectra of the surface region shows peaks of approximately equal areas at 400.5 and 405.8 eV which are appropriate for the pyrrole nitrogen and the nitro nitrogen atoms, respectively (8). Therefore the p-nitrophenylpyrrole structure remains intact in the film. Peaks for carbon and oxygen are also present in the ESCA spectra. The scanning electron micrograph of the surface of the film shows that it is a continuous film with a fairly even surface as was observed with the polypyrrole films (2).

The electroactive behavior of the nitrophenyl group is particularly intriguing. Although the fully-charged film appears to have the anionic charges localized on the nitrophenyl group, the electron transfer process between the platinum and the film for the reduction reaction may involve electron exchange between the unsaturated pyrrole backbone and the pendent

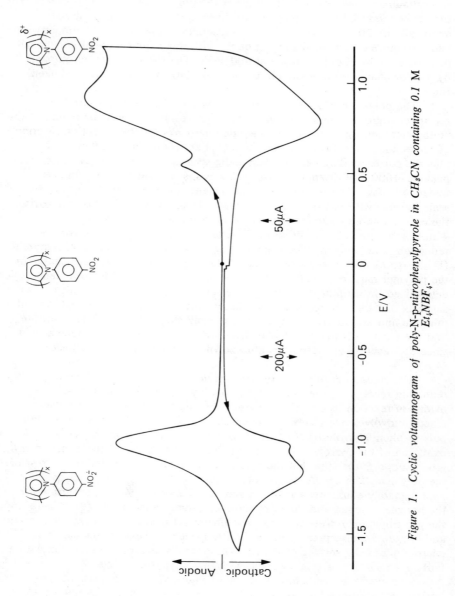

Figure 1. Cyclic voltammogram of poly-N-p-nitrophenylpyrrole in CH₃CN containing 0.1 M Et₄NBF₄.

nitrophenyl groups rather than a hopping process between the groups. This proposed mechanism is reasonable since pyrrole is known to form π-complexes with acceptor molecules (9), plus the fact that adjacent nitrophenyl groups along the chain are probably held apart in a near 180° orientation and are too far away to interact directly. As expected, the nitro group is electrochemically reduced to the amine structure in the presence of water, which provides a convenient way to further modify the film. The accessibility of these amino groups for further modification of these films needs to be determined.

As regards the electrooxidation of the corresponding monomers, they have less anodic E_{pa} values than N-phenylpyrrole even with the nitro substituent and the reactions remain irreversible. The substituents influence the oxidation of these monomers much more than was observed with pentaphenylpyrrole. For example, substitution of a p-methoxy group in the N-phenyl of the latter produces a 20 mV cathodic shift in the E_{pa} value (10). The dimethylaminophenyl and nitrophenyl groups show reversible redox behavior and appear to behave independent of the pyrrole moiety in these derivatives.

In summary, the phenyl group provides a practical way to chemically modify the polymer film. Polypyrrole films containing the N-phenyl group are as conducting as those containing the N-methyl group (ca. 10^{-3} (Ωcm)$^{-1}$) and ca. 10^5 less conducting than the unsubstituted films (4). While good films can be prepared when the substituted phenyl group on the monomer is electroactive and easily reduced, we have not been able to prepare good films when there is a substituted phenyl group which is easily oxidized.

LITERATURE CITED

1. Diaz, A. F.; Castillo, J.; Kanazawa, K. K.; Logan, J. A.; Salmón, M.; Fajardo, O. J. Electroanal. Chem. 1981, 0000.
2. Diaz, A. F.; Kanazawa, K. "Extended Linear Chain Compounds"; Miller, J., Ed., Plenum Press, 1982, Vol. 3.
3. Salmón, M.; Diaz, A. F., unpublished results.
4. Diaz, A. F.; Castillo, J. I.; Logan, J. A.; Lee, W. Y. J. Electroanal. Chem. 1981, 0000.
5. Van de Mark, M. R.; Miller, L. L. J. Amer. Chem. Soc. 1978, 100, 3223.
6. Kerr, J. B.; Miller, L. L.; Van de Mark, M. R. J. Amer. Chem. Soc. 1980, 102, 3383.
7. Kaufman, F. B.; Schroeder, A. H.; Engler, E. M.; Kramer, S. R.; Chambers, J. Q. J. Amer. Chem. 1980, 102, 483.
8. Robinson, J. W., Ed.; "Handbook of Spectroscopy"; CRC Press, 1974, Vol. I.

9.   Jones, R. A. "Physiochemical Properties of Pyrroles"; Katritzky, A. R.;
     Boulton, A. J., Eds.; Acad. Press, 1970, Vol. 11, p. 383.
10. Cauquis, G.; Genies, M. Bull. Soc. Chim. Fr. 1967, 3220.
11. Weinberg, N. L. "Techniques of Electroorganic Synthesis"; John Wiley
     and Sons, 1975, Vol. V, Pt. II, p. 811.

RECEIVED November 12, 1981.

Simulation of the Cyclic Voltammetric Characteristics of a Second Order EC Catalytic Mechanism

DENNIS M. DIMARCO, PAUL A. FORSHEY and THEODORE KUWANA

Ohio State University, Department of Chemistry, Columbus, OH 43210

This paper describes a general method for the elucidation of rate parameters for second order homogeneous ec catalytic reactions, using cyclic voltammetry as the diagnostic electrochemical tool. It is being written so that others besides the everyday practitioners of electrochemistry can relate the mechanistic aspects to the diagnostics, and hence, can appreciate the beauty of the ec mechanism for the design of catalytic electrodes. In doing so, it assumes that cyclic voltammetry remains a convenient and powerful diagnostic tool for the study of this mechanism, that the ec catalytic mechanism is a viable approach to the design and fabrication of catalytic electrodes, and that redox mediators serving as catalysts can be thoroughly characterized in a solution coupled ec mechanism and then transferred to the electrode surface via their immobilization. Previous reports invoking the ec mechanism have been well documented both in this lab (1-4) and others (5). In this paper we will restrict our discussion to the homogeneous case. Cyclic voltammetric current-potential profiles were computer simulated for the ec catalytic reduction of molecular oxygen by water-soluble iron porphyrin. These profiles were in good agreement with experimental ones for a mechanism involving oxygen reduction to water through hydrogen peroxide in a series pathway.

The reaction sequence of an ec catalytic regeneration mechanism is illustrated, for a reduction by reactions 1 and 2:

0097-6156/82/0192-0071 $7.75/0

$$M_{ox} + n_M e^- \overset{k_{sM}}{\underset{}{\rightleftarrows}} M_r \qquad\qquad E^{O\prime}_M \qquad (1)$$

$$M_r + S_{ox} \overset{k_f}{\rightarrow} M_{ox} + S_r \qquad\qquad (2)$$

where $M_{ox/r}$ denotes the redox mediator and $S_{ox/r}$ represents the solution reactant species (hereafter referred to as the reactant). The electrode reaction of $S_{ox/r}$ is shown in re-action 3.

$$S_{ox} + n_S e^- \overset{k_{s,S}}{\underset{}{\rightleftarrows}} S_r \qquad\qquad E^{O\prime}_S \qquad (3)$$

When $k_{s,M}$ is large, the concentration ratio M_{ox}/M_r is Nernstian. The equilibrium constant, K_{eq}, of reaction 2 is determined by $E^{O\prime}_M$ and $E^{O\prime}_S$ values of reactions 1 and 3, respectively ($K_{eq} = \exp((E^{O\prime}_S - E^{O\prime}_M)F/RT)$ when $n_M = n_S = 1$.

For some of the less complex ec processes, cyclic volt-ammetry (i-E) waves have been used to show, qualitatively, the effects of the follow-up reaction (reaction 2). The model first developed for this scheme consider only pseudo first-order conditions where the heterogeneous process was either reversible (6,7) or irreversible (7,8). Accordingly, when the homogeneous rate constant was very large, the i-E scan appeared similar to a conventional polargraphic wave without any peaks. The complications of Nicholson and Shain (7) provide cyclic i-E data that can be compared directly to experimental results. While these data can be used to fit the case represented by equations 1 and 2 ($n_M = 1$), more complex schemes involving second or higher order homogeneous reactions, conditions of unequal diffusion coefficients, and mechanisms in which $k_{s,M}$ is in the quasi-reversible regime have not been described in detail.

More recently Andrieux et. al. (5a,5b) have described a procedure for computer simulation of a second-order ec cata-lytic mechanism. In their work cyclic voltammetric data were calculated while changing the rate and reversibility of the follow-up reaction. Using the implicit finite-difference method these authors calculated voltammetric waves for dimensionless homogeneous rates ($k_f \cdot C_a$) as large as 5×10^5 M^{-1} s^{-1}. The results were then applied to cases where $n_S = 2 \cdot n_M$. Qualitative information was obtained from several experimental systems by observing changes in the i–E wave shape. Homogeneous rate constants were also evaluated. Their model did not take into consideration slow heterogeneous kinetics. Additional complexities are involved when all the diffusion coefficients of the species involved are not equal. Unfortunately many catalytic systems are multistepped and have non–infinite heterogeneous charge transfer rates. In the particular case of oxygen reduction, catalyzed by water soluble porphyrins (1,2), many of the complexities listed above occur, so that analysis of this reaction using published data is difficult. Thus we have digitally simulated i–E waves for the ec catalytic process with the purpose of elucidating mechanistic pathways and the associated rate constants.

The explicit, finite difference method (9,10) was used to generate all the simulated results. In this method, the concurrent processes of diffusion and homogeneous kinetics can be separated and determined independently. A wide variety of mechanisms can be considered because the kinetic flux and the diffusional flux in a discrete solution "layer" can be calculated separately and then summed to obtain the total flux. In the simulator, time and distance increments are chosen for convenience in the calculations. Dimensionless parameters are used to relate simulated data to real world data. The dimensionless heterogeneous and homogeneous rate parameters are given by y_s and y_f, respectively. Table I lists the different dimensionless parameters used in this paper. For a more thorough explanation of the required calculations the reader is referred to appropriate texts (9,10). The use of optimizing techniques that reduce the time needed to complete the calculations, have not been attempted in the present work (11). All simulations have been computed on either an in-lab NOVA III S/12 minicomputer with 32k memory, or the AMDAHL 470 computer at the O.S.U. computer center. All programs were written in FORTRAN.

The discussion will be divided into four sections. The first part will introduce the method and demonstrate typical digital simulation results. Secondly, diagnostic tests will affirm the operation of the program. Next, we will demonstrate several methods that can be used to compare experimental and simulated data. The diagnostic utility of these methods will be compared and approaches suggested for determination of the homogeneous rate constant. Finally we will describe the application of these methods to the homogenous catalysis of oxygen reduction. Three possible mechanisms will be evaluated and curves plotted to show the fit between the simulated and the experimental parameters.

TABLE I

Fig. No.	C_M C_S	D_M D_S	k_f ($M^{-1}s^{-1}$)	y_s	k_s ($cm\ s^{-1}$)	y_s	v ($V\ s^{-1}$)
1A	1	1	0	0	5×10^{-9}(a)	8×10^{-7}	.10
1A	1	1	Var.	Var.	1.0	160	.10
2A	1	1	Var.	Var.	1.0	160	.10
2B	1	1	Var.	Var.	1.0	160	.10
2C	1	1	2×10^{6}	500	Var.	Var.	.10
3	1	1	Var.	Var.	Var.	Var.	.10
4	1	1	Var.	Var.	Var.	Var.	.10
5	1	1	Var.	Var.	Var.	Var.	.10
6	1	1	Var.	Var.	Var.	Var.	.10
7	1	1	1×10^{4}	Var.	Var.	Var.	Var.
8A	Var.	1	Var.	Var.	1.0	160	.10
8B	Var.	1	Var.	Var.	1.0	160	.10
9	1	9	5×10^{5}	125	1.0	160	.10
10A	1	9	Var.	Var.	.005	5.0	.10
10B	1	9	2×10^{6}	500	Var.	Var.	.10
11	Var.	9	Var.	Var.	.005	2.5	.05

a) $k_{s,S}$

VERIFICATION

Digital simulation using the explicit, finite-difference method can be used to describe a wide range of electro-chemical reaction mechanisms. With only a slight increase in programming sophistication one can cover the range from the uncomplicated, one-electron reaction, to more complex mechanisms with homogeneous coupling and/or surface inter-actions. Before venturing into the more complex sequences, however a simpler mechanism is chosen to verify the proposed calculations.

Heterogeneous Electron Transfer

Agreement with previously published results, when possible, is one way of assuring that the computations are correct. By making the homogeneous rate constant equal to zero we effectively simulate the uncomplicated, single electron transfer case. The difference between our simulated i-E curves and those of Nicholson and Shain was less that 1.0% for current greater than 10% of the maximum current for both the reversible and irreversible cases. Since this comparison has been published elsewhere (7), we will not elaborate further here.

The ec Mechanism

The work of Nicholson and Shain (7) is also a convenient resource for the study of the pseudo first-order ec cata-lytic mechanism. Pseudo first-order conditions were simu-lated in the present study by making the reactant concen-tration (C_S) greater than the catalyst concentration (C_M) by a factor of 10^4. Again the divergence from the previously tabulated data is less than 1.0%.

The ability to change concentrations, rate constants, diffusion coefficients, alpha, temperature, and even uncom-pensated resistance is available with the present programs (15). Changes in the stoichiometry are accomplished through alterations in the "kinetic" section of the program. Thus our simulations allow us to investigate a wide range between the reversible and irreversible heterogeneous cases, which have not previously been investigated for the ec catalytic mechanism.

Unless otherwise noted in the figures and discussion to follow, the potential will be reported with respect to the redox potential of the mediator couple and the current will be normalized to the current calculated for the reversible one electron transfer of the mediator (16). Catalysis of a reduction is considered here. The analogy to an oxidation process is direct. In figures 1 through 5 the simple second order case is considered. The concentrations and diffusion coefficients of the mediator and the reactant are equivalent. The stoichiometric ratio ($N = n_S/n_M$) of unity will be used as shown in reaction 2. Pertinent dimensionless parameters used in the simulations are shown in Table I.

DEMONSTRATION

To appreciate the effect of the catalysis to the i-E wave of the reactant, it is instructive to consider first the separate electrode reactions of reactant and mediator, and then the results of their homogeneous coupling. Fig. 1A shows the irreversible reaction of the reactant with $k_{s,S} = 5 \times 10^{-9}$ cm s^{-1}. Fig. 1B shows the results of the simulation of reactions 1, 2 and 3 in which k_f varies from 0.0 to 2.0 $\times$ 10^4 M^{-1} s^{-1}. With $k_f = 0.0$, as in curve 1, the more positive peak represents the mediator, which reacts reversibly at the electrode ($k_{s,M} = 1.0$ cm s^{-1}). The second cathodic wave is the result of the irreversible reaction of the reactant ($k_{s,S} = 5.0 \times 10^{-9}$ cm s^{-1}) at the electrode. The difference between $E^{o'}_S$ and $E^{o'}_M$ is 0.25 volts. Curves two through five demonstrate the effect of the homogeneous coupling reaction on the mediator and the gradual shift of the E_{pc} initially in the negative and then in the positive direction are characteristic features of the increasing homogeneous rate constant. Note that the uncatalyzed reactant peak decreases to zero as k_f increases, indicative of the depletion of the reactants in the diffusion layer. The reverse mediator wave (oxidation wave in this case) is still observed which is a behavior not found in pseudo first-order cases. The changes in i_{pc} and E_{pc} and other features of this mechanism will be discussed in later sections that describe diagnostic applications.

Additional interesting features of the i-E wave shape become evident at values of k_f that are higher than those shown in Fig. 1. In Fig. 2A this dependence of the i-E wave on k_f is shown. As

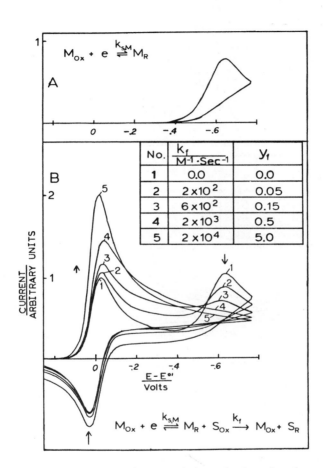

Figure 1. Cyclic voltammetry of the ec catalytic mechanism plotted as normalized current ($i_{pc}/i_{pc,0}$) versus normalized potential ($E - E_M{}^{o\prime}$). Key: $C_M = C_S = 10^{-3}$ M, $D_M = D_S = 10^{-5}$ cm²/s, $E_S{}^{o\prime} - E_M{}^{o\prime} = 0.25$ V, and $v = 0.10$ V/s; (A) $k_{s,M} = 0$, $k_{s,S} = 5 \times 10^{-9}$ cm/s, and $k_f = 0$; (B) $k_{s,M} = 1.0$ cm/s, $k_{s,S} = 5 \times 10^{-9}$ cm/s.

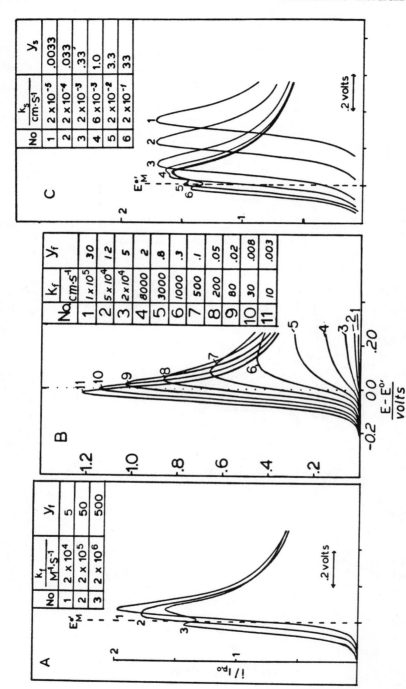

Figure 2. Effects of k_f and k_s on the CV characteristics of an ec catalytic mechanism for large values of k_f. Key: A, normalized current of the catalyzed wave versus potential; B, normalized current contribution of the reactant (i.e. $(i - i_0)/i_{pc,0}$) versus potential; and C, normalized current of the catalyzed wave plotted versus potential.

k_f increases, i_{pc}'s increase, reach a maximum (at k_f = 5.0 x 10^4 M^{-1} s^{-1}), and then decrease. The decrease is caused by separation of the single peak into two individual peaks. The double peak phenomenon, which has been previously ascribed to the depletion of the reactant at low concentrations of M_r, has also been found to occur experimentally (5b). This phenomenon can be visualized by considering the effect of k_f in two ways. The first and most obvious one is the increase in the effectiveness of the mediator within the diffusion layer. The result is an increase in the current under the mediator wave that is dependent on k_f. The second effect is the shifting of the catalyst wave in the positive direction. This shift is directly proportional to log k_f (5b) when y_f is very large (i.e. y_f > 10 for the conditions shown above).

To explain this further, consider the total current to be a sum of contributions from the mediator and the reactant. An i-E plot of the reactant contribution is shown in Fig. 2B. This contribution was obtained by subtracting the current due to the reversible mediator from the total current for the catalytic process (i.e. that shown in Fig. 1B or 2A). The reactant contribution will be related to the rate of the homogeneous reaction (reaction 2).

$$\text{RATE} = k_f \bullet c(M_r) \bullet C(S_{ox}) \tag{4}$$

When k_f is small and $C(S_{ox})$ is relatively constant within the diffusion layer, the maximum rate occurs when $C(M_r)$ approaches the bulk mediator concentration. Under Nernstian conditions this will occur negative of the E_{pc} of the mediator. As k_f increases, $C(S_{ox})$ in the diffusion layer is no longer constant for the duration of the voltage scan. The i-E wave of the reactant contribution now resembles that of a normal cyclic wave with its peak potential dependent on k_f. This is shown in Fig. 2B when y_f is greater than 0.1. The maximum current contributed by the reactant will still occur when $C(S_{ox}) \bullet C(M_r)$ is the largest, but this product will be maximized at successively lower values of $C(M_r)$ that is, earlier in the i-E scan. The maximum current contributed by the reactant exceeds $i_{pc,0}$ for y_f greater than 5.0. This agrees with results whosn recently by Andrieux et al. (5b). With very large values of k_f the reactant is depleted (and its current contribution has reached its peak) before the current due to the mediator is significant. At this point the dual peak phenomenon is observed and the reactant peak is separated from the mediator peak. When the mediator is under Nerstian control the two peaks will increase in separation as k_f continues to increase (5b). Thus for effective catalysis both k_f and k_s must be large. Thermodynamic considerations highlight the advantage of having a positive value of $E^{o'}_S - E^{o'}_M$ for catalysis of a reduction (17).

The transition from the reversible to the irreversible case is demonstrated in Fig. 2C. The changes incurred as $k_{s,M}$ dereases are: 1) the shift of the peak potential in the negative direction and, 2) the disappearance of the dual peak phenomena. In curve 1 of Fig. 2C, the voltage is scanned with overvoltage increasing in the negative (reducing) direction. At the foot of the wave, the current is limited by the heterogeneous rate of electron transfer to the mediator. The reactant will not be depleted until significant concentrations of M_r are formed; thus both mediator and reactant will be depleted at approximately the same time. Compare this to the case where $k_{s,M}$ is large and there is no limitation by heterogeneous charge transfer. Without $k_{s,M}$ limitation the reactant can be depleted prior to depletion of the mediator, resulting in the formation of two peaks. In the transition from the reversible to the irreversible case, behavior intermediate to the two preceeding cases is displayed.

To summarize, in order to observe the double peak wave, both dimensionless rate constants, k_f and $k_{s,M}$, need to be large, and the C_S/C_M ratio approximately equal to unity.

DIAGNOSTICS

Introduction

The method of overlaying digitally calculated i-E curves with experimental ones is frequently used as a verification of the proposed mechanism for the reaction involved. In order to use the simulated data diagnostically, the behavior of a certain mechanism must be calculated over a wider range of conditions. In the course of these simulations one finds which parameters are most useful and then quantitates their dependence on changes in such variables as rate constants, scan rates, and concentration ratio. In this section we will first display the dependence of the peak current and peak potential on the two rate constants, k_f and $k_{s,M}$. Then the effects of experimentally variable parameters (i.e. scan rate and concentration ratio) will be examined. The data in this section will deal with a single electron transfer reaction followed by a second order catalytic regeneration step, as shown by reactions 1 and 2. Dimensionless rate constants were calculated using nominal experimental values incorporated into the appropriate dimensionless groups (see Table 1).

Effects of k_f

The dependence of i_{pc} on k_f is shown in Fig. 3. At low values of k_f the peak current depends solely on $k_{s,M}$. As the homogeneous rate increases ($100 < k_f < 5 \times 10^4$ M^{-1} s^{-1}) the i_{pc} increases

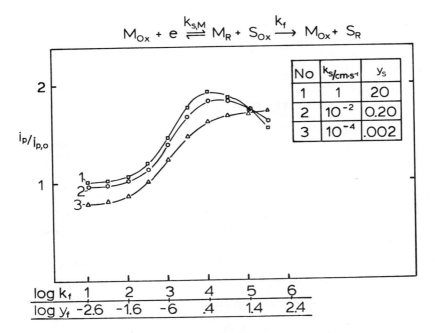

Figure 3. Normalized peak current as a function of the homogeneous rate constant. Data for three values of k_s are shown. Other parameters are the same as for Fig. 1.

smoothly with k_f. The decrease in i_{pc} with $k_f > 5 \times 10^4$ M^{-1} s^{-1} is due to the double peak phenomena as already discussed. When $k_{s,M}$ is small there is no actual separation of the two waves. Note that when the two peaks actually separate, the first peak (i.e. that due to the reduction of the reactant) is used in the i_{pc} versus k_f plots.

The shift in E_{pc} with k_f is shown in Fig. 4. At very high values of y_f, E_{pc} shifts positive of $E^{O'}_M$. Some aspects of this behavior have also been shown previously (5b,19).

Effects of $k_{s,M}$

The effects of $k_{s,M}$ on E_{pc} can be seen in Fig. 5. At large values of y_s, E_{pc} is constant as long as y_f is constant. As y_s decreases and the heterogeneous reaction becomes irreversible, the peak potential changes by 120 mv per decade change in y_s (7). The dependence of i_{pc} is independent of $k_{s,M}$ under reversible and irreversible conditions. For the highest value of k_f the peak current decreases as $k_{s,M}$ increases due to the double peak formation (cf. Fig. 2).

Comparison of Fig. 3 to Fig. 6 shows that the peak current of the catalyst wave is much more dependent on k_f than on $k_{s,M}$. A similar comparison of Figs. 4 and 5 shows the following characteristics: 1) When $k_{s,M}$ is large the peak shift depends only on changes in k_f. Under these conditions, E_{pc} values positive of E_{pc} for the mediator alone can be used for diagnostic criteria for k_f. Peak potentials negative of the mediator peak however would produce ambiguous results since they could be generated by more than one value of k_f; and 2) under conditions where the catalyst reaction is not Nernstian, the peak potential is dependent on both k_f and $k_{s,M}$. Thus in this regime the determination of both rate constants would be difficult.

Since $k_{s,M}$ for the mediator is normally obtained experimentally, a set of working curves for the particular case under consideration can be generated using experimental values for all necessary parameters and plotting i_{pc} and E_{pc} versus k_f. It may be necessary to adjust the experimental conditions to obtain useful values of the diagnostic parameters. For example, if one finds that values of i_{pc} are very near those for the catalyst alone (i.e. in Fig. 3, near $k_f \to 0.0$), then increasing the value of y_f will move i_{pc} to higher (and more diagnostically useful) values. From

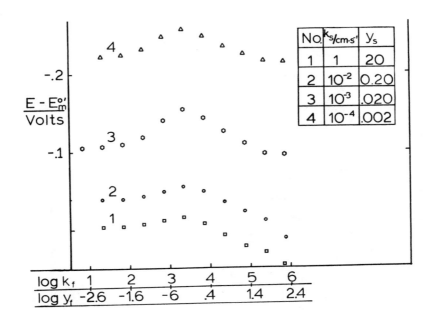

Figure 4. Normalized peak potential versus the homogeneous rate constant. Different values of k_s demonstrate the dependence of peak potential on the heterogeneous rate constant. Other parameters are the same as for Fig. 1.

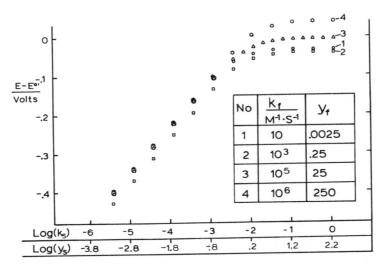

Figure 5. Normalized peak potential as a function of y_s. Different values of y_f are used; other parameters are the same as for Fig. 1.

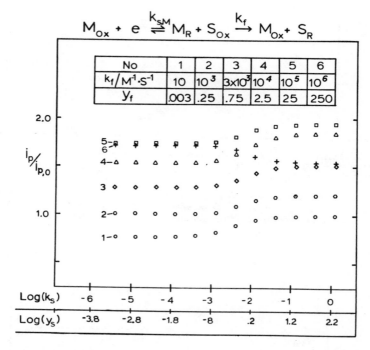

Figure 6. The dependence of i_{pc} on y_s is shown for different values of y_f. Other parameters are the same as for Fig. 1.

Fig. 3 we see that k_f needs to lie between 100 and 2×10^4 M^{-1} s^{-1} (for the conditions shown in Fig. 3) for greatest utility. The dimensionless homogeneous rate can be increased by either increasing the concentration of the reactants, or be decreasing the scan rate (v). Care must be exercised in changing v as both k_f and $k_{s,M}$ are related to v through the dimensionless parameters. In the reversible region ($k_{s,M}$ large) this is no problem since neither i_{pc} or E_{pc} vary much with $k_{s,M}$; however in the quasi-reversible region or irreversible regime, changes in E_{pc} and/or i_{pc} will occur on varying $y_{s,M}$ via changes in v.

In general the i_{pc} is most diagnostically useful at intermediate values of y_f and the change in E_{pc} is more useful for large values of k_f C/a. A good point of delineation is k_f C/a = 10.

Effects of Scanrate

In order to verify a proposed mechanism it is useful to know the behavior of the simulation through a range of experimental variables. Probably most useful is the correlation of peak potential or current to scanrate (v). Both $k_{s,M}$ and k_f are related to v via the dimensionless parameters (Table 1). Fig. 7B shows that a decrease in scanrate increases the contribution of the follow-up catalytic process to the peak current. As discussed earlier the dimensionless homogeneous rate is inversely proportional to v. In fact, for large values of $k_{s,M}$, where the peak current is independent of $k_{s,M}$, a plot of $i_{pc}/i_{pc,0}$ versus log 1/v would resemble a plot of $i_{pc}/i_{pc,0}$ versus log k_f (cf. Fig. 3).

Changes in E_{pc} with v likewise reflect both k_s and k_f. For the case where $k_{s,M}$ is large the change in $y_{s,M}$ generated by varying v, does not shift E_{pc}. The resultant shift in E_{pc} with v is due to the effective change in k_f. Thus as k_f increases or v decreases, the peak shifts slightly negative and then back in the positive direction. Eventually it becomes more positive than the E_{pc} in the absence of homogeneous kinetics. This is similar to the behavior that was shown in Fig. 4 for the change in E_{pc} due to $k_{s,M}$. When the rate of the heterogeneous process decreases, changes in v affect both $y_{s,M}$ and y_f. The solid lines plotted in Fig. 7A depict the shift of E_{pc} with ln(v) for an irreversible one electron transfer wave (7). The simulated points for curves 4 and

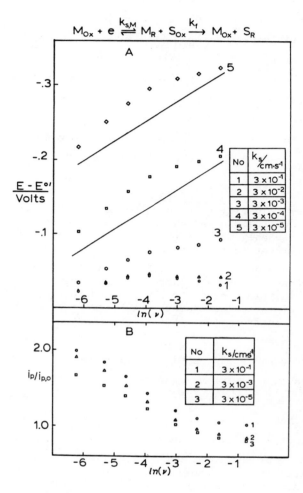

Figure 7.   *The variation of E_{pc} (top) and i_{pc} (bottom) as a function of ln (scan rate) is shown. $K_f = 4 \times 10^2/M\ s$.*

5 in Fig. 2A appear to be the sum of the potential shift due to y_f and that due to y_s.

Diagnostic plots of one parameter as a function of the dimensionless rate are common in numerical analyses of rate constants. Manipulation of the scan rate is one way to experimentally change the dimensionless rate constants. Having more than one adjustable rate constants which depend on the scanrate make the determination of rate constants less straightforward. Changes in v can however, be used to show the qualitative changes in the i–E scan that are characteristic of the ec mechanism. This will be demonstrated later.

Concentration Ratio Effects

Another system variable that can be manipulated experimentally is the concentration ratio, C_M/C_S. Fig. 8 shows the dependence of normalized reactant peak current on C_M/C_S and k_f. In Fig. 2 the reactant current was plotted as a function of potential when this concentration ratio was equal to unity. In these figures the current is normalized to $i_{pc,0}$ for the substrate. Increasing either the C_M/C_S ratio or k_f, increases the turnover of the reactant. When the C_M/C_S ratio is very small, very large values of k_f are required for high turnover of the reactant. The limit of the reactant contribution as k_f gets very large is approximately $1.35i_{pc,0}$, in agreement with similar results obtained for y_f approaching 5×10^5 M^{-1} s^{-1}.

Although this discussion has so far been limited to the case where $n_S = n_M = 1$, and $D_S/D_M = 1$, we can apply the same diagnostics to a wide range of similar cases. For the cyclic voltammetric results described herein, the concept of a concentration ratio can be expanded to a more general cyclic voltammetry "flux ratio" which would include the n and $D^{\frac{1}{2}}$ ratios of the mediator and reactant. Thus our previous results for $C_S/C_M = 1$ will apply to all experimental situations in which the following ratio holds:

$$n_S \cdot C_S \cdot D_S^{\frac{1}{2}} = n_M \cdot C_M \cdot D_M^{\frac{1}{2}} \tag{5}$$

Applying this concept to Fig. 8 one can then use $(n_S \cdot C_S \cdot D_S^{\frac{1}{2}})/ (n_M \cdot C_M \cdot D_M^{\frac{1}{2}})$ in place of C_S/C_M. Thus this analysis for the simple case can be applied to cases in which D_S is not equal to D_M and n_S is not equal to n_M. These results show that one can determine

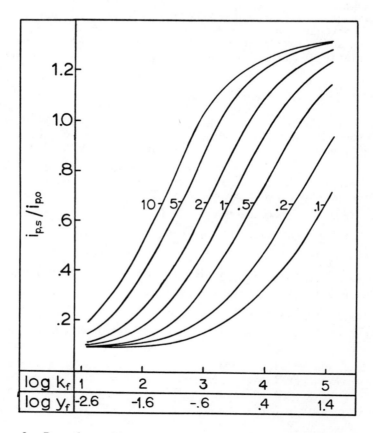

Figure 8.   Dependence of $i_{pc,reactant}/i_{pc,0}$ on C_M/C_S, and k_f. For comparison, plots of $i_{pc,reactant}$ (or $i - i_0$) versus E are shown in Fig. 2B.   The value of $i_{pc,0}$ is due to the reversible electron transfer of a species whose concentration is equal to that of the reactant species.

N through the use of equation 5 and peak current data over a wide range of concentration ratios.

The first part of this section showed how the diagnostic parameters ($i_{pc}/i_{pc,0}$ and E_{pc}) varied with the rate constants. When the dimensionless homogeneous rate ($k_f C/a = y_f$) goes from 0.01 to 10, the peak current ratio increases from 1 to near 2. With an independent determination of $k_{s,M}$ a working curve can be constructed to determine k_f. For y_f above 10 the peak current ratio will decrease again. Thus data should be taken over a wide enough range of y_f so that the specific regime can be identified. In the $y_f > 10$ range the peak potential shift can also be used to determine the rate constant. According to Andrieux and coworkers the peak potential shift 30 mV per decade increase in k_f for very large y_f (5b). This particular determination is dependent on Nernstian response of the mediator. The present work allows the behavior of an ec catalytic system to be predicted over the full range of $k_{s,M}$ for the mediator.

The variation due to $k_{s,M}$ was similar to the case of a single electron transfer. The E_{pc} was independent of $k_{s,M}$ under reversible conditions and shifted by 120 mV/decade $k_{s,M}$ under irreversible conditions. In the quasi-reversible region the respective parameters varied smoothly between the two limiting cases. The object of the exercise with $k_{s,M}$ has been to understand how it can effect the diagnostic parameters used for the determination of k_f.

The final two parts of this section showed how to experimentally obtain working curves that could be compared to simulated data. Plots of peak current versus v should be used discriminately since b effectively varies both y_f and y_s. As long as $y_s \gg 1$ or $y_s \ll 1$, i_{pc} is independent of the dimensionless heterogeneous rate. In addition to this, plots of i_{pc} versus concentration can be used to match the simulated i_{pc} versus y_f plots.

EXPERIMENTAL AND SIMULATED EC CATALYSIS

The Catalysis of Oxygen Electro-reduction

A problem that has been prominent for many years has been the catalysis of oxygen electro-reduction. The objective and problem with oxygen are illustrated by the cyclic voltammetric i-E waves shown in Fig. 9. Curve a is the computer simulated i-E wave for a reversible, four electron reduction of oxygen to water ($E^{O'}$ = +1.23 V vs NHE). The i_{pc} value is 8 times the peak height that

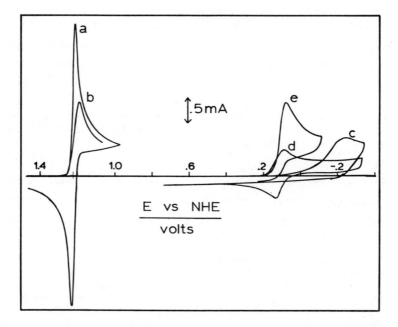

Figure 9. CV i–E scans pertinent to oxygen reduction catalysis. Key: a, simulated, reversible, four electron reduction of oxygen to water; b, simulated ec catalytic mechanism, $N = 4$ with $E_M{}^{\circ\prime} = 1.23$ volts; c, experimental oxygen reduction on glassy carbon; d, experimental FeTMPyP reduction on glassy carbon; and e, experimental oxygen reduction catalyzed by FeTMPyP (on glassy carbon).

would have been obtained if oxygen was reduced only to the super-oxide ion, an one electron reduction. The factor of 8 appears because the number of electrons, n, in the reduction of oxygen to water is raised to a power of 3/2 in the Randles-Sevcik equation (16). If it were possible to mediate (i.e. catalyze) the re-duction of oxygen at the reversible potential using an one elec-tron mediator, the increase in current by oxygen conversion to water (N = 4) would be a direct multiple of N, the stoichiometric coefficient. Thus for a follow-up reaction like:

$$N \cdot M_r + S_{ox} = N \cdot M_{ox} + S_r \qquad (6)$$

the current would be given by:

$$i = i_M + N \cdot i_S \qquad (7)$$

where i_M is the current due to the mediator and i_S is that con-tributed by the ec catalysis of the reactant species. Thus for oxygen, an one electron mediator would produce a peak height $(N \cdot i_{p,S})$ due to oxygen catalysis of curve b in Fig. 9. For the conditions shown, $N \cdot i_{p,S}$ is only four times that of the one elec-tron reduction of oxygen. One can draw similar conclusions re-garding the reduction of oxygen to hydrogen peroxide (N = 2). Curve C in the same figure is the experimental i-E curve for the reduction of oxygen at a highly polished glassy carbon electrode in 0.1M H_2SO_4. This reduction is highly irreversible with the peak potential shifted negative of the reversible peak by about 1.5 volt and the peak current is about one-fifth the height of the reversible peak (curve a). Curve d shows the reversible redox i-E wave for the iron tetrakis(N-methyl-4-pyridyl)porphyrin (abbr: FeTMPyP) which has been shown to be an effective catalyst for the reduction of oxygen on glassy carbon (1). In earlier studies in which the FeTMPyP and oxygen concentrations were equal to 2.4 x 10^{-4} M (air-saturated solution), H_2O_2 was concluded to be the pro-duct of the oxygen reduction, from the analysis of the CV i-E wave heights (1). Curve e in Fig. 9 is the i-E wave for the above con-ditions. To date all of the data are consistent with an ec cata-lytic mechanism for this reduction.

Three different ec catalytic mechanisms are considered in the simulation of the i-E curves for oxygen reduction catalyzed by FeTMPyP. These are:

1.   e step: $Fe(III)TMPyP + e^- = Fe(II)TMPyP$ (8)

            c step: $2Fe(II)TMPyP + O_2 + 2H^+ =$

                     $2Fe(III)TMPyP + H_2O_2$ (9)

2.   reaction 8 followed by:

$$4Fe(II)TMPyP + O_2 + 4H^+ =$$

$$4Fe(III)TMPyP + 2H_2O \qquad\qquad (10)$$

3.   Reactions 8 and 9 followed by:

$$2Fe(II)TMPyP + H_2O_2 + 2H^+ =$$

$$2Fe(III)TMPyP + 2H_2O \qquad\qquad (11)$$

where reactions 9, 10 and 11 reflect the reactant stoichiometry in the homogeneous step. The simulated i-E waves showing an N = 2 stoichiometry for oxygen catalysis by Fe(II)TMPyP are given in Fig. 10 A and B. The experimental $k_{s,M}$ value of 5 x 10^{-3} cm s^{-1} is used in Fig. 10 A as the k_f value of reaction 9 is varied, while in Fig. 10 B, the k_f is fixed at 2 x 10^6 M^{-1} s^{-1} as the value of $k_{s,M}$ is varied. These values of k_f and K_s had been previously estimated from CV data (19). The i_{pc} values are about 5 times greater than those previously seen in Fig. 2 for similat values of $k_{s,M}$ and k_f because of the larger ratios of n_S/n_M = 2 and D_S/D_M = 9 for the oxygen/FeTMPyP case.

More recently, it (19) has found that the extent of oxygen catalysis by FeTMPyP was concentration dependent. The i_{pc} normalized to $i_{pc,0}$ (where $i_{pc,0}$ is the peak current for reduction of oxygen to superoxide ion) was found to approach four at FeTMPyP/oxygen concentration ratios greater than two. This result suggested that oxygen could be catalytically reduced to water. In this case the overall reaction has a stoichiometry of four.

Characterization of this reaction by changes in the concentration ratio is shown in Fig. 11, A and B. The results reflect the large homogeneous rate constant in two ways: 1) the rapid increase in i_{pc} with C_M, and 2) the shift of E_{pc} positive of the $E_{pc,0}$ of the mediator. The experimental results can be compared to different mechanisms for mediated oxygen reduction. The peak currents for oxygen reduction are higher than that expected of a two electron process. This model is therefore considered inappropriate. The simulated peak currents for the mediated N = 4 case are greater than that obtained experimentally. Thus under these conditions the reaction is somewhere between the two and four electron processes. Of course the peak currents for the four electron stoichiometry can be decreased by decreasing the homogeneous rate; this will be discussed later. Using mechanism 3 the values of $i_{pc,0}$ closely match the experimental results. In add-

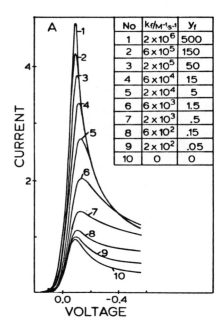

No	$k_f/M^{-1}s^{-1}$	y_f
1	2×10^6	500
2	6×10^5	150
3	2×10^5	50
4	6×10^4	15
5	2×10^4	5
6	6×10^3	1.5
7	2×10^3	.5
8	6×10^2	.15
9	2×10^2	.05
10	0	0

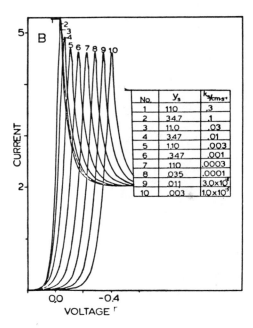

No.	y_s	$k_{s,M}/cm \cdot s^{-1}$
1	110	.3
2	34.7	.1
3	11.0	.03
4	3.47	.01
5	1.10	.003
6	.347	.001
7	.110	.0003
8	.035	.0001
9	.011	3.0×10^{-5}
10	.003	1.0×10^{-5}

Figure 10. Simulated i–E scans for the ec catalytic mechanism when $N = 2$, and $D_S/D_M = 9$. Effects of changing k_f, with $k_{s,M} = 5 \times 10^{-3}$ cm/s (top); and $k_{s,M}$ when $k_f = 2 \times 10^6$/M s (bottom).

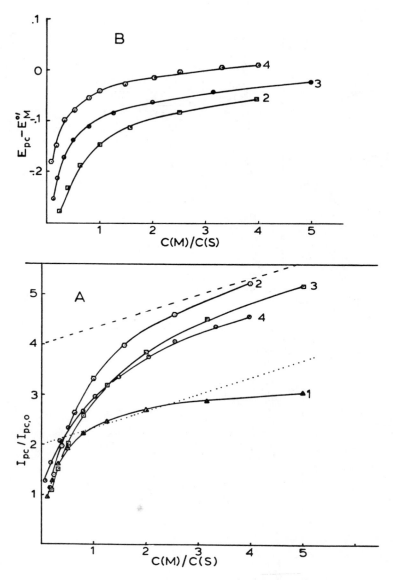

Figure 11. Dependence of E_{pc} (top) and i_{pc} (bottom) on the concentration ratio C_M/C_S. Key: $D_S/D_M = 9$; curve 1, $N = 2$, $k_f = 1 \times 10^6/M\ s$, $k_s = 0.01\ cm/s$; curve 2, $N = 4$, $k_f = 2 \times 10^5/M\ s$, $k_s = 0.01\ cm/s$; curve 3, $N = 2 + 2$ (scheme three), k_f (rxn 8) = $5 \times 10^5/M\ s$, k_f (rxn 10) = $5 \times 10^5/M\ s$, $k_s = 0.01\ cm/s$; and curve 4, experimental reduction of oxygen using water soluble FeTMPyP.

ition to this, Fig. 11 B shows the peak potential shifts of the catalyzed wave (with mechanism 1 excluded). The results clearly demonstrate that the peak potentials for mechanism 3 more closely match the experimental peak shifts. The peak currents for mechanism 2 can be lowered to approach the experimental i_{pc}'s by lowering the homogeneous rate constant. However, the concomitant shift of E_{pc} in the negative direction makes this lowering of k_f unacceptable (cf. Fig. 11 B). Further details of the mechanistic pathways for the reduction of oxygen catalyzed by this water soluble iron porphyrin will be published (19).

CONCLUSION

CV, i-E waves can be used pictorially to demonstrate the characteristics oa an ec catlytic mechanism. Wave parameters (i_{pc} and E_{pc}) can be used diagnostically to obtain shoichiometric and kinetic information. Use of these parameters in conjunction with digitally simulated data can provide qualitative to semi-quantitative information on very complex ec mechanisms. The determination of the homogeneous rate constants is especially useful for oxygen catalysis by water-soluble metal porphyrins, which can be transferred to the surface by immobilization for heterogeneous catalysis. There is evidence already in the case of immobilized iron porphyrin (4) that the N value does depend on the "coverage" of the catalyst, in agreement with the homogeneous results. It is our purpose to continue the study of the relationships between homogeneous and immobilized ec catalytic systems and to apply the tools developed in this study to the diagnosis of surface modified for electrocatalytic purposes.

ACKNOWLEDGEMENTS

We gratefully acknowledge the support of this work by grants from the Air Force Office of Scientific Research (grant No. 78-3672) and the National Institute of Health (grant No. 19181). The discussions and helpful comments by H.N. Blount of the University of Delaware are gratefully appreciated.

Key to Symbols and Abbreviations

a	$n \cdot F \cdot v / (R/T)$
alpha	transfer coefficient for an electrochemical reaction
C_M	bulk concentration of the mediator: M
C_S	bulk concentration of the reactant: M
CV	cyclic voltammetry
D_M	diffusion coefficient of the mediator: $cm^2\ s^{-1}$
D_S	diffusion coefficient of the reactant: $cm^2\ s^{-1}$
$E^0{}'M$	formal electrode potential of the $M_{ox/r}$ couple
$E^0{}'S$	formal electrode potential of the $S_{ox/r}$ couple
ec	designates an electrocatalytic scheme involving an homogeneous step following a heterogeneous electron transfer
E_{pc}	cathodic peak potential: Volts
F	Faradays constant: 96500 coulombs
i_{pc}	peak cathodic current
$i_{pc,0}$	peak cathodic current for a $1e^-$, reversible reaction
K_{eq}	equilibrium constant
k_f	homogeneous rate constant for forward reaction: $M^{-1}\ s^{-1}$
$k_{s,M}$	heterogeneous rate constant of the mediator: $cm\ s^{-1}$
$k_{s,S}$	heterogeneous rate constant of the reactant: $cm\ s^{-1}$
$M_{ox/r}$	mediator in ex catalytic scheme
N	stoichiometric ratio equal to n_S/n_M
n_M	number of electrons transferred per molecule of $M_{ox/r}$
n_S	number of electrons transferred per molecule of $S_{ox/r}$
ox	oxidized form of a redox couple
R	gas constant: 8.314 joules/mole·degree
r	reduced form of a redox couple
$S_{ox/r}$	reactant in an ec catalytic scheme
T	temperature in degrees kelvin
v	scanrate: $V\ s^{-1}$
y_f	dimensionless homogeneous rate $= k_f \cdot C / a$
y_s	dimensionless heterogeneous rate $= k_s / d_M \cdot a^{\frac{1}{2}}$

Literature Cited

1. T. Kuwana, M. Fujihira, K. Sunakawa, and T. Osa, J. Electro-
    anal. Chem., 88 (1978) 299.
2. T. Kuwana and A. Bettelheim, Anal. Chem., 51 (1979) 2257.
3. T. Kuwana, R.J. Chan and A. Bettelheim, J. Electroanal. Chem.,
    99 (1979) 391.
4. T. Kuwana, R.J. Chan and A. Bettelheim, J. Electroanal. Chem.,
    110 (1980) 93.
5. For example, see the following papers and the references list-
    ed therein: a) C.P. Andrieux, J.M. Dumas-Bouchiat and J.M.
    Saveant, J. Electroanal. Chem., 87 (1978) 39-53; b) C.P.
    Andrieux, C. Blocman, J.J. Dumas-Bouchiat, F. M'Halla and J.M.
    Saveant, J. Electroanal. Chem., 113 (1980) 19-40; and c) M.K.
    Hanafey, R.L. Scott, T.H. Ridgway and C.N. Reilley, Anal.
    Chem., 50 (1978) 116.
6. J.M. Saveant and E. Vianello in "Advances in Polarography",
    I.S. Longmuir (Ed.), Vol. I, p. 367, Pergammon Press. N.Y.,
    1960.
7. R.S. Nicholson and I. Shain, Anal. Chem., 36 (1974) 706-723.
8. J.M. Saveant and E. Vianello, Electrochim. Acta., 10 (1965)
    905.
9. S.W. Feldberg in A.J. Bard (Ed.), "Electroanalytical Chem-
    istry", Vol. 3, Marcel Dekker, New York, 1969, pp. 199-296.
10. D. Britz, "Lecture Notes in Chemistry" Digital Simulation in
    Electrochemistry". Springer-Verlag Berlin. Heidelberg, New
    York, 1981.
11. For example the heterogeneous equivalent approximation (12),
    the unequal box size method (13), the orthogonal collocation
    technique (14) and the aforementioned implicit scheme all will
    lead to decreased computer time, although a price is usually
    paid in generality and/or accuracy.
12. J. Ruzic and S.W. Feldberg, J. Electroanal. Chem., 50 (1974)
    153-162.
13. T. Joslin and D. Pletcher, J. Electroanal. Chem., 49 (1974)
    171-186.
14. B. Speiser and A. Rieker, J. Electroanal. Chem., 102 (1979)
    1-20.
15. Several programs used in this study, as well as added insights
    into the ec catalytic mechansim were provided by Prof. Henry
    Blount of the University of Delaware.
16. (a) J.E.B. Randles, Trans. Faraday Soc., 44 (1948) 327, (b)
    A. Sevcik, Collect. Czech. Chem. Commun., 13 (1948) 349.
17. Recent results by Anson (18) and Saveant (5a) indicate that
    this driving force is not necessary as long as a sufficiently
    rapid follow-up reaction occurs which effectively removes the
    product (S_r) of reaction 2.
18. F.C. Anson, J. Phys. Chem., 84 (1980) 3336-3338.
19. P. Forshey and T. Kuwana, submitted for publication (1981).
20. H. Matsuda and Y. Ayabe, Z. Electrochem., 59 (1955) 494.

RECEIVED March 19, 1982.

Chemically Derivatized Semiconductor Photoelectrodes

MARK S. WRIGHTON

Massachusetts Institute of Technology, Department of Chemistry,
Cambridge, MA 02139

Highlights of research results from the chemical
derivatization of n-type semiconductors with (1,1'-
ferrocenediyl)dimethylsilane, I, and its dichloro
analogue, II, and from the derivatization of p-type
semiconductors with {N,N'-bis[3-trimethoxysilyl)-
propyl]-4,4'-bipyridinium}dibromide, III are
presented. Research shows that molecular derivatization with II can be used to suppress photoanodic corrosion of n-type Si; derivatization of
p-type Si with III can be used to improve
photoreduction kinetics for horseheart ferricytochrome c; derivatization of p-type Si with III
followed by incorporation of Pt(0) improves
photoelectrochemical H₂ production efficiency.
Strongly interacting reagents can alter semicon-
ductor/electrolyte interface energetics and surface
state distributions as illustrated by n-type WS₂/I⁻
interactions and by differing etch procedures for
n-type CdTe.

Derivatization of the surface of semiconductor photoelectrodes may be useful in suppressing corrosion reactions of
the electrode (1-5), accelerating the rate of desired redox
processes (6-8), measuring rate constants for reactions of
surface-confined redox reagents (9,10), bringing about changes in
the energetics of the semiconductor/electrolyte interface(11,12),
and altering the distribution of surface states associated with
the semiconductors.(13,14) Work in this laboratory has concerned
the study of n-type semiconductor photoelectrode materials such
as Si, Ge, and GaAs derivatized with reagents based on ferrocene
such as those represented by I and II. Work with p-type
semiconductor photoelectrode materials such as Si concerns the
use of the N,N'-dialkyl-4,4'-bipyridinium-based derivatizing

0097-6156/82/0192-0099 $9.25/0

reagent represented by <u>III</u>. The results from these studies do suggest that surface derivatization may be useful in certain practical and fundamental applications. The highlights of the studies to date along with the limitations associated with chemical derivatization will be summarized in this article.

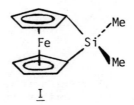

<u>I</u>

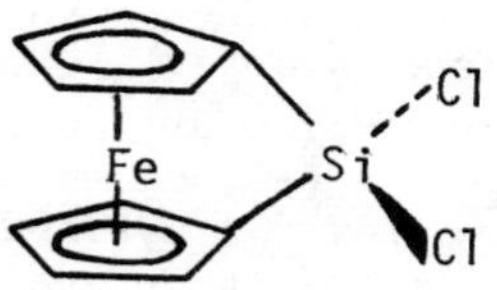

<u>II</u>

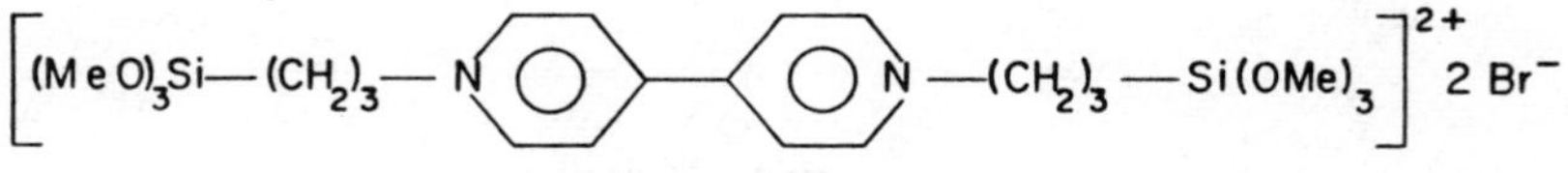

$$\left[(MeO)_3Si-(CH_2)_3-N\bigcirc\!\!-\!\!\bigcirc N-(CH_2)_3-Si(OMe)_3 \right]^{2+} 2\,Br^-$$

<u>III</u>

Suppression of Photoanodic Corrosion of N-Type Semiconductors

All n-type semiconductors are thermodynamically unstable
when irradiated with supra band gap energy light in the presence
of liquid electrolytes.(15-17) However, it is well known that
durable n-type semiconductor/electrolyte/redox couple
combinations do exist.(18,19) For example, it has been found
that n-type Si, that can undergo surface photooxidation according
to equation (1) can be protected from corrosion.(20)   In equation

$$Si + 2xh^+ + xH_2O \longrightarrow SiO_x + 2xH^+ \qquad (1)$$

(1) h^+ represents the photogenerated minority carrier (hole) that
comes to the semiconductor surface under depletion conditions as
illustrated in Scheme I. If the oxidative decomposition of Si
proceeds too far the SiO_x thickness ultimately blocks the flow of
current and useful photoelectrochemical effects cease. The oxidative decomposition can be suppressed if some redox active
species A can compete for the h^+, equation (2). Since the photo-

$$A + h^+ \longrightarrow A^+ \qquad (2)$$

anodic decomposition of semiconductors is generally a multistep
process it would seem that fast, one-electron reductants would be
able to completely suppress photoanodic corrosion by neutralizing
the h^+ before the decomposition process can begin. A priori the
species A should have fast heterogeneous electron transfer
kinetics, be durable in both the A and A^+ oxidation levels, be
optically transparent, be present at high effective concentration, and have an $E^{\circ\prime}(A^+/A)$ that gives a good efficiency from
the point of view of output photovoltage, E_V. Referring to
Scheme I, E_V for the photoanode is the extent to which the
oxidation occurs at a potential more negative than the E_{redox} of
the solution. Concerning n-type Si it was found that EtOH/0.1 M
[n-Bu₄N]ClO₄ solutions containing A = ferrocene and A^+ = ferricenium result in a constant output of electrical energy from an
illuminated photoelectrochemical device configured as in Scheme
II.(20)   The ferrocene captures the photogenerated h^+ at a rate
that precludes photoanodic corrosion of the n-type Si. The
purpose in using EtOH solvent is to remove as much H_2O as
possible from the solvent to reduce the importance of the photooxidation process (1).

The experiments with the n-type Si/ferrocene in EtOH/0.1 M
[n-Bu₄N]ClO₄ prompted the initial work in this laboratory on the
surface derivatization of photoelectrodes. The ferrocene-based
reagent, II, was anchored to the surface according to equation
(3).(1-3)   The resulting polymer confronts the n-type Si

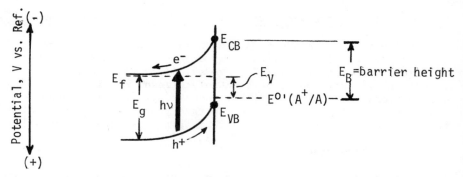

Scheme I. Interface energetics for an n-type semiconductor under
illumination giving an uphill oxidation of A to A+ to the extent of
of E_V. Generally, the desired oxidation is only competitive with the
anodic decomposition of the semiconductor. In the diagram E_f represents
the electrode potential; E_{CB} the bottom of the conduction band; and E_{VB}
the top of the valence band. At open-circuit $E_V \approx E_B$.

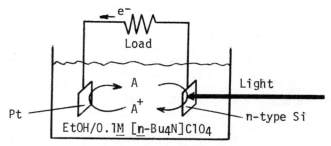

Scheme II. Representation of an n-type Si photoanode-based
cell for the conversion of light to electricity.

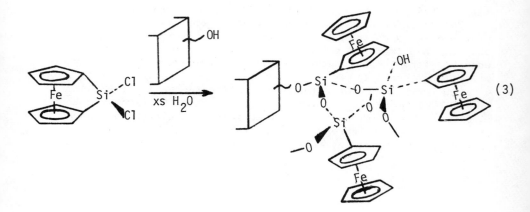

$$(3)$$

surface with a high effective concentration of the reducing agent
A. The important fact with respect to suppressing electrode
corrosion was the finding that n-type Si functionalized with II
is capable of being used in aqueous electrolyte solution under
conditions where the naked (non-derivatized) electrode suffers
photodecomposition at a rate that precludes any reproducible
photoelectrochemistry. When the reagent A is confined to the
photoelectrode surface sustained current flow results from the
sequence represented by equations (4)-(5) where the photo-

$$\text{surface-A} + h^+ \xrightarrow{\;k_4\;} \text{surface-A}^+ \tag{4}$$

$$\text{surface-A}^+ + B \xrightarrow{\;k_5\;} \text{surface-A} + B^+ \tag{5}$$

generated, surface-confined oxidant, A^+, reacts heterogeneously
with a solution species B to form B^+ and reduce A^+ to A.(2,3,9,
10) For the surfaces resulting from treatment with II the surface
oxidant is a ferricenium derivative and anything oxidizeable with
ferricenium should be oxidizeable with a photoanode derivatized
with II. A number of aqueous species B have been photooxidized
using n-type Si derivatized with II including $Ru(NH_3)_6^{2+}$,
$Fe(CN)_6^{4-}$, $Co(2,2'-bipyridine)_3^{2+}$, and I^-.(2,3,9,10) In every
case the photocurrent is relatively constant compared to that
from a naked n-type Si photoanode. Quite interestingly, no
aqueous redox additive has been demonstrated to suppress
photooxidation of Si to the extent that can be achieved using the
surface derivatization procedure. However, even electrodes
functionalized with I do not last indefinitely in aqueous
solution. Typically, naked n-type Si photoanodes give a photocurrent that declines by >90% in <5 min under conditions where
the derivatized electrode shows <20% in 60 min. In such experi-
mentation it has been demonstrated that each ferrocene center on
the surface can be oxidized and reduced $>10^5$ times without
significant loss of electroactive material.(2,3) The decline in
efficiency found for n-type Si photoanodes derivatized with II
seems to be attributable to the slow growth of an SiO_x layer
between the bulk Si and the derivatizing layer.

The ability to observe sustained electrical output from
n-type Si-based cells after derivatization of the surface of Si
with II indicates that such surface chemistry may prove useful.
The maximum value of E_V is ~0.5 - 0.6 V for n-type Si derivatized
with II which is not too bad considering that the band gap, E_g,
of Si is only 1.1 eV. The ferrocene system is fairly durable in
both oxidation states and its heterogeneous electron transfer

kinetics are good; k_4 is large. Further, the ferricenium does not appear to be capable of effecting Si oxidation to an extent that a thick, insulating SiO_x layer results. Unfortunately, the features that make the ferricenium/ferrocene couple attractive also detract from its usefulness in the generation of energy-rich compounds using the photoanode-based cells. First, ferricenium is an oxidant, but a weak one; $E°'$(ferricenium/ferrocene) for the surface species derived from II is ~+0.5 V vs. SCE. Some data for $E°'$ for various electrodes are given in Table I. Second, and more important, ferricenium is a one-electron, outer-sphere oxidant. Most of the desired photoanodic process for fuel formation involve multi-electron transfer processes: O_2 from H_2O, Br_2 from Br^-, etc. Thus, while there are many aqueous reagents B that can be oxidized with a large value of k_5, equation (5), the generation of useful, powerful oxidatants is either thermo-dynamically forbidden or kinetically sluggish. Electrodes only derivatized with II thus do not provide evidence that useful oxidation processes can be effected. However, it may be possible to introduce oxidation catalysts into the derivatizing layer from II that will accelerate the multi-electron processes of interest, as has been done for H_2 evolution, vide infra.(7,8)

Work in other laboratories has demonstrated that n-type Si or GaAs can be protected from photocorrosion using a derivatizing procedure involving the polymerization of pyrrole to coat the surface with an electronically conducting film.(4,5) This procedure is analogous to coating the electrode with a uniform metal overcoat to yield a "buried" photosensitive interface. In such a case, the h^+ does not contact the liquid electrolyte at all and thus photocorrosion is only possible if there are pinholes in the polymer overcoat. As for the surfaces derived from II, the polypyrrole-coated electrodes likely suffer from poor kinetics for processes such as O_2 generation and surface catalysts are needed. Again, however, considerable improvement in durability is attainable compared to naked photoanodes.

Catalysis of H_2 Generation from P-Type Semiconductor Photocathodes

Many p-type semiconductors should be capable of effecting the generation of H_2 from H_2O using light as the driving force, since it can be shown that the bottom of the conduction band, E_{CB}, can be more negative than $E°'$(H_2O/H_2). Work in this labor-atory has focused on the use of p-type Si as a photocathode.(7,8) It was shown that N,N'-dimethyl-4,4'-bipyridinium, MV^{2+}, can be photoreduced to MV^+ in aqueous solution at a pH where $E°'$($MV^{2+/+}$) ≈ $E°'$(H_2O/H_2) establishing the interface energetics to be as represented in Scheme III.(21,22) For MV^{2+} reduction to MV^+ the maximum E_V was found to be ~0.5 V. For p-type photocathodes E_V is the extent to which the photoreduction can be effected at a

TABLE I.   Formal Potentials and Photovoltages for
Surface-Confined Ferrocene Reagents

Derivatizing Reagent	Electrode Substrate	$E^{\circ\prime}$, V vs. SCE ± 0.03[a]	E_V, V[b]
I	Pt	+0.43	---
	Au	+0.43	---
	n-type Si	[+0.43][c]	~0.4 - 0.6
II	Pt	+0.50	---
	Au	+0.45	---
	n-type Si	[+0.45][c]	~0.5 - 0.6
	n-type GaAs	[+0.45][c]	~0.7
	n-type Ge	[+0.45][c]	~0.2

[a]Data for Pt and Au electrodes are from cyclic voltammograms in
$CH_3CN/0.1$ M [n-Bu$_4$N]ClO$_4$. Data are from a number of
determinations as given in: Wrighton, M.S.; Palazzotto, M.C.;
Bocarsly, A.B.; Bolts, J.M.; Fischer, A.B.; Nadjo, L. J. Am.
Chem. Soc., 1978, 100, 7264; Bolts, J.M.; Wrighton, M.S. ibid.,
1978, 100, 5257 and 1979, 101, 6179; Bruce, J.A.; Wrighton, M.S.
J. Electroanal. Chem., 1981, 122, 93; Fischer, A.B. Ph.D.
Thesis, M.I.T., 1981.
[b]E_V is the photovoltage obtained for the derivatized n-type
semiconductor photoanodes. We assume $E^{\circ\prime}$ to be the values given
in brackets and E_V is the extent to which the peak of the
photoanodic current is more negative than $E^{\circ\prime}$ under $\geqslant E_g$
illumination. Data are from references given in (a).
[c]We assume $E^{\circ\prime}$ to be the same on the n-type semiconductors as on
metallic electrodes but these values have not been measured,
since the n-type semiconductors generally are not reversible.

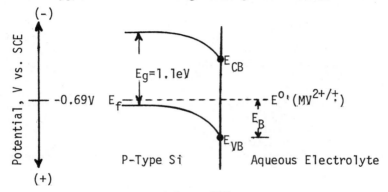

Scheme III

more positive potential than E_{redox} of the redox species. Good
photocurrent-voltage curves were found for the p-type $Si/MV^{2+/+}$
system.

Under the conditions where the MV^{2+} reduction occurs with
good output parameters the reduction of H_2O does not occur,
despite the fact that formation of MV^+ is as difficult thermodynamically as the formation of H_2 from H_2O. Not unexpectedly,
the formation of H_2 from H_2O is kinetically more difficult than
the one-electron, outer-sphere reduction of MV^{2+}. At this point,
work in this laboratory commenced toward the use of reagent III
as a derivatizing agent for p-type Si, since the reducing power
of the MV^+ is sufficiently great to evolve H_2 from H_2O at pH ≤ 7.
Exploiting the reducing power, though, requires the use of a
catalyst to equilibrate the $(MV^{2+/+})$ with (H_2O/H_2). Our work has
been involved with the use of polymers derived from III that are
confined to the p-type Si surface, $[(PQ^{2+} \cdot 2Br^-)_n]_{surf.}$, that have
been further functionalized to include either Pt(0) or Pd(0) to
equilibrate the $[(PQ^{2+/+})_n]_{surf.}$ with the (H_2O/H_2) couple.

A number of physical techniques have been used to characterize electrode surfaces derivatized with III. In the first
study (23), the cyclic voltammetry of Pt and p-type Si electrodes
bearing $[(PQ^{2+} \cdot 2Br^-)_n]_{surf.}$ was used to confirm the surface
attachment of polymeric quantities of PQ^{2+} centers. In
CH_3CN/electrolyte solution the positions of waves on Pt for the
$[(PQ^{2+/+})_n]_{surf.}$ and $[(PQ^{+/0})_n]_{surf.}$ systems are very close to
those expected from the $E°'$ for $(MV^{2+/+})$ in solution.(23) Some
representative data for the N,N'-dialkyl-bipyridinium systems are
given in Table II. Notice that the $E°'$ for $[(PQ^{2+/+})_n]_{surf.}$ in
H_2O electrolyte is somewhat more positive (~100-150 mV) than the
$E°'$ for the $(MV^{2+/+})$ solution species. We attributed(8) this
shift to the fact that the radical monocations of such species
are known to reversibly dimerize as shown in equation (6) for the

$$2MV^+ \quad \rightleftarrows \quad (MV)_2^{2+} \qquad (6)$$

$$\text{blue} \qquad\qquad\qquad \text{violet}$$
$$\lambda_{max} \approx 603 \text{ nm} \qquad \lambda_{max} \approx 550 \text{ nm}$$

MV^+ case.(24) Optical spectral changes as a function of the
concentration of the MV^+ (or the one-electron reduced form of
III)(25) are consistent with the reversible equilibrium
represented by equation (6). The $[(PQ^{2+/+})n]_{surf.}$ system is
violet in color(25), not blue, consistent with aggregation of the
PQ^+ centers due to the high effective concentration. Since the
$E°'$ data for $(MV^{2+/+})$ in H_2O solution are for low concentrations,
the $E°'$ is not directly comparable to that for the
surface-confined analogue. These properties (optical spectra and
$E°'$) associated with aggregation of the redox center represent
one of the ways that the surface-confined species may depart from

Table II.   Formal Potentials and Photovoltages for Surface-
Confined N,N'-Dialkyl-4,4'-Bipyridinium Reagents and
For Solution N,N'-Dimethyl-4,4'-Bipyridinium

Species[a]	Electrode	Solvent	$E°'$,V vs. SCE[b]	E_V, V[c]
$(MV^{2+/+})_{soln.}$	Pt,Au,n-Si	CH_3CN	-0.45	---
	p-Si	CH_3CN	$[-0.45]^d$	~0.5
	p-InP	CH_3CN	$[-0.45]^d$	~0.8[e]
	Hg, n-Si	$H_2O(pH=1-7)$	-0.69	---
	Pt, Au	$H_2O(pH=7)$	-0.69	---
	p-Si	$H_2O(pH=1-7)$	$[-0.69]^d$	~0.5
	p-InP	$H_2O(pH=1-7)$	$[-0.69]^d$	~0.8[e]
$(III)_{soln.}$	Pt,Au,n-Si	CH_3CN	-0.45	---
	Pt,Au,n-Si	$H_2O(pH=7)$	-0.66	---
$[(PQ^{2+/+})_n]_{surf.}$	Pt,Au,n-Si	CH_3CN	-0.45	---
	Pt,Au,n-Si	$H_2O(pH=7)$	-0.55	---
	W, n-MoS$_2$			
	p-Si	CH_3CN	$[-0.45]^d$	~0.5
	p-Si	$H_2O(pH=1-7)$	$[-0.45]^d$	~0.5

[a] MV^{2+}=N,N'-Dimethyl-4,4'-bipyridinium; $(III)_{soln.}$ is the species
(III) dissolved in solution; in H_2O, of course, III hydrolyzes;
$[(PQ^{2+/+})_n]_{surf.}$ is the surface-confined material from functionalization with III.
[b] Data are from ref. 8 and are from the average position of the
reduction and oxidation wave of cyclic voltammetry scans.
[c] E_V is the photovoltage obtained from the p-type semiconductors
for the reduction of the oxidized form of the redox couple. We
assume $E°'$ to be the values in brackets and E_V is the extent to
which the cathodic current peak is more positive than $E°'$ under
$>E_g$ illumination.
[d] We assume $E°'$ to be the same at the p-type semiconductors as on
the reversible electrodes, but these values have not been
measured because the p-type semiconductors are not reversible.
[e] These data from Dominey, R.N.; Lewis, N.S.; Wrighton, M.S.
J. Am. Chem. Soc., 1981, 103, 1261.

expectations from measurements for the solution species at low concentration.

In addition to optical spectra and cyclic voltammetry, Auger spectra and Auger spectra while sputtering surfaces modified with III have been crucial to the development of a surface catalyst for improving H_2 kinetics. For example, recording Auger signal intensity for various elements while sputtering the surface of p-type Si derivatized with III gives an analysis of elemental composition as a function of depth from the outer surface. So-called depth profile analyses yielded the essential representation of the interface given in Scheme IV.(7) A key feature revealed is the presence of a SiO_x layer between the bulk p-type Si and the polymer. The oxide is likely the air oxide found on Si and is in the range of 20 Å in thickness and non-stoichiometric.(26,27) The consequence of the non-stoichiometric oxide is that there remains a significant density of surface states at the p-type Si/SiO_x interface such that Fermi level pinning occurs.(13,28)

There is considerable reservation concerning the use of Auger spectroscopy and sputtering techniques for organic materials owing to problems typically encountered from e^- beam and sputtering beam damage.(29) In our system we have been fortunate to be able to test whether there are problems of this sort by using the fact that ion exchange reactions can occur as in equation (7) that lead to the persistent electrostatic binding

$$[(PQ^{2+} \cdot 2Br^-)_n]_{surf.} + nK_2IrCl_6 \rightarrow [(PQ^{2+} \cdot IrCl_6{}^{2-})_n]_{surf.} + 2nKBr \quad (7)$$

of reversibly electroactive anions as has been done earlier by other workers.(30-32) Analysis of the amount of the electro-active anion present relative to the amount of PQ^{2+} on the surface can be established by cyclic voltammetry. Subsequent analysis of the same surfaces by depth profile analysis reveals excellent consistency with the data from cyclic voltammetry. Table III summarizes Auger and cyclic voltammetry analyses of electrode surfaces bearing PQ^{2+} that were exposed to $H_2O/0.1$ M K_2SO_4/K_2IrCl_6.(33) Note that under the conditions employed, the Ir complex is ultimately present in the polylmer as the $IrCl_6{}^{3-}$ and that >25 μM $IrCl_6{}^{2-}$ is sufficient to completely charge compensate the PQ^{2+} system. At low $IrCl_6{}^{2-}$ concentrations the $SO_4{}^{2-}$ is competitively bound to the surface and there is an excellent correlation with Cl (from $IrCl_6{}^{3-}$) Auger signal intensity with the cyclic voltammetry data. A number of such competitive ion binding experiments have given us confidence in the depth profile technique for the substrate/$[(PQ^{2+} \cdot 2X^-)_n]_{surf.}$ systems. We regard Auger signal intensities to give relative elemental composition to ~±20% for these systems.

The ion exchange reaction represented by equation (7) is directly relevant to our studies of H_2 evolution in that we

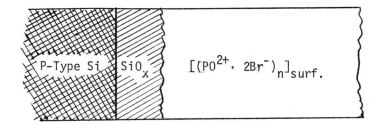

Scheme IV. Side view of the interface resulting from functionalization of p-type Si with reagent III. At about 10^{-8} mol of PQ^{2+} per cm^2 the thickness of the polymer is in the vicinity of 1000 Å.

Table III. Correlation of Auger and Cyclic Voltammetric Analysis of $Pt/[(PQ^{2+} \cdot 2/3xIrCl_6{}^{3-} \cdot (1-x)SO_4{}^{2-})_n]surf.^a$

Electrode Number	$[K_2IrCl_6]$, μM^b	Cyclic Voltammetry		x^d	Auger Cl/C^e
		Coverage^c $[(PQ^{2+/+})_n]surf.$	Coverage^c $[IrCl_6{}^{3-}]surf.$		
1	0	5.0×10^{-9}	0	0.0	0
2	1.0	7.6×10^{-9}	0.5×10^{-9}	0.1	0.04
3	2.5	7.6×10^{-9}	1.1×10^{-9}	0.2	0.15
4	5.0	5.0×10^{-9}	1.8×10^{-9}	0.5	0.35
5	25.0	7.3×10^{-9}	3.9×10^{-9}	0.8	0.55
6	50.0	7.3×10^{-9}	5.1×10^{-9}	1.0	0.73

[a] Data are from ref. 33.
[b] K_2IrCl_6 is present at various concentrations indicated; K_2SO_4 is present at 0.1 M in H_2O.
[c] Coverage determined by integration of cyclic voltammetry waves for $[(PQ^{2+/+})_n]surf.$ and then for $[IrCl_6{}^{2-/3-}]surf.$ after equilibration. Units are mol/cm^2 and error is ±5%.
[d] x is the stoichiometric coefficient determined by the ratio of the coverage of $[(PQ^{2+})]surf.$ and electrostatically bound $IrCl_6{}^{3-}$. x ranges from 0–1 in $[(PQ^{2+} \cdot 2/3xIrCl_6{}^{3-} \cdot (1-x)SO_4{}^{2-})_n]surf.$
[e] Auger data are from surface analysis after withdrawing the electrode and washing with distilled H_2O. Data given are the observed relative signal intensity and are not corrected for element sensitivity. C is constant and associated with $[(PQ^{2+})_n]surf.$ and Cl is associated with bound $IrCl_6{}^{3-}$. Ratios are ~±20%.

recognized that the $[(PQ^{2+})_n]_{surf.}$ itself does not react with H_2O
to yield H_2 even though such is thermodynamically possible for pH
below ~5. Thus, we incorporated Pt(0) into the surface-confined
polymer according to equations (8) and (9) in order to

$$[(PQ^{2+}\cdot 2Br^-)_n]_{surf.} + nK_2PtCl_6 \longrightarrow$$

$$[(PQ^{2+}\cdot PtCl_6{}^{2-})_n]_{surf.} + 2nKBr \qquad (8)$$

$$[(PQ^{2+}\cdot PtCl_6{}^{2-})_n]_{surf.} \longrightarrow$$

$$[(PQ^{2+}\cdot 2Br^-\cdot Pt(0)_n]_{surf.} + 6nKCl \qquad (9)$$

equilibrate the $[(PQ^{2+/+})_n]_{surf.}$ couple with the (H_2O/H_2) couple.
(7,8) Direct evidence that this can be done comes from
functionalization of the inside of a Pyrex test tube with III
followed by ion exchange with $PtCl_6{}^{2-}$ and chemical reduction of
the surface-confined system with H_2 at pH $\approx$ 7. Reduction of
$[(PQ^{2+})_n]_{surf.}$ to $[(PQ^+)_n]_{surf.}$ using H_2 can be monitored
spectrophotometrically as a function of pH.(8) In the absence of
Pt(0) no detectable reaction occurs. For $[(\overline{PQ}^{2+/+}\cdot Pt(0))_n]_{surf.}$
we find that the spectral changes with pH under 1 atm H_2 yield an
$E°'$ for the $[(PQ^{2+/+})_n]_{surf.}$ couple that is the same, within
experimental error, as that found from cyclic voltammetry.(34)
        Photocathode material p-type $Si/[(PQ^{2+}\cdot 2Cl^-\cdot Pt(0))_n]_{surf.}$
does yield much improved H_2 evolution compared to naked p-type
Si. In particular, the naked electrode gives no significant
photocurrent at E_f more positive than $E°'(H_2O/H_2)$. This means
that there is no output photovoltage for the H_2 evoultion and
light (to create carriers) and electrical energy are needed to
reduce H_2O. In fact, less total electrical energy would be
needed to reduce H_2O with a good conventional H_2 electrode such
as platinized Pt. For the derivatized p-type Si photoelectrode
we observe that $[(PQ^{2+})_n]_{surf.}$ can be reduced to $[(PQ+)_n]_{surf.}$
under $\geqslant E_g$ illumination at E_f up to ~0.5 V more positive than $E°'$
for $[(PQ^{2+/+})_n]_{surf.}$. Thus, at the high light intensity limit we
find $E_V \approx 0.5$ V. The incorporation of Pt(0) into the surface
polymer thus allows realization of an $E_V \approx 0.5$ V for the
reduction of H_2O to H_2. Photocurrent for H_2 evolution from the
p-type $Si/[(PQ^{2+}\cdot 2Cl^-\cdot Pt(0))_n]_{surf.}$ onsets at the potential
where the reduction of $[(PQ^{2+})_n]_{surf.}$ occurs. Since the $E°'$ for
$[(PQ^{2+/+})_n]_{surf.}$ is essentially independent of pH, Table II, and
$E°'(H_2O/H_2)$ varies 59 mV/pH, there is an optimum pH where rate
(current) times E_V is a maximum. Table IV shows some typical
sets of power output (photocurrent x E_V) data vs. pH for the
p-type $Si/[(PQ^{2+}\cdot 2Cl^-\cdot Pt(0))_n]_{surf.}$ photocathodes. These data
are consistent with a mechanism for rate improvement involving
first reduction of the $[PQ^{2+}]_{surf.}$ followed by equilibration of

Table IV. Comparison of pH Dependence on Photoelectrochemical H_2 Generation Efficiency from p-Type Si/Pt(0) and from p-Type $Si/[(PQ^{2+} \cdot 2Cl^{-} \cdot Pt(0))_n]_{surf.}$ Photocathodes.[a]

Electrode[b]		pH	Input Pwr at 632.8 nm, mW/cm^2	η,%[c]
p-Si/Pt(0)				
	#1	1.1	11.8	0.4
		3.9	11.8	2.3
		6.5	11.8	4.1
	#2	1.1	11.8	3.5
		3.9	11.8	6.9
		5.4	11.8	7.1
p-Si/[(PQ^{2+}/2Cl^{-}·Pt(0))$_n$]$_{surf.}$				
	#1	1.0	10.9	0.9
		4.0	10.8	5.0
		5.5	11.2	1.8
	#2	1.0	6.9	1.8
		4.0	6.9	3.8
		8.0	6.9	2.3
	#3	1.0	20.8	0.5
		4.0	20.8	3.7
		5.5	20.8	2.7

[a]Data are from ref. 8.
[b]Electrodes p-Si/Pt(0) have been prepared by electrodeposition of Pt(0) from PtCl$_6^{2-}$ directly onto p-Si/SiO$_x$; approximate coverage is ~5 x 10^{-8} mol/cm^2. The p-Si/[(PQ^{2+}·2Cl^{-}·Pt(0))$_n$]$_{surf.}$ electrodes were prepared by first treating with III followed by ion exchange with PtCl$_6^{2-}$ and reduction to yield Pt(0) dispersed in the polymer. The coverage of PQ^{2+} is typically 10^{-8} mol/cm^2; the ion exchange incorporates one Pt atom per PQ^{2+} center.
[c]Power conversion efficiency. The input power is that from a He/Ne laser (632.8 nm). The output power is E$_V$ times photocurrent. Thus η in % is given by (output power/input power) x100%. Data given are representative of a number of determinations given in ref. 8.

the $[(PQ^{2+/+})_n]$surf. couple with the (H_2O/H_2) couple via the dispersed Pt(0).

The elemental Pt(0) is dispersed throughout the surface polymer as determined by depth profile analysis,(7) and a representation of the interface is given in Scheme V. According to this view there is a certain amount of Pt(0) in contact with the thin SiO_x overlayer on the bulk p-type Si. This is a relevant structural feature, since direct deposition of Pt(0) onto photocathode surfaces is known to improve the efficiency for the reduction of H_2O to H_2. Thus, we expect that, for an interface like that depicted in Scheme V, there will be a certain amount of the H_2 evolution occurring by direct catalysis of the reaction of the photoexcited electrons with H_2O at the SiO_x/Pt(0) interfaces. In the extreme of a uniform, pinhole-free coverage of Pt(0) on p-type Si/SiO_x one expects that the photocathode would operate as a buried photosensitive interface and in fact would be equivalent to an external solid state photovoltaic device driving a photoelectrolysis cell with a Pt(0) cathode. In such a case the maximum power from the device (photocurrent times E_V) would be independent of the pH of the solution. However, for Pt(0) electrochemically deposited onto p-type Si/SiO_x photocathodes in amounts of ~10^{-8} mol/cm^2, we find that the output depends on pH such that a lower efficiency is found at the low pH's, Table IV.(7,8) For the p-type Si/SiO_x/Pt(0) photocathodes the pH-efficiency data demand a different mechanism for improvement of efficiency compared to that for p-type Si/SiO_x/$[(PQ^{2+} \cdot 2Cl^- \cdot Pt(0))_n]$surf.. The key fact is that the efficiency appears to peak at a particular pH for the redox polymer system, consistent with the pH independent reducing power of the redox couple. For the case of Pt(0) on the p-type Si/SiO_x the efficiency rises from low to high pH and does not show a peak. The fact that there is a pH dependence at all indicates that the photosensitive interface is not completely buried. The Pt(0) can be regarded as a catalyst for the reactions of the excited electrons and does not completely dominate the behavior of the interface with respect to photovoltage.

The ambiguity associated with the Pt(0) at the SiO_x in Scheme V has prompted us to synthesize interfaces where the catalyst used to equilibrate the $[(PQ^{2+/+})_n]$surf. couple with the (H_2O/H_2) couple is not dispersed throughout the polymer.(35) Additionally, to better test the interface structure we have turned to use of Pd(0) instead of Pt(0) as the catalyst. The kinetics for the equilibration of (H_2O/H_2) with Pd(0) are expected to be as good as for Pt(0),(36) but Pd(0) has the advantage of being much more easily detected (~25x more sensitive)(37) by Auger than is Pt(0). This allows better signal to noise in the depth profile analyses used to establish the distribution of catalyst in the polymer.

The interfaces represented by the sketch in Scheme VI have been prepared and characterization by Auger/depth profile analysis is consistent with the preparation procedure.(35) For

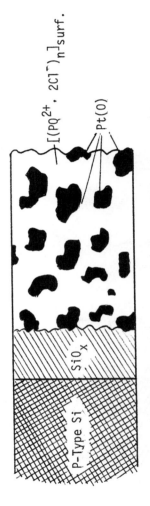

Scheme V. Side view of interface resulting from ion exchange of interface shown in Scheme IV with $PtCl_6^{2-}$ followed by reduction to form $Pt(0)$ dispersed through the polyion.

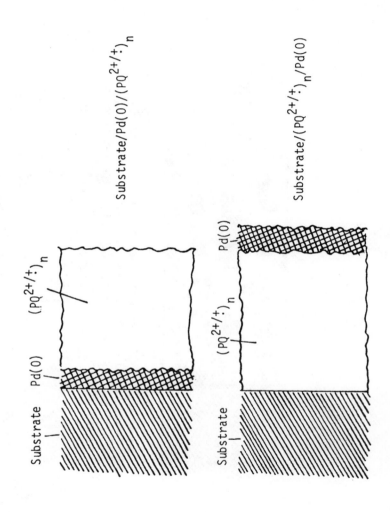

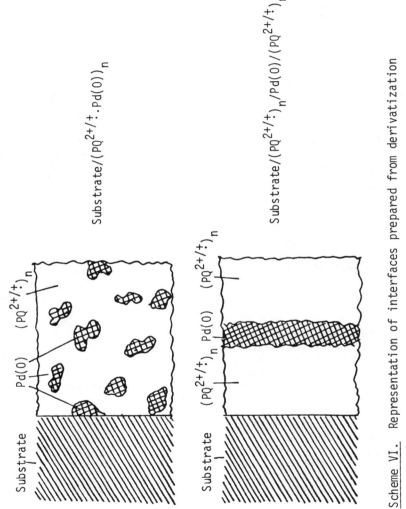

Scheme VI. Representation of interfaces prepared from derivatization of substrates with III and Pd(0). From ref. 35. See also Figures 1 and 3 for Auger depth profile analyses supporting structural assignments.

example, in determining that Pt(0) is distributed throughout the polymer we had no proof that different distributions would yield different depth profiles. Depth profiles for the interfaces represented by Scheme VI do confirm the viability of the use of the technique to determine interface structure. Figure 1 shows representative data for a substrate/$[(PQ^{2+} \cdot 2X^-)_n/Pd(0)/-(PQ^{2+} \cdot 2X^-)_n]_{surf.}$ interface prepared by electrodeposition of the first $(PQ^{2+})_n$ layer by holding the metal electrode at -0.6 V vs. SCE in an aqueous KCl solution of 1 mM III at pH = 7 until the coverage of $[(PQ^{2+} \cdot 2Cl^-)_n]_{surf.}$ equalled 2.3 x 10^{-8} mol/cm^2 from integration of the cyclic voltammogram for the surface—confined material. The electrode was then withdrawn, washed and immersed in aqueous 0.1 M KCl and potentiostatted at -0.6 V vs. SCE to reduce the $[(PQ^{2+})]_{surf.}$ partially to $[(PQ^+)_n]_{surf.}$. While the electrode was held at -0.6 V vs. SCE, K_2PdCl_4 was added to the electrolyte and cathodic current immediately resulted, consistent with reduction of $PdCl_4{}^{2-}$ to Pd(0). At this point, a depth profile analysis is consistent with a substrate/$[(PQ^{2+} \cdot 2Cl^-)_n/-Pd(0)]_{surf.}$ interface. Electrodeposition of an additional 1.6 x 10^{-8} mol/cm^2 of PQ^{2+} from reduction of III in pH $\approx$ 7 KCl yields the depth profile given in Figure 1 that is consistent with the substrate/$[(PQ^{2+} \cdot 2Cl^-)_n/Pd(0)/(PQ^{2+} \cdot 2Cl^-)_n]_{surf.}$ detailed in Scheme VII.

An electrode such as W/$[(PQ^{2+} \cdot 2Cl^-)_n/Pd(0)/-(PQ^{2+} \cdot 2Cl^-)_n]_{surf.}$ gives improved H$_2$ evolution properties compared to naked W in that the H$_2$ overvoltage is reduced.(35) However, the current—voltage curves for such an electrode indicate that the improvement only occurs for pH's where the $[(PQ^{2+/+})_n]_{surf.}$ has the reducing power to reduce H$_2$O to H$_2$. It would appear that these findings accord well with the conclusion that the dominant mechanism for H$_2$ evolution catalysis requires reduction of the $[(PQ^{2+})_n]_{surf.}$. Findings for $[(PQ^{2+} \cdot 2Cl^-)_n/-Pd(0)]_{surf.}$ where the Pd(0) is only on the outermost surface are also consistent with the mechanism, Figures 2 and 3. These results fully confirm the conclusion drawn from the earlier studies(7,8) of the redox polymer/Pt(0) catalyst systems where Pt(0) is dispersed throughout the polymer.

In our experiments the role of the $[(PQ^{2+})_n]_{surf.}$ is to rapidly capture the photoexcited electrons; the Pt(0) or Pd(0) equilibrates the $[(PQ^{2+/+})_n]_{surf.}$ with the (H$_2$O/H$_2$) couple. Overall, the result is the catalysis of the process represented by equation (10). All mechanisms for catalysis of this process

$$2e^- + 2H^+ \longrightarrow H_2 \qquad\qquad (10)$$

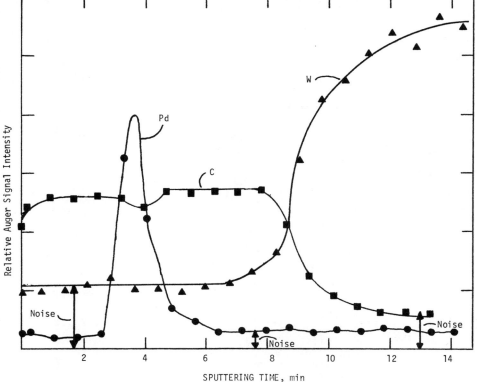

Figure 1. Auger depth profile analysis of a W electrode derivatized first with III to yield $W/[(PQ^{2+} \cdot 2Cl^-)_n/Pd(0)/PQ^{2+} \cdot 2Cl^-)_n]_{surf}$ after removal from 0.1 M KCl solution as described in the text.

The Auger instrument is a Physical Electronics Model 590A employing a 5-KeV e^- beam with a beam current of 0.5 to 1 μA. Sputtering was done using a 2-KeV Ar^+ beam from a Physical Electronics Model 04-303 ion gun. Auger signals monitored were: Pd (330 eV); C, (272 eV); and W (1736 eV). Key: ●, Pd; ▲, W; and ■, C.

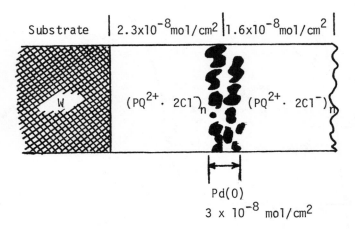

Scheme VII.   Representation of the interface characterized by the depth profile analysis of Figure 1. Coverages indicated were determined electrochemically. Data from reference 35. See text for synthetic procedures used to prepare this interface.

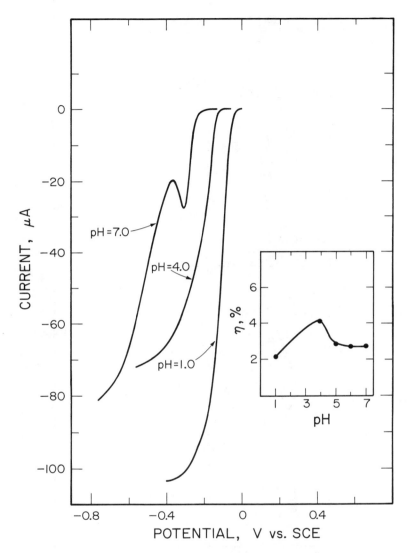

Figure 2.   Photocurrent–voltage curves (10 mV/s) for a p-type Si/[(PQ^{2+} · 2Cl$^-$)$_n$/ Pd(0)]$_{surf}$ photocathode where Pd(0) is deposited only on the outer surface of the redox polymer. The illumination source is a He–Ne laser, 632.8 nm, at ~10 mW/ cm^2, and the exposed electrode area is ~0.1 cm^2. The inset shows the power conversion efficiency peaking at ~pH = 4. Steady-state photocurrent corresponds to H$_2$ evolution. Data are from Ref. 35.

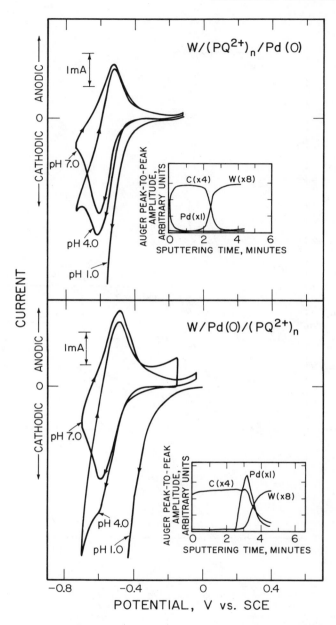

Figure 3.   Comparison of pH dependence on H₂ evolution for two different inter-
faces: top, the derivatization with III is followed by Pd(0) deposition and only
when [(PQ²⁺)ₙ]ₛᵤᵣ𝒻 is reduced, current for H₂ is observed; and bottom, Pd(0) deposi-
tion directly onto W is followed by derivatization with III and H₂ evolution shows
the usual 59 mV/pH shift expected.   The insets show Auger depth profile analyses
after the electrodes were used.   Data from Ref. 35.

can give the same ultimate efficiency. For example, the direct
platinization can improve H_2 evolution, Table IV. The
polymer/Pt(0) system should only work well at pH's where the
polymer is a sufficiently good reductant. The directly
platinized surfaces do not have such a pH dependence. It is true
that deliberate manipulation of the polymer can effect changes in
the $E°'$ so that the cells could operate at optimum efficiency at
other pH's. However, it is not clear that a redox polymer is the
procedure of choice to improve H_2 evolution. Direct platinization may suffer from the requirement of using a large amount of
Pt in order to achieve the buried junction likely needed to
achieve durability. At this point, the only safe conclusion is
that the redox polymer/Pt(0) or Pd(0) systems do improve H_2
evolution kinetics for cathodes such as illuminated p-type Si or
W in the dark. Whether the approach is viable for practical
systems is not presently known.

Improvement of Kinetics for Photoreduction of Horseheart Ferri-cytochrome c̲: A Prototype Example of Superior Properties from Molecular Derivatization

Many biological molecules that can undergo simple,
one-electron transfer processes often have very poor electrode
kinetics owing in some cases to the fact that the redox center is
buried deep inside the macromolecule.(38) However, such reagents
sometimes do undergo rapid bimolecular redox reactions with small
redox reagents called mediators.(39) For example, horseheart
ferricytochrome c, cyt $c_{(ox)}$, is only sluggishly reduced at most
electrode surfaces,(40) but cyt $c_{(ox)}$ reacts with MV^+, equation
(11), with a very large bimolecular rate constant.(41) This

$$\text{cyt } c_{(ox)} + MV^+ \longrightarrow \text{cyt } c_{(red)} + MV^{2+} \tag{11}$$

raises the possibility of anchoring known mediators to electrode
surfaces for the purpose of improving electron transfer kinetics.
In our laboratory reagent III was used to functionalize Au, Pt,
or p-type Si surfaces for the purpose of illustrating this
principle.(6)

The reversible systems Au or Pt/$[(PQ^{2+}\cdot 2Br^-)_n]_{surf.}$ were
shown to be superior electrodes for cyt $c_{(ox)}$ reduction compared
to the naked electrodes.(6) Reduction of cyt $c_{(ox)}$ was found to
be mass transport limited when the electrode potential was held
sufficiently negative to reduce the $[(PQ^{2+})_n]_{surf.}$ to
$[(PQ^+)_n]_{surf.}$. Thus, the results accord well with a mechanism
where the reduction of cyt $c_{(ox)}$ occurs in a mass transport
limited reaction with surface-confined PQ^+ centers.

P-type Si photocathodes functionalized with III also effect
the reduction of cyt $c_{(ox)}$ with superior kinetics compared to the
naked electrode.(6) The naked p-type Si does not effect the

reduction at a significant rate. The illuminated p–Si/–
[(PQ^{2+}·2Br$^-$)$_n$]$_{surf}$. cathode can be used to effect the
reduction of cyt c$_{(ox)}$ at a potential ~0.5 V more positive than
at Au or Pt, consistent with the value of E$_V$ for the
[(PQ$^{2+/+}$)$_n$]$_{surf}$. system, Table II.

It is important to recognize that E°' for (MV$^{2+/+}$) or
[(PQ$^{2+/+}$)$_n$]$_{surf}$. is significantly more negative than E°'(cyt
c$_{(ox)}$/cyt c$_{(red)}$) = +0.02 V vs. SCE.(42) In terms of practical
consequence this means that the reversible electrodes, Au or Pt,
do not respond to (cyt c$_{(ox)}$/cyt c$_{(red)}$) at the thermodynamic
potential. To do this requires a surface–confined mediator
having an E°' in the vicinity of that for the cyt c system while
preserving the large rate constants.

The data for illuminated p–type Si indicate that reduction
of cyt c$_{(ox)}$ can be effected at more positive potentials, but the
objective would be to obtain a good value of E$_V$ with respect to
the biological couple. Again this requires a better match of the
E°' of the surface mediator with that of the biological reagent.
It is known that the (MV$^{2+/+}$) system is a mediator system for a
large number of biological redox systems including enzymes
capable of catalyzing important multielectron transfer
reactions.(43) Future studies may take advantage of the redox
polymer systems to equilibrate the biological catalysts with the
oxidizing and reducing carriers created by absorption of light by
semiconductor electrodes. However, the practical consequences
will remain small unless the photoelectrodes can be shown to have
sufficiently good efficiency for the redox reaction of the
mediator system. For example, the E$_V$ of ~0.5 V for the
p–Si/[(PQ^{2+}·2X$^-$)$_n$]$_{surf}$. system (Table II) is too low to give high
efficiency. The E$_V$ for p–InP/[(PQ^{2+}·2Cl$^-$)$_n$]$_{surf}$. system is
~0.8 V but there appear to be greater problems with interface
stability.(44,45) In any event, surface attachment of mediators
would appear to be a rational approach to equilibrating
biological redox agents with conductors and is an area where the
molecular derivatization procedure is promising. Unlike H$_2$
evolution that can be improved by direct platinization or
corrosion that can be suppressed by overcoats of electronically
conducting material, the equilibration of biological redox
substances with surfaces will likely require the molecular
approach.

Measurement of Electron Transfer Rate Constants Involving Surface–Confined Redox Reagents

Semiconductor electrodes provide an excellent substrate for
the study of redox reactions of surface–confined redox reagents.
This follows from the fact that the ratio of oxidized to reduced
form of a redox couple on a photoelectrode responds to two
stimuli, light and potential, rather than to only potential as is

the case for a redox couple confined to a reversible electrode.
For example, the generation of surface-confined ferricenium from
ferrocene on n-type Si requires $\geqslant E_g$ illumination and an electrode
potential that is sufficiently positive. The oxidation of
ferrocene does not occur in the dark, but the reduction of
ferricenium will occur provided the electrode potential is moved
sufficiently negative because there are plenty of majority charge
carriers avilable. Thus, we have used the two stimuli response
to determine rate constants such as k_5 of equation (5).(9,10) The
measurement involves the determination of the time dependence of
the surface concentration of A^+ = ferricenium in the presence of
B and as a function of the concentration of B. The concentration
of the surface oxidant is easily measured in the dark after
reaction time t_i by a rapid potential sweep to a potential where
the surface ferricenium is reduced, equation (12). Integration

$$\text{surface-ferricenium} + e^- \longrightarrow \text{surface-ferrocene} \qquad (12)$$

of the current associated with equation (12) gives the remaining
surface-ferricenium concentration. The experiment is possible on
a semiconductor photoanode and not on a reversible electrode
because once the ferricenium is photogenerated and illumination
terminated there will be no additional ferricenium generated. By
way of contrast, a reversible electrode will always have a ratio
of oxidized to reduced material on the surface that is dependent
only on the potential. For the photoanode the surface oxidant
can be reduced by a solution reductant in the dark and the
reaction can be monitored electrochemically. For n-type Si
electrodes functionalized with I or II, measurements of k_5 have
been performed. The data show that equations (4) and (5) can
account for 100% of the photocurrent. The data rule out any
significant component of electrocatalysis not involving a redox
reaction of a surface-ferricenium and a solution reductant.
Further, the variation in k_5 with B accords well with
expectations from self-exchange rates of (B^+/B) couples, the
self-exchange rate of (ferricenium/ferrocene), and the driving
force of reaction.(9,10)

Similarly, rate constants for reaction of photogenerated
surface reductants on p-type semiconductors can be measured.
Thus, for the p-type Si electrodes derivatized with III, we are
concerned with processes represented by equations (13) and (14).

$$[(PQ^{2+})_n]_{surf.} + ne^- \xrightarrow{k_{13}} [(PQ^+)_n]_{surf.} \qquad (13)$$

$$[(PQ^+)_n] + nB^+ \xrightarrow{k_{14}} nB + [(PQ^{2+})_n]_{surf.} \qquad (14)$$

For B^+ = cyt $c_{(ox)}$ we have examined the time dependence of the
surface concentration of $[(PQ^+)_n]_{surf.}$ in the dark.(6) We find
that the oxidation of $[(PQ^+)_n]_{surf.}$ is limited by the rate of

mass transport of cyt $c_{(ox)}$ up to the surface, consistent with data for reduction at rotating disk $Pt/[(PQ^{2+/+})_n]surf.$ electrodes. Again, the direct electrochemical measurement of the time dependence of the surface concentration of PQ^+ allows the conclusion that the mechanism for cyt $c_{(ox)}$ reduction only involves a redox mediation and no other surface catalysis, such as that observed by other workers(46,47) for other systems, need be invoked in the case. It is the ability to directly electrochemically monitor surface concentrations of the redox reagent that makes the semiconductor surface unique compared to reversible electrode surfaces. This allows an assessment of mechanism and predictability of redox reactivity from theory and measurements involving solution species.

At this point, it is worth noting that polymer-coated electrodes may suffer from a problem associated with charge transport through the polymer. For example, the reduction of $Ru(NH_3)_6^{3+}$ according to equation (15) has been studied at

$$[(PQ^+)_n]surf. + nRu(NH_3)_6^{3+} \xrightarrow{k_{15}}$$

$$[(PQ^{2+})_n]surf. + nRu(NH_3)_6^{2+} \qquad (15)$$

rotating disk $[(PQ^{2+}\cdot2Cl^-)_n]surf.$ electrodes.(8) For coverages of $\sim10^{-8}$ mol/cm^2 it appears thaat linear plots of cathodic current vs. $\omega^{1/2}$ can be obtained only up to certain current densities, ~20 mA/cm. This limit depends on the concentration of the supporting KCl electrolyte and decreases with decreasing KCl concentration. These data are consistent with the conclusion that current is ultimately limited by charge transport in the polymer. This limitation may be quite important in practical applications and requires additional studies. For example, current densities of >20 mA/cm^2 could be expected for an efficient solar photoelectrochemical device. Transport of ions and electrons must both be fast in order to overcome this limitation even if the specific rate constants such as k_5, k_{14}, or k_{15} are sufficiently large.

Alteration of Interface Energetics and Surface States by Chemical Modification

Semiconductor electrodes modified with reagents I-III exhibit properties that are fairly well predicted from the properties associated with the naked semiconductors in contact with ferrocene or MV^{2+}. Strongly interacting modifiers may alter the interface energetics and surface state distribution in useful ways.(11-14) A classic example of altering surface state distribution comes from electronic devices based on Si.(48) The semiconducting Si has a large density of surface states situated between the valence band and the conduction band. Oxidation of the surface to produce a Si/SiO$_x$ interface results in a substantial diminution of the states between the valence and conduction band edges of the Si, but the density of surface states depends on the surface chemistry. Another example of surface state alteration may be the example of the improvement of output parameters for n-type GaAs-based photoelectrochemical devices from surface pretreatment of n-type GaAs with RuCl$_3$.(14) Recent results in this laboratory have shown that oxidizing etches for pretreating n-type CdTe can yield a Te-rich overlayer on the surface resulting in Fermi level pinning.(49,50) A reducing etch pretreatment can lead to an n-type CdTe photoanode having nearly ideal variation of the barrier height, E$_B$, with changes in E$_{redox}$ of the solution, Figure 4.(49) These examples illustrate possible consequences of semiconductor surface modification not encountered with molecular reagents. These sorts of modification would appear to be crucial to practical achievements, since interface states will likely control e$^-$ - h$^+$ recombination rates and E$_V$. Thus, controlled modification of semiconductor surfaces will be needed to achieve the high efficiency required in solar energy devices.

Ion adsorption to an electrode surface can also be regarded as a type of surface modification that can have a profound effect on photoelectrochemistry.(11,12) A classic example here is the pH dependence of the band edge positions of metal oxide electrodes.(51) Recently, work in this laboratory has illustrated that ion adsorption can dramatically alter the photoelectrochemical performance of a semiconductor.(11) It was shown that the presence of as little as 1 mM I$^-$ in 6 M H$_2$SO$_4$/1 M SO$_2$ can alter the band edge positions of WS$_2$ as illustrated in Schemne VIII. The ~0.6 V negative shift allows a fairly good E$_V$ to be obtained with respect to E$^\circ$'(SO$_4^{2-}$/SO$_2$). Further, the photooxidation of the I$^-$ significantly improves the overall rate of SO$_2$ oxidation via equations (16) and (17). In the absence of I$^-$ the

$$3I^- + 2h^+ \longrightarrow I_3^- \qquad (16)$$

$$2H_2O + SO_2 + I_3^- \longrightarrow SO_4^{2-} + 3I^- + 4H^+ \qquad (17)$$

E$^\circ$'(SO$_4^{2-}$/SO$_2$) indicates that SO$_2$ oxidation should occur in the dark, since E$_{CB}$ is more positive. However, SO$_2$ oxidation has poor kinetics(52), and oxidation of the SO$_2$ is not found either in the dark or upon ≥E$_g$ illumination. The I$^-$ thus plays the dual role of favorably altering the interface energetics (to give a good E$_V$) and providing a mechanism to give good kinetics. Figure 5 illustrates the effect of I$^-$ on the photoelectrochemical oxidation of SO$_2$ at illuminated MoS$_2$ that behaves in a manner similar to that for WS$_2$.(11) The n-type WS$_2$ is able to effect the overall process represented by equation (18). The H$_2$ is evolved at the dark cathode and the process can be effected with

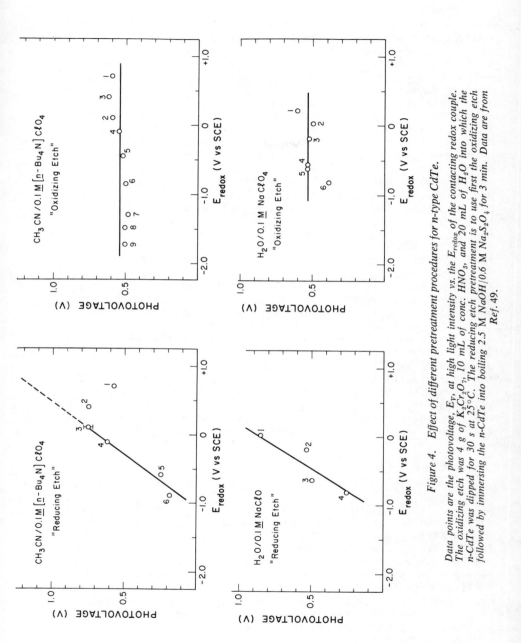

Figure 4.   Effect of different pretreatment procedures for n-type CdTe.

Data points are the photovoltage, E_V, at high light intensity vs. the E_{redox} of the contacting redox couple. The oxidizing etch was 4 g of $K_2Cr_2O_7$, 10 mL of conc. HNO_3, and 20 mL of H_2O into which the n-CdTe was dipped for 30 s at 25°C. The reducing etch pretreatment is to use first the oxidizing etch followed by immersing the n-CdTe into boiling 2.5 M NaOH/0.6 M $Na_2S_2O_4$ for 3 min. Data are from Ref. 49.

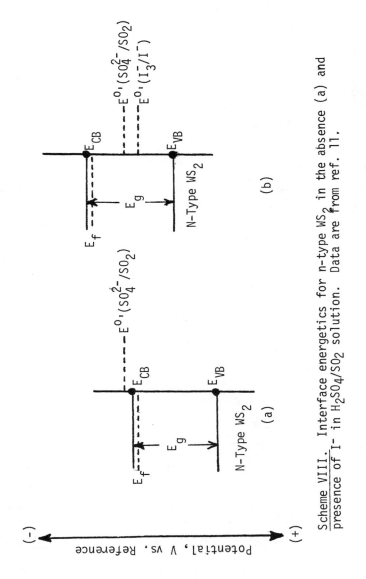

Scheme VIII. Interface energetics for n-type WS_2 in the absence (a) and presence of I^- in H_2SO_4/SO_2 solution. Data are from ref. 11.

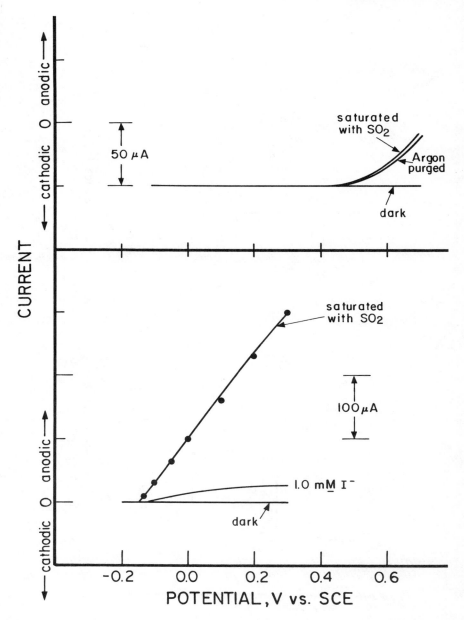

Figure 5.   Effect of I⁻ adsorption onto n-type MoS₂ on the photoelectrochemical oxidation of 1 M SO₂ in 6 M H₂SO₄. In the absence of I⁻ (top), no dark or photooxidation of SO₂ occurs. In the presence of 1 mM I⁻ (bottom) the mediated oxidation of SO₂ occurs at a potential corresponding to the onset for I⁻ oxidation. The electrode (0.07 cm²) was irradiated at 632.8 nm (~40 mW/cm²). Data are from Ref. 11.

$$2H_2O + SO_2 \xrightarrow[\text{I^- catalyst}]{\text{$\geqslant$1.3 eV light}} H_2SO_4 + H_2 \qquad (18)$$

no energy input other than the light. At ~50% H_2SO_4 the process
is ~0.3 V uphill(52) and the surprisingly rugged n-type WS_2 gives
632.8 nm power conversion efficiencies of up to ~13% (~6 mW/cm^2
input) with no other energy input.

Ions are not typically persisitently bound and their
lability may preclude general utility. However, the WS_2/I^-
system provides evidence that modification of the proper sort can
yield extraordinary consequences. Modification procedures
resulting in an irreversible interface change like that from I^-
adsorption would be useful.

Conclusion

Chemical treatment of the surfaces of semiconductor photoelectrode surfaces can result in profound, positive changes in
interface properties and overall performance of the photoelectrodes. Illustrations of the use of one-electron surface
reagents to suppress photocorrosion and to improve electrode
kinetics for large biological molecules establishes a possible
role for such species in future studies and possibly in
applications. However, the important overall processes in
photoelectrochemical energy conversion are multi-electron
processes that will likely require reagents that involve inner
sphere redox character. Combinations such as the redox polymer/-
Pt(0) are prototype electron transfer catalysts that can improve
kinetics for multi-electron transfer processes. Surface modification to remove surface states and alter interface energetics
requires elaboration in order to achieve high efficiency devices.
At this point it appears that chemical pretreatments of photoelectrode surfaces will be the rule rather than the exception.
The procedures will range from etches for increasing surface area
to molecular derivatization for improvement of the rate of
equilibration of large biological redox systems with the semiconductor surface.

Acknowledgements

Research performed in this laboratory and cited in the
references has been supported in part by the United States
Department of Energy, Office of Basic Energy Sciences, Division
of Chemical Sciences. Work on cadmium telluride was partially
supported by the Office of Naval Research. Support from the Dow
Chemical Company and GTE Laboratories, Inc. is also gratefully
acknowledged.

LITERATURE CITED

1. Wrighton, M.S.; Austin, R.G.; Bocarsly, A.B.; Bolts, J.M.;
    Haas, O.; Legg, K.D.; Nadjo, L.; Palazzotto, M.C. J. Am.
    Chem. Soc., 1978, 100, 1602.
2. Bolts, J.M.; Bocarsly, A.B.; Palazzotto, M.C.; Walton, E.G.;
    Lewis, N.S.; Wrighton, M.S. J. Am. Chem. Soc., 1979, 101,
    1378.
3. Bocarsly, A.B.; Walton, E.G.; Wrighton, M.S. J. Am. Chem.
    Soc., 1980, 102, 3390.
4. (a) Noufi, R.; Tench, D.; Warren, L.F. J. Electrochem.
    Soc., 1980, 127, 2310; (b) Noufi, R.; Frank, A.J.; Nozik,
    A.J. J. Am. Chem. Soc., 1981, 103, 1849; (c) Skotheim, T.;
    Lundstrom, I.; Prejza, J. J. Electrochem. Soc., 1981, 128,
    1625.
5. Fan, F.-R. F.; Wheeler, B.L.; Bard, A.J.; Noufi, R.N. J.
    Electrochem. Soc., 1981, 128, 2042.
6. Lewis, N.S.; Wrighton, M.S. Science, 1981, 211, 944.
7. Bookbinder, D.C.; Bruce, J.A.; Dominey, R.N.; Lewis, N.S.;
    Wrighton, M.S. Proc. Natl. Acad. Sci., U.S.A., 1980, 77,
    6280.
8. Dominey, R.N.; Lewis, N.S.; Bruce, J.A.; Bookbinder, D.C.;
    Wrighton, M.S. J. Am. Chem. Soc., 1982, 104, 0000.
9. Lewis, N.S.; Bocarsly, A.B.; Wrighton, M.S. J. Phys. Chem.,
    1980, 84, 2033.
10. Lewis, N.S.; Wrighton, M.S. ACS Symposium Series, 1981,
    146, 37 "Photoeffects at Semiconductor-Electrolyte
    Interfaces", A.J. Nozik, ed.
11. Calabrese, G.S.; Wrighton, M.S. J. Am. Chem. Soc., 1981,
    103, 6273.
12. Ginley, D.S.; Butler, M.A. J. Electrochem. Soc., 1978, 125,
    1968.
13. Bard, A.J.; Bocarsly, A.B.; Fan, F.-R.F.; Walton, E.G.;
    Wrighton, M.S. J. Am. Chem. Soc., 1980, 102, 3671.
14. Heller, A.; Lewerenz, H.J.; Miller, B. Ber. Bunsenges.
    Phys. Chem., 1980, 84, 592.
15. Bard, A.J.; Wrighton, M.S. J. Electrochem. Soc., 1977, 124,
    1706.
16. Gerischer, H. J. Electroanal. Chem., 1977, 82, 133.
17. Park. S.M.; Barber, M.E. J. Electroanal. Chem., 1977, 99,
    67.
18. Wrighton, M.S. Accs. Chem. Res., 1979, 12, 303.
19. Heller, A. Accs. Chem. Res., 1981, 14, 154.
20. Legg, K.D.; Ellis, A.B.; Bolts, J.M.; Wrighton, M.S. Proc.
    Natl. Acad. Sci., U.S.A., 1977, 74, 4116.
21. Bookbinder, D.C.; Lewis, N.S.; Bradley, M.G.; Bocarsly,
    A.B.; Wrighton, M.S. J. Am. Chem. Soc., 1979, 101, 7721.
22. Bocarsly, A.B.; Bookbinder, D.C.; Dominey, R.N.; Lewis,
    N.S.; Wrighton, M.S. J. Am. Chem. Soc., 1980, 102, 3683.

23.   Bookbinder, D.C.; Wrighton, M.S.   J. Am. Chem. Soc., 1980,
      102, 5123.
24.   Kosower, E.M.; Cotter, J.L.   J. Am. Chem. Soc., 1964, 85,
      5524.
25.   Bookbinder, D.C.; Wrighton, M.S., to be submitted to
      J. Electrochem. Soc.
26.   Schmidt, P.F.; Michel, W.J.   J. Electrochem. Soc., 1957,
      104, 230.
27.   Raider, S.I.; Flitsch, R.; Palmer, M.J.   J. Electrochem.
      Soc., 1975, 122, 413.
28.   McGill, T.C.   J. Vac. Sci. Technol., 1974, 11, 935.
29.   Davis, R.E.; Faulkner, J.R.   J. Electrochem. Soc., 1981,
      128, 1349.
30.   Oyama, N.; Anson, F.C.   J. Electrochem. Soc., 1980, 127,
      247, and Anal. Chem., 1980, 52, 1192.
31.   Shigerhara, K.; Oyama, N.; Anson, F.C.   Inorg. Chem., 1981,
      20, 518.
32.   Oyama, N.; Sato, K.; Matsuda, H.   J. Electroanal. Chem.,
      1980, 115, 149.
33.   Bruce, J.A.; Wrighton, M.S.   J. Am. Chem. Soc., 1982, 104,
      0000.
34.   Bookbinder, D.C.; Lewis, N.S.; Wrighton, M.S.   J. Am. Chem.
      Soc., 1981, 103, 0000.
35.   Bruce, J.A.; Murahashi, T.; Wrighton, M.S.   J. Phys. Chem.,
      1982, 86, 0000.
36.   Bockris, J. O'M.; Reddy, A.K.N.   "Modern Electrochemistry",
      Vol. 2, Plenum: New York, 1970, p. 1238.
37.   Davis, L.E.; MacDonald, N.C.; Palmberg, P.W.; Riach, G.E.;
      Weber, R.G. "Handbook of Auger Electron Spectroscopy", 2nd
      ed., Physical Electronics Division, Perkin-Elmer Corp., Eden
      Prairie, MN, 1972.
38.   Margoliash, E.; Schejter, A. in "Advances in Protein
      Chemistry", Vol. 21, Chap. 2, Anfinsen, C.B.; Edsall,
      J.T.; Richards, F.M.,eds., Academic Press: New York, 1966.
39.   Kuwana, T.; Heineman, W.R.   Accs. Chem. Res., 1976, 9, 241.
40.   (a) Kono, T.; Nakamura, S.   Bull. Agric. Chem. Soc. Jpn.,
      1958, 22, 399; (b) Haladjian, J.; Bianco, P.; Serve, P.A.
      J. Electroanal. Chem., 1979, 104, 555; (c) Betso, S.R.;
      Klapper, M.H.; Anderson, L.B.   J. Am. Chem. Soc., 1972, 84,
      8197.
41.   Land, E.J.; Swallow, A.J.   Ber. Bunsenges. Phys. Chem.,
      1975, 79, 436.
42.   Margalit, R.; Schejter, A.   Eur. J. Biochem., 1973, 32, 492.
43.   Summers, L.A.   "The Bipyridinium Herbicides", Academic
      Press: London, 1980, pp. 122-124.
44.   Dominey, R.N.; Lewis, N.S.; Wrighton, M.S.   J. Am. Chem.
      Soc., 1981, 103, 1261.
45.   Dominey, R.N.; Wrighton, M.S., to be submitted.

46. Eddowes, M.J.; Hill, H.A.O.; Uosaki, J. J. Am. Chem. Soc.,
     1979, 101, 7113.
47. Landrum, H.L.; Salmon, R.T.; Hawkridge, F.M. J. Am. Chem.
     Soc., 1977, 99, 3154.
48. Sze, S.M. "Physics of Semiconductor Devices", Wiley: New
     York, 1969.
49. Tanaka, S.; Bruce, J.A.; Wrighton, M.S. J. Phys. Chem.,
     1981, 85, 0000.
50. Aruchamy, A.; Wrighton, M.S. J. Phys. Chem., 1980, 84,
     2848.
51. Morrison, S.R. "Electrochemistry at Semiconductor and
     Oxidized Metal Electrodes", Plenum: 1980.
52. Lu, P.W.T.; Ammon, R.L. J. Electrochem. Soc., 1980, 127,
     2610.

RECEIVED April 8, 1982.

Transfer of Solution Reactivity Properties to Electrode Surfaces

HECTOR D. ABRUNA,[1] JEFFREY M. CALVERT, PETER DENISEVICH,[2]
CHARLES D. ELLIS, THOMAS J. MEYER, WILLIAM R, MURPHY, JR.,
ROYCE R. MURRAY, BRIAN P. SULLIVAN, and JERRY L. WALSH[3]

University of North Carolina, Department of Chemistry, Chapel Hill, NC 27514

Polypyridyl complexes of ruthenium and especially those based on 2,2'-bipyridine have an extensive and well-developed solution chemistry. The observed chemistry includes important photochemical reactions and reactions of coordinated ligands. Successful procedures have been developed for the preparation of electrode interfaces which contain Ru-bpy chemical sites. The procedures are based on silane attachments to metal oxide surfaces, physical adsorption of polymers, and electropolymerization. The results of electrochemical experiments on the resulting interfaces show that the Ru-bpy sites retain many of their solution chemical properties, which include two examples of sustained oxidative catalysis. However, the interface itself can play a significant role in determining properties. Perhaps the most dramatic cases are those where the interface contains spatially separated bilayers containing Ru-bpy sites having different redox potentials or those containing a single layer exposed to a redox couple in the external solution. In either case, directed (unidirectional) charge transfer through the inner layer and charge trapping outside the inner layer can be shown to occur.

It is difficult to overestimate the importance of events which occur at interfaces involving metals and semiconductors. They range from corrosion to catalysis to device fabrication. Unfortunately, compared with reactions in solution, it is difficult to study and control interfacial events because of the lack of routine measurement techniques, the absence of conclusive structural information about the surface chemical sites which control reactivity, and the difficulty of making routine chemical changes in the mater-

[1] Current address: University of Texas at Austin, Austin, TX.
[2] Current address: Chevron Research Laboratories, Richmond, CA 94802.
[3] Current address: Lafayette College, Easton, PA.

ial. In contrast to interfacial phenomena, reactions based on molecules in solution can be followed by well-developed, routine techniques on structures which are well-defined, at least before and after the reaction occurs. If important reactions are discovered, systematic synthetic changes can often be used to change reactivity by modifying the chemical site.

The theme of this account is an attempt at a synthesis. The synthesis involves the attachment of sites which are chemically well-defined in solution to the solid-solution interface. It opens the possibility of fabricating new interfacial structures in which properties inherent in the chemical sites are incorporated at the interface. The synthesis raises questions concerning the effects of the interface on the chemical sites and of the chemical sites and the material that surrounds them on the properties of the interface.

What follows is intended as a review of our own work, which is a small part of a rapidly growing area of chemistry. Note, for example, reference 1. Our emphasis has been on redox events at chemically fabricated metal and semiconductor interfaces. Given the chemical sites used and the configuration of the resulting structures, the presence of the electrode automatically provides a method of analysis and a means for monitoring interfacial events. The electrode also serves as a controlled potential source of oxidizing or reducing equivalents for the interface.

Background Chemistry

In order to explore whether reactivity properties can be transferred to electrode surfaces it is advantageous, and probably essential, to identify a versatile chemical system. Versatility implies access to a group of related compounds where changes in structure can be made which lead to systematic variations in chemical and physical properties. For our purposes an ideal chemical system should possess as many of the following characteristics as possible:

1) The availability of reversible redox couples. Many important interfacial events involve electron transfer or net redox changes. 2) A broadly based synthetic chemistry with which to make variations. 3) A synthetic basis for creating the interface. 4) High chemical stability in more than one oxidation state. 5) Potentially exploitable excited state or catalytic properties. 6) A well-developed and diverse solution chemistry, including detailed mechanistic information. 7) Convenient spectral or other physical properties which can be used to make measurements at the interface.

We have developed an extensive background over a period of years with a type of chemical system--polypyridyl complexes of ruthenium--which appear to have all of the desired characteristics. As examples consider the following: 1) $Ru^{III/II}$ couples based on the bis-2,2'-bipyridine (bpy) complexes $Ru^{II}(bpy)_2L_2^{2+}$ (L = Cl$^-$,

NCS^-, NH_3, PR_3, py, CNR,...) have reversible potentials ranging from -0.3 to $+2.0$ V in acetonitrile vs. the saturated sodium chloride calomel (SSCE) reference electrode (2) and electron transfer involving such couples is known to be facile (3). Ru(IV) is also an accessible oxidation state at relatively low potentials by loss of 2 protons from bound water following oxidation, $Ru(bpy)_2(py)H_2O^{2+}$ $\xrightarrow[-2H+]{-2e-}$ $Ru(bpy)_2(py)O^{2+}$ (py is pyridine)(4). 2) There is a well-developed background synthetic chemistry which is based on: changes in the polypyridyl ligands (e.g., modified bpy, 1,10-phenanthroline or phosphines in place of bpy); changes in the non-polypyridyl ligands based on the incorporation of halides, pseudo-halides, pyridines, phosphines, etc.; reactions of coordinated ligands (5); photochemical reactions (6); and the preparation of dimeric and oligomeric complexes based on ligand bridges (7, 8). 3) Because of the availability of the background synthetic chemistry, several viable strategies exist for binding sites to metal or semiconductor surfaces. 4) With some exceptions, many of which are useful in other ends, the series of complexes is coordinatively stable in both the Ru(II) and Ru(III) oxidation states. 5) Redox catalysts are known (18, 19) and the metal-to-ligand charge transfer (MLCT) excited state of $Ru(bpy)_3^{2+}$ has provided a basis for numerous photocatalytic schemes. 6) The known reactions of the series of complexes are diverse. In addition to simple electron transfer, (9) well-defined reactions are known involving coordinated ligands (4, 5, 10-12), complex redox steps (13, 14, 15), and there is an extensive and growing photochemistry (9, 16, 17). 7) The complexes have characteristic π^*(polypyridyl) $\leftarrow d\pi$(Ru(II)) MLCT transitions and characteristic IR and Raman vibrational spectra.

Even with access to both a viable chemical system and a routine procedure for monitoring interfacial events based on electrochemistry, it is necessary to develop appropriate strategies for attachment of the chemical sites to electrode surfaces. We have investigated three different approaches based on: a) chemical links using covalent bond formation, b) physical adsorption of premade polymers, c) electropolymerization at the electrode surface. All three techniques have their own particular nuances and will be discussed in more or less the chronological order in which they were applied to the attachment of Ru-bpy complexes.

Covalent Attachments Based on Organosilanes. Organosilane reagents are known to form stable chemical bonds to the surfaces of metal oxide electrodes (20, 1n). Included in this category are silane attachments to thin platinum oxide layers on platinum which are formed when clean Pt surfaces are held at positive potentials ($+1.0$ V vs. SCE) in aqueous solution. The subsequent attachment chemistry is based on the known propensity of chloro- and alkoxysilanes to undergo reactions in which Si-O-M bonds are formed by metathesis, e.g.,

$$-Pt-OH(surface) + (CH_3O)_3Si-R \rightarrow -Pt-O-Si-R(surface) + CH_3OH \qquad (1)$$

Using silane reagents which contain chemically active functional groups provides the necessary entré into interface fabrication. For our purposes it was a question of matching the chemistry of the functional group with chemical properties that could be built into the Ru-bpy complexes.

   Two strategies were adopted. In the first, the key was the availability of a free amine site bound to the platinum-platinum oxide surface via eq. 1.

$$Pt/PtO + (CH_3O)_3Si(CH_2)_3NH(CH_2)_2NH_2 \longrightarrow$$

$$Pt/PtO/Si(CH_2)_3NH(CH_2)_2NH_2 \qquad (2)$$

The shorthand nomenclature used here and later to describe the attachment chemistry is imposed by the absence of structural infor-mation concerning either the surface or the mode of binding of the silane to the surface.

   Following eq. 2, attachment of the redox couple to the elec-trode was achieved by amide bond formation based on the presence of a carboxylic acid group in the complex as shown in eq. 3. The reactions were carried out in dry acetonitrile in the presence of the dehydrating agent dicyclohexylcarbodiimide (DCC) which removes water as it forms in the coupling reaction. As suggested in eq. 3,

$$Pt/PtO/Si(CH_2)_3NH(CH_2)_2NH_2 + [Ru(bpy)_2(4-pyCO_2H)Cl]^+$$

$$\xrightarrow[-H_2O]{+DCC} Pt/PtO/[Si(CH_2)_3NH(CH_2)_2NHC(O)-4-pyRuCl(bpy)_2]^+ \qquad (3)$$

the point of attachment is probably at the terminal amine group since earlier work had shown that the internal amine is less reac-tive, apparently because of interactions with the electrode sur-face.

   The amide linkage procedure has proven to be successful in a general way. We have been able to attach to platinum electrodes $Ru(bpy)_2(4-pyCO_2H)Cl^+$ and $Ru(bpy)_2(4-pyCO_2H)_2^{2+}$, either singly or simultaneously, and also to attach the bpy-diacid complex shown below (21).

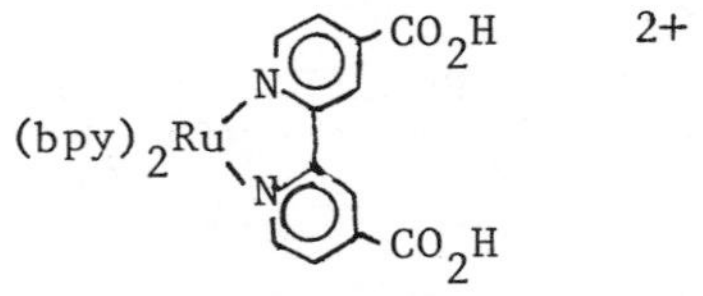

$$[(bpy)_2Ru(bpy\text{-}diacid)]^{2+}$$

   Cyclic voltammetric measurements on the resulting electrodes clearly show the presence of the complexes, and, from $E_{\frac{1}{2}}$ values for the $Ru^{III/II}$ couples, that they survive the attachment proce-dure with their characteristic redox properties intact. XPS (X-Ray

Photoelectron Spectroscopy) analysis of the surface shows the presence of Ru^{II} by the appearance of a band at a binding energy of 280.8 eV for the $3d_{5/2}$ level. Surface coverages (Γ in mol/cm^2) were estimated from the areas under voltammetric waves assuming the molecular dimensions ($r \sim 7.1$Å for Ru(bpy)$_3{}^{2+}$) for the chemical sites. Under carefully controlled conditions, it was found that close to monolayer coverages could be reproducibly obtained. Higher coverages were occasionally observed, and their origin was apparently in an extended Si-O-Si oligomerization caused by trace water.

In the second attachment strategy, the surface link was made by a ligand displacement reaction in which a labile group (1,2-dimethoxyethane, DME) was displaced by a surface-bound pyridine (eq. 4). Once again, voltammetric measurements showed that $E_{\frac{1}{2}}$ (Ru^{III}/^{II}) for the surface couple was close to the potential for the analogous solution couple, Ru(bpy)$_2$(py)Cl$^{2+/+}$ ($E_{\frac{1}{2}}$ = 0.76V vs. SSCE). For either surface, voltammetric wave shapes were characteristic of nondiffusing, immobilized sites, e.g., ΔE_p < 58mV where ΔE_p is the potential difference between the oxidative and reductive peak currents in a cyclic voltammetry experiment. The interfaces are stable indefinitely (months) when stored either dry or in an acetonitrile solution and are also stable to repeated cycling through the Ru^{III}/^{II} wave although some decomposition is observed after thousands of cyclic scans.

The early experiments were of value in demonstrating that surface attachments were feasible and that simple redox properties could be transferred to an electrode interface. The next set of experiments were based on a more complex system, nitro and nitrosyl complexes of ruthenium, where an extensive chemistry is known based on the reactions of coordinated ligands (Scheme 1). In the redox sense, the most interesting reactions are at the bottom of Scheme 1; reversible, ligand-based nitrosyl reduction (A); acid-base, nitrosyl-nitro interconversion, reaction (B); oxidation of the coordinated nitro group to nitrate, reaction (C). The mechanism for the oxidation of the nitro group has been studied in detail (<u>14</u>) and appears to involve the sequence of reactions shown later in Scheme 3. In the presence of an added redox "scavenger" like PPh$_3$, the reactive Ru(III) intermediate can be intercepted before ligand oxidation occurs (<u>18</u>). The combination of the reversible

$$(\text{bpy})_2\underset{\overset{|}{\text{py}}}{\text{Ru-NO}_2}{}^{2+} + \text{PPh}_3 \longrightarrow (\text{bpy})_2\underset{\overset{|}{\text{py}}}{\text{Ru-}\overset{\cdot\cdot}{\text{N}}\text{O}}{}^{2+} + \text{OPPh}_3 \qquad (5)$$

acid-base and nitrosyl reduction reactions in Scheme 1 (reactions (B) and (A)) with eq. 5 provides a basis for the catalytic oxidation of PPh$_3$ (Scheme 2). The reactions are carried out in acetonitrile containing water and an added organic base, B, like collidine to tie up released protons. Unfortunately, catalytic applications to other substrates are limited because of the competing oxidation of the nitro group in Ru(bpy)$_2$(py)NO$_2{}^{2+}$ to nitrate.

Equation 4

$$Pt/PtO/Si-CH_2CH_2-\langle\bigcirc\rangle N + Ru(bpy)_2(DME)Cl^+ \xrightarrow{-DME}$$

$$Pt/PtO/Si-CH_2CH_2-pyRu(bpy)_2Cl^+$$

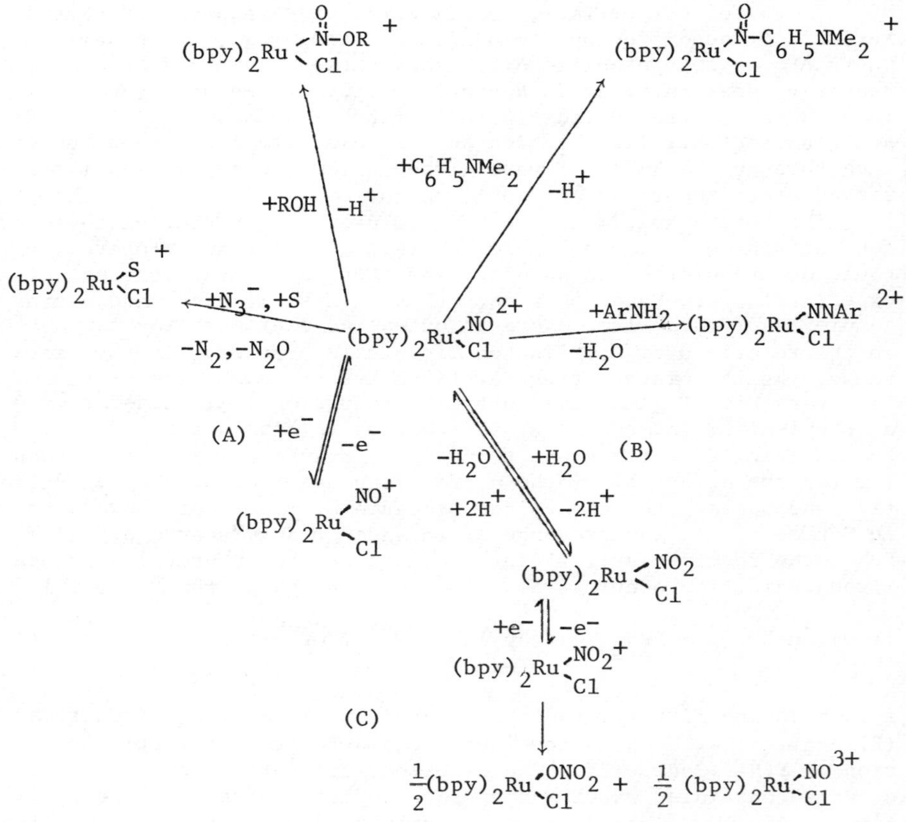

Scheme 1

$2BH^+$ $Ru(bpy)_2(py)NO_2^+$ $\xrightarrow{-e^-}$ $Ru(bpy)_2(py)NO_2^{2+}$ PPh_3

$2B + H_2O$ $Ru(bpy)_2(py)NO^{3+}$ $\xleftarrow{-e^-}$ $Ru(bpy)_2(py)NO^{2+}$ $OPPh_2$

Scheme 2

The transfer of the $Ru^{II}-NO_2$ group to an electrode interface offered the possibility of a series of comparisons in reactivity between interface and solution sites and the appealing possibility that immobilization might inhibit oxidation of the nitro group because of the *bimolecular* nature of the reaction (Scheme 3). The complex $[Ru(bpy)_2(NO_2)(4-pyCO_2H)]^+$ was successfully attached to a silanized Pt/PtO electrode using the procedure described in eq. 3 (23). Initial electrochemical experiments using acetonitrile as solvent showed immediately that although much of the basic redox chemistry was retained on the surface, there were significant changes in detail. From successive scan cyclic voltammograms, following oxidation of $-(py)Ru^{II}(bpy)_2NO_2^+$ to Ru(III), both the nitrato ($E_{1/2} = 0.93V$ vs. SSCE) and nitrosyl ($E_{1/2} = 0.50V$) complexes appeared on the surface. However, the rate of decay of the Ru-(III)-nitro group was several orders of magnitude slower than in solution and, curiously, although both the nitrato and nitrosyl products appear initially, only the wave for the nitrato product continues to grow after the first stage. The final nitrato/nitrosyl ratio is far greater than 1:1. Attachment of the complex to the electrode proved to be of great advantage in the determination of the mechanism of nitro oxidation. Because of the attachment: 1) The retardation of the bimolecular reaction on the surface provided a more convenient time domain for observation. 2) Low temperature experiments (-78°C in n-butyronitrile) were easy to perform and allowed a key intermediate to be observed. 3) It was possible to use faster cyclic voltammetry sweep rates (up to 200 V/s) for surface couples because their peak current variation with sweep rate has the same functional dependence ($i_p \propto v$) as for double layer charging currents while for solution couples, $i_p \propto v^{1/2}$ (24). Based on our electrochemical observations the detailed mechanism for nitrite oxidation in Scheme 3 evolved.

The key features uncovered by the surface study were clear evidence for the isomerization of N-bound $-(py)Ru(bpy)_2NO_2^{2+}$ to the O-bound, nitrito form, $-(py)Ru(bpy)_2ONO^{2+}$, and the appearance of a second pathway ((B) in Scheme 3) for oxidation of the bound nitro group to nitrate. The bimolecular solution pathway is shown as (A) in Scheme 3. In path (B) the mechanism has changed to the one-electron oxidation of $-(py)Ru(bpy)_2ONO^{2+}$, perhaps through the intervention of a surface state at the electrode. After the fact, it was shown that path (B) also exists in solution, by observing the nitrato-nitrosyl ratio when $Ru(bpy)_2(py)NO_2^+$ was oxidized by increasing amounts of the one-electron oxidant $Ru(bpy)_3^{3+}$.

In retrospect, the effect of surface attachment on catalyst stability was a success in that the bimolecular oxidation of the

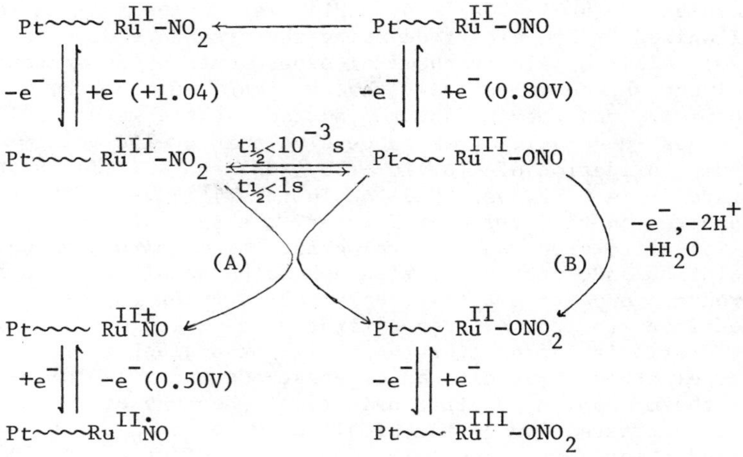

$$\text{Pt}\sim\sim \text{Ru}^{II}\text{-NO}_2 \longleftarrow \qquad \text{Pt}\sim\sim \text{Ru}^{II}\text{-ONO}$$

$$-e^- \updownarrow +e^- (+1.04) \qquad\qquad -e^- \updownarrow +e^- (0.80V)$$

$$\text{Pt}\sim\sim \text{Ru}^{III}\text{-NO}_2 \underset{t_{\frac{1}{2}}<1s}{\overset{t_{\frac{1}{2}}<10^{-3}s}{\rightleftharpoons}} \text{Pt}\sim\sim \text{Ru}^{III}\text{-ONO}$$

$$-e^-,-2H^+$$
$$+H_2O$$

(A)   (B)

$$\text{Pt}\sim\sim \text{Ru}^{II+}_{}\text{NO} \qquad\qquad \text{Pt}\sim\sim \text{Ru}^{II}\text{-ONO}_2$$

$$+e^- \updownarrow -e^- (0.50V) \qquad\qquad -e^- \updownarrow +e^-$$

$$\text{Pt}\sim\sim\sim\text{Ru}^{II}\overset{\bullet}{\text{NO}} \qquad\qquad \text{Pt}\sim\sim \text{Ru}^{III}\text{-ONO}_2$$

(Pt$\sim\sim$ Ru -NO$_2$ is Pt/PtOSi(CH$_2$)$_3$NHC(O)pyRu(bpy)$_2$NO$_2^+$, note eq. 3)

$$\text{Os(PPhMe}_2)_3\text{Cl}_3 \xrightarrow{\text{Glassy C/}\atop\text{PVP}} -(\text{py})\text{Os(PPhMe}_2)_3\text{Cl}_2$$

$$-e^- \updownarrow +e^-$$

$$-(\text{py})\text{Os(PPhMe}_2)_3\text{Cl}_2^+ \rightleftharpoons -(\text{py})\text{Os(PPhMe}_2)_3\text{Cl}_2^{2+}$$

Scheme 3

nitro group is inhibited as shown by the enhanced stability of the $-(py)Ru(bpy)_2NO_2^{2+}$ site. The inhibition is not surprising since there are severe orientational demands associated with the bimolecular oxo-transfer process which leads to ligand oxidation. The appearance of some nitrosyl product suggests that initially there are pairs of sites which are adequately disposed orientationally to undergo reaction by path (A), but they are soon depleted and the reaction proceeds to completion by path (B).

Unfortunately, the surface immobilization procedure was successful in avoiding one decomposition pathway, but it also uncovered the existence of a second. Nonetheless, it was possible to show that the catalytic abilities of the Ru-nitro group on the surface are unimpaired. Addition of acid to $-(py)Ru(bpy)_2NO_2^+$ in dry acetonitrile gives the nitrosyl complex which can be reconverted into the nitro form by the addition of a base and trace water (eq. 6). Oxidation of $Ru^{II}-NO_2$ to $Ru^{III}-NO_2$ in the presence of

$$-(py)Ru(bpy)_2NO_2^+ \quad \xrightleftharpoons[+H_2O, -2H^+]{+2H^+, -H_2O} \quad -(py)Ru(bpy)_2NO^{3+} \tag{6}$$

$P(p-C_6H_4Cl)_3$ results in the quantitative production of $-(py)Ru(bpy)_2NO^{3+}$ on the surface. The acid-base and redox steps are key elements in the catalytic sequence in Scheme 2. Oxidation of $-(py)Ru^{II}(bpy)_2NO_2^+$ to Ru^{III} in acetonitrile containing the phosphine, acetate ion, and a little water resulted in sustained catalytic currents although the catalysis is not persistent because of slow solvolysis of the nitro group to give $-(py)Ru(bpy)_2(CH_3-CN)^{2+}$.

Physical Adsorption of Polymers. The silane attachment procedure and the resulting interfaces have limitations. They include fragility--the electrode--chemical site link is susceptible to hydrolysis--the inability to fabricate controlled multilayers, and the fact that the fabrication procedures are somewhat difficult and tedious. A second approach, which has the advantage of extreme simplicity, is physical adsorption of pre-made polymers either by dipping the electrode into a polymer solution or by controlled evaporation of a solution on the electrode surface. If the composition of the external solution with regard to solvent and pH is controlled, reasonably stable interfaces can be prepared by simple adsorption.

Nearly all of our work on preformed polymers has been based on the polymer poly-4-vinylpyridine (PVP) whose structure is shown below.

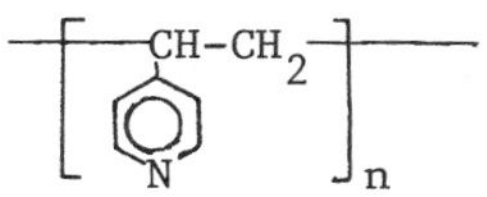

(poly-4-vinylpyridine; PVP)

The polymer has attractive features based on the presence of the pyridyl groups and the availability of well-established procedures for preparing the polymer (25). Earlier work on the attachment of Ru-bpy complexes to PVP had been reported (26) but was based on commercially available, high molecular weight polymer samples. The resulting materials were difficult to work with because of a lack of solubility. By heating solutions containing low molecular weight PVP ($M_n \approx 3900$) and $Ru(trpy)(bpy)H_2O^{2+}$ in ethanol it was possible to prepare and isolate a series of well-defined metallo-polymers where the py/Ru ratio varied from ~2/1 to ~20/1 (27). The py/Ru ratio is the ratio of totally available pyridyl sites on the polymer to those with Ru attached. The samples were charac-terized by 'H-NMR and UV-Vis spectroscopy. It was possible to show that on the polymers the Ru sites retained the properties of monomers in solution. The evidence was provided by the results of absorption, emission and electrochemical studies. However, some unusual effects did occur whose existence depended critically on the py/Ru ratio. In "dilute" samples where py/Ru > 3/1, absorp-tion or emission spectra were identical to those of the monomer, $Ru(trpy)(bpy)py^{2+}$. In more concentrated samples significant spec-tral shifts and intensity changes were observed which suggested the onset of interactions between the chromophores along the poly-mer chain. The py/Ru ratio also influences the electrochemistry. In concentrated samples the oxidative and reductive components of cyclic voltammetry waves are symmetrical with ΔE_p < 60 mV as is characteristic for surface waves involving kinetically facile cou-ples (1,28). However, as the thickness of the films is increased or the metal content diluted, ΔE_p increases and the waves take on a more diffusional-like shape with distinct tailing edges. These observations clearly suggest the intervention of charge transport limitations within the films as they are made thicker or are made more dilute in redox sites.

Our next efforts were directed toward the preparation of PVP polymers which contained the group $-(py)Ru(bpy)_2(H_2O)^{2+}$. In this case the materials were prepared in solution either by a reaction between $Ru(bpy)_2(H_2O)OH^+$ and PVP or by photoaquation of the twice-bound bis-pyridyl complex,

$$(bpy)_2Ru(N\bigcirc\text{-}CHCH_2)_2^{2+} \xrightarrow[h\nu]{+H_2O} (bpy)_2Ru(H_2O)(N\bigcirc\text{-}CHCH_2)^{2+}$$

$$+ py\overset{|}{C}HCH_2-$$

a reaction initially reported by Clear, et al.(26a) and expected based on the photochemical properties of the monomer analog, Ru-$(bpy)_2(py)_2^{2+}$ (6). Earlier work on the monomers $Ru(bpy)_2(py)H_2O^{2+}$ and $Ru(trpy)(bpy)H_2O^{2+}$ had shown: 1) The existence of pH dependent $Ru^{IV/III}$ and $Ru^{III/II}$ couples (4); note the Latimer-type diagram in Scheme 4. 2) An extraordinary H_2O/D_2O solvent kinetic isotope effect of 16 for the reaction between $Ru(bpy)_2(py)O^{2+}$ and $Ru(bpy)_2$-$(py)(H_2O)^{2+}$ (29). 3) Reduction of NO_3^- to NO_2^- by $Ru(bpy)_2(py)$-

H_2O^{2+} (13) and oxidation of coordinated ammonia to nitrate in Ru-(trpy)(bpy)NH_3^{2+} (30). 4) Sustained electrocatalytic oxidation of a series of organic compounds, e.g., alkyl substituents on aromatic hydrocarbons or olefins, primary and secondary alcohols (19).

$$Ru(bpy)_2(py)O^{2+} \xrightarrow{\ 0.53\ } Ru(bpy)_2(py)OH^{2+} \xrightarrow{\ 0.42\ } Ru(bpy)_2(py)H_2O^{2+}$$

$$0.47$$

(potentials are vs. the SSCE at 25°, pH 6.8)

Scheme 4

Spectral studies on polymer samples (py/Ru ~ 5/1) containing $-(py)Ru(bpy)_2(H_2O)^{2+}$ showed that the intrinsic properties of the polymer-bound sites were relatively unchanged in the polymer but unusual effects were observed for films adsorbed on glassy carbon electrodes (31). Because of the proton dependences of the couples in Scheme 4, the $Ru^{IV/III}$ and $Ru^{III/II}$ potentials are pH dependent. Their $E_{1/2}$ values decrease 59mV per pH unit as pH is increased ($2 \leq$ pH ≤ 9) as predicted by the Nernst equation. The same pH dependences are observed for the polymer-bound couples in acidic solution. However, when the pK_a of the free pyridyl groups in PVP is reached (pH ~ 3.5) the pH registered by the surface couples remains constant and does not change further with changes of pH in the external solution. One interpretation of the effect is that protonation of the pyridyl groups gives an interface open to the external solution and the external solution dictates the pH properties within the polymer film. The loss of charge associated with deprotonation leads to partial exclusion of the polar solvent and its buffer component. The result is that the local environment at the complex is dictated by the acid/base properties of the polymer. By cycling between acidic and basic solutions, it is possible to show that the pH-induced opening and closing of the interface occurs on a timescale of minutes.

Except at very slow scan rates i_p values for the $Ru^{IV/III}$ couple are smaller than i_p for the $Ru^{III/II}$ couple. The origin of the effect appears to be that the direct reaction at the electrode is slow because of the necessity of a proton-coupled electron transfer (eq. 7) (29),

$$(bpy)_2Ru-OH^{2+} \underset{+H^+,+e^-}{\overset{-H^+,-e^-}{\rightleftharpoons}} (bpy)_2Ru=O^{2+} \tag{7}$$

$$\text{py} \hspace{5cm} \text{py}$$

and the electrochemical mechanism involves initial disproportionation of $Ru(bpy)_2(py)OH^{2+}$, for which $k_{H_2O}/k_{D_2O} = 16:1$. Disproportionation is followed by rapid oxidation of $Ru(bpy)_2(py)H_2O^{2+}$ at the electrode (32). Because of the indirect pathway, the $Ru^{IV/III}$ wave in the films is extremely sensitive to the presence of D_2O.

$$2 \ Ru(bpy)_2(py)OH^{2+} \longrightarrow Ru(bpy)_2(py)H_2O^{2+} + Ru(bpy)_2(py)O^{2+}$$

$$(\Delta G = +0.11V)$$

The sensitivity to D_2O provides a basis for measuring the deuterium content in H_2O/D_2O mixtures and the rate of H-D exchange between the film and bulk solvent ([32]).

Another pH-related property is the ability of the films containing the aquo complex to act as ion exchangers when protonated ([31]). At pH 7.4, an electrode coated with ~10 layers of polymer is totally blocking towards the $Fe(CN)_6^{4-/3-}$ couple at millimolar concentration. Upon acidification to pH ~ 2, the film opens to the external solution and a wave appears at 0.37V for the Fe-$(CN)_6^{3-/4-}$ couple which has ΔE_p ~ 40mV. The E_p value, which is lower than the 58mV expected for an ideal solution couple, shows that the $Fe(CN)_6^{4-/3-}$ pair is behaving as a surface couple held by electrostatic binding. Because of the labile nature of the binding, the redox couple is lost when the film is exposed to a fresh solution free of $Fe(CN)_6^{4-}$ or $Fe(CN)_6^{3-}$.

The feature of the $-(py)Ru(bpy)_2(H_2O)^{2+}$ which interested us most, at least initially, was their use in catalytic applications. For adsorbed films on Pt or carbon electrodes, catalytic currents were observed upon stepping the electrode potential to potentials more positive than the $Ru^{IV/III}$ couple in the presence of isopropanol, p-toluic acid or a mixture of the xylenes. In the latter case, the surfactant sodium dodecylsulfate (0.02$\underline{M}$) was also added to the solution. The electrocatalytic oxidation of all three substrates had been demonstrated previously based on the $Ru(trpy)-(bpy)O^{2+}/Ru(trpy)(bpy)OH_2^{2+}$ couple ([19]). Using the isopropanol → acetone conversion as a model reaction, we were able to show that catalytic currents--$i_{cat} \cong 1\mu A$ for $[(CH_3)_2CHOH] = 0.4\underline{M}$ using a $0.146cm^2$ glassy carbon electrode--increased with increasing isopropanol concentration, were essentially independent of film thickness in the range 1-20 layers, and increased with increasing electrode surface area. The relative insensitivity of the catalytic current to film thickness suggests that only the outer layers of the film are catalytically active. The basis for such a limitation arises from the rather severe constraints imposed by the oxidation mechanism. The mechanism involves a hydride transfer from the C-H bond of isopropanol and the kinetic isotope effect in comparing the perprotio and perdeutero alcohols is $k_H/k_D = 18$ ([33]). The catalytic currents are not persistent but slowly decay. Typically, the catalytic current falls by half after ~30 catalytic turnovers, calculated as if each Ru site in the film were involved in the catalysis. The performance in the film represents a stability enhancement of a factor of ~6 compared to the solution couple Ru-$(bpy)_2(py)O^{2+}/Ru(bpy)_2(py)OH_2^{2+}$ for which a pyridyl group is slowly lost. The problem of loss of pyridine appears not to be a problem in the films. However, as in the case of the silane-based interface, a new decay pathway appears. With the sites in the films in the Ru(IV) state, an, as yet, undefined redox reaction occurs to give a product with $E_{1/2} \sim 0.6V$ and the catalytic properties of the film are lost.

It is worth repeating that one of the real advantages of preparing interfaces by simple adsorption of a preformed polymer is ease of fabrication. Another is chemical versatility which is limited only by the synthesis of new polymers. One recent synthetic development is reductive loss of Cl^- followed by re-oxidation and pyridyl incorporation, all of which can be made to occur within a preformed electrode-polymer interface, as shown on the next page. The work is described in another paper in this volume (34). Another development is the preparation of an extended series of related PVP polymers based on Ru-bpy chemistry, $-(py)Ru(bpy)_2X^{2+}$ ($X = py$, H_2O, CH_3CN, N_3^-, Cl^-, NO_2^-,...) (34, 35).

The $Ru^{II}-NO_2$ oxidative chemistry is a useful "test case" for comparing solution and interfacial reactivity. For the premade metallopolymer complex $-(py)Ru(bpy)_2NO_2^+$ (py/Ru $\sim$ 5/1) adsorbed on a glassy carbon electrode, a clean two-electron oxidation to the nitrato complex is observed with water (0.1M Na_2SO_4; pH = 2.0) as the external solvent. There is no evidence for the nitrosyl product. Presumably the translational/orientational demands of the bimolecular O-atom transfer pathway in the polymer film dilute in Ru are too restrictive. Oxidation of the ligand occurs solely by the one-electron transfer path in reaction (B) of Scheme 3. The nitro→nitrato oxidation in the films has synthetic value. If, following the oxidation step, Ru^{III} is reduced to Ru^{II}, nitrate aquation occurs rapidly to give the aquo complex. The sequence of reactions is notable since it provides a simple means for converting the interface from one catalytically active form into another (32).

$$-(py)Ru(bpy)_2(NO_2)^+ \xrightarrow[\substack{+H_2O \\ -2H^+}]{-2e^-} -(py)Ru(bpy)_2(ONO_2)^+ \xrightarrow[-NO_3^-]{+H_2O}$$

$$-(py)Ru(bpy)_2(H_2O)^{2+} \qquad (8)$$

Ru^{III}-azido complexes are unstable in solution because oxidation is followed by loss of the coordinated ligand as N_2 (5c). The reaction opens up a coordination site which is rapidly occupied by a neighboring solvent molecule. In a film (py/Ru $\sim$ 5/1) on Pt with

$$Ru(bpy)_2(py)N_3^+ \xrightarrow{-e^-} Ru(bpy)_2(py)N_3^{2+} \xrightarrow[+CH_3CN]{-3/2\ N_2}$$

$$Ru(bpy)_2(py)(CH_3CN)^{2+}$$

CH_3CN as the external solvent, the course of the reaction changes. As shown by an experiment on an optically transparent tin oxide electrode, the product is the twice-bound, bis-pyridyl complex

rather than the solvent complex. However, the resulting film is
not electroactive. A reasonable suggestion is that extensive

$$-(py)Ru(bpy)_2N_3^{2+} + py- \xrightarrow{\ -3/2\ N_2\ } -(py)Ru(bpy)_2(py)-^{2+}$$

cross-linking occurs in association with formation of the bis-pyridyl complex and the cross-linking creates an inhibition to charge
transfer either by restriced counterion or electron transport. It
is interesting to note that the bis-pyridyl polymer of the same
composition but prepared by heating solutions containing $Ru(bpy)_2$-
$(H_2O)_2^{2+}$ and PVP is electroactive when adsorbed.

In solution, the photochemical properties of the bis-pyridyl
polymer (py/Ru ~ 5/1) are related to those of analogous monomers
in solution (32). The photochemical loss of pyridine from Ru-
$(bpy)_2(py)_2^{2+}$ is a high efficiency reaction which has proven to be

$$Ru(bpy)_2(py)_2^{2+} \xrightarrow[H_2O]{h\nu} Ru(bpy)_2(py)H_2O^{2+} + py$$

synthetically useful for the preparation of complexes of the types
$Ru(bpy)_2(py)X^{2+}$ or $Ru(bpy)_2X_2^{2+}$ (X = Cl$^-$, Br$^-$, NCS$^-$,...) (6). In
acetonitrile, the polymer-bound chromophore has a diminished lifetime (600 ns compared to 20 ns) and a diminished quantum yield for
ligand loss (~30% compared to ~8%) (32). As with related monomers, the polymers can be shown to undergo light-induced redox reactions. Quenching and flash photolysis experiments have shown
that following excitation the sites on the polymer can undergo
oxidative or reduction quenching, e.g., Scheme 5, in acetonitrile
solution (32).

$$-(py)_2Ru(bpy)_2^{2+} \longrightarrow -(py)_2Ru(bpy)_2^{2+*}$$

$$-(py)_2Ru(bpy)_2^{2+*} + TMPD \longrightarrow -(py)_2Ru(bpy)_2^+ + TMPD^+$$

$$-(py)_2Ru(bpy)_2^+ + TMPD^+ \longrightarrow -(py)_2Ru(bpy)_2^{2+} + TMPD$$

$$(TMPD\ is\ Me_2N\underset{}{\bigodot}NMe_2)$$

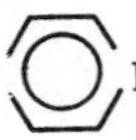

Scheme 5

The involvement of the polymer-based excited states in electron
transfer reactions is notable both because it can lead to polymer
units containing multiple reducing or oxidizing sites and because
it may portend a related chemistry on surfaces.

Although the very short lifetime and photodecomposition of
the bis-pyridyl polymer render it far from an ideal case, we have
used it to obtain sensitized photocurrents at a semiconductor
electrode (37). Thick films ($\Gamma \sim 10^{-8}$ moles/cm^2) of the polymer
on n-TiO$_2$ show an obvious emission when irradiated with visible
light. In acetonitrile solution with hydroquinone as supersensitizer, stable photocurrents (0.2-0.3 μA/cm^2) are observed and the

photocurrent action spectrum agrees reasonably well with the absorption spectrum of the polymer. The origin of the photocurrents is probably in an electron transfer to the conduction band of the semiconductor by Ru-bpy excited states in the polymer (Scheme 6). The supersensitizer is added to reduce the Ru^{III} sites in the film once formed to Ru(II).

$$TiO_2/-(py)_2Ru(bpy)_2^{2+} \xrightarrow{h\nu} TiO_2/-(py)_2Ru(bpy)_2^{2+*} \longrightarrow$$

$$\overset{\ominus}{TiO_2}/-(py)_2Ru(bpy)_2^{3+} \xrightarrow[-e^-]{hydroquinone} TiO_2/-(py)_2Ru(bpy)_2^{2+}$$

Scheme 6

This kind of experiment, the observation and manipulation of photo-effects at interfaces containing Ru-bpy and related chromophores, is becoming of increasing importance to us, especially given the possibilities for preparing multilayer interfaces which are described in the next section.

Electropolymerization Based on 4-Vinylpyridine and Related Ligands. The third technique for preparing electrode/film interfaces is in many ways the most interesting both in terms of the chemistry involved and the results so far obtained. The strategy is to induce polymerization directly at the electrode surface by oxidation or reduction and our emphasis has been on the reduction of coordinated 4-vinylpyridine and related compounds. It is known that 4-vinylpyridine is susceptible to anionic polymerization (38).

A characteristic feature of the chemistry of Ru^{II}-bpy complexes is the existence of reversible, bpy-localized reductions in the range −1.0 to −2.0V, which occur in addition to the metal-based oxidations in the potential range 0-2.0V. For example, for the complex $Ru(bpy)_2(vpy)_2^{2+}$ (vpy is 4-vinylpyridine, $NC_5H_4CH=CH_2$) in acetonitrile, reversible, bpy-based waves occur at $E_{\frac{1}{2}} = -1.36$ and −1.52 V (vs. SSCE). In addition, at more negative potentials, an irreversible wave appears for reduction of the vinylpyridine groups. Following repeated negative scans from 0 V past the ligand reductions, a polymer film appears on the electrode. The growth of the film is shown by the appearance and growth of cyclic voltammetric waves at potentials expected for the $Ru^{III/II}$ oxidation and bpy-based reductions (39, 40). With continued scanning in solutions containing the monomer, the metallic appearance of the electrode changes into the gold color of the polymer film. One of the remarkable features of the electropolymerization procedure is that the extent of surface coverage and the rate of polymer growth are controllable in a reproducible manner by making variations in: 1) monomer concentration, 2) the extent of the scan in the negative direction, and 3) the number of scans. As before, the extent of surface coverage was determined by measuring areas under voltammetric traces assuming reasonable molecular volumes for the redox sites. The films are mechanically stable and can be stored indefinitely either dry or in contact with acetonitrile. The films appear to be insoluble in a range of solvents from di-chloromethane to concentrated nitric acid, which suggests the pre-sence of long polymer chains, given the solubility characteristics of related monomers and oligomers. In $1\underline{M}$ $HClO_4$, platinum oxide forming and stripping waves at the metal surface are clearly evi-dent, even beneath the polymer layer. The fact that the electro-chemistry of the metal surface is relatively unchanged suggests that the electrode-polymer interaction at the electrode surface must involve physical adsorption and not strong chemical bonding (40).

The insolubility of the polymer has limited our ability to characterize it in detail, but the following observations are re-vealing: 1) Elemental analysis data on a sample of polymer mechan-ically removed from an electrode are consistent with the formula-tion shown below.

$$[(bpy)_2Ru(N\bigcirc\!\!\!\!\!-CH-CH_2-)_2](ClO_4)_2$$

2) There is good agreement ($\sim$20 mV) between potential values for surface and solution redox couples. 3) Resonance Raman experiments show the presence of expected 2,2'-bpy vibrations. 4) The visible absorption spectrum of $Ru(bpy)_2(vpy)_2^{2+}$ after electropolymerization on an optically transparent SnO_2 electrode is essentially unchanged from the spectrum of $Ru(bpy)_2(py)_2^{2+}$ in solution. 5) The films can act as ion exchangers as shown by the appearance of the $Fe(CN)_6^{4-/3-}$ couple in the films after exposure to solutions containing either the $Fe(CN)_6^{4-}$ or $Fe(CN)_6^{3-}$ ions. From cyclic voltammetry experiments, differences between oxidative and reduction peak po-tentials are small ($\Delta E_p \leq 20$ mV) for thin films (e.g., $\Gamma = 1.8$ x 10^{-9} mole/cm^2; $\sim$20 monolayers) and vary linearly with sweep rate. For thicker films (e.g., $\Gamma = 1.6$ x 10^{-8} mole/cm^2) ΔE_p is much lar-ger ($\sim$200 mV), the peak current sweep rate dependence becomes low-er than first order, and the wave shapes develop tailing edges.

One peculiar feature in the electrochemistry of the films is the appearance of a prewave before the $Ru^{III/II}$ wave on an oxida-tive scan and before the first $bpy^{0/-}$ wave on a reductive scan. The properties of the prewaves are reminiscent of the bilayer in-terfaces described below. Because of the similarities, their ori-gins may lie in a chemical decomposition process which leads to two different types of spatially separated sites in the films. Alter-natively, the prewaves may have a non-Faradaic, structural origin in which changes occur as a consequence of the gain or loss of counterions in the films upon oxidation or reduction.

$$[-(py)_2Ru^{II}(bpy)_2]X_2 \xrightarrow[+X^-]{-e^-} [-(py)_2Ru^{III}(bpy)_2]X_3$$

$$[-(py)_2Ru^{II}(bpy)_2]X_2 \xrightarrow[-X^-]{+e^-} [-(py)_2Ru^{II}(b\bar{p}y)(bpy)]X$$

Charge transfer through the films could be controlled by electron or counterion transport, by the rate of anion transfer between phases at the interface, or by a combination of the three (40, 41). From potential step chronoamperometry measurements on the electropolymerized vinylpyridine complex mentioned below, charge transfer is facile in the films and probably only a factor of 10-100 slower than the rate of electron transfer between associated $Ru(bpy)_3^{2+}$ and $Ru(bpy)_3^{3+}$ ions in acetonitrile solution (42).

$$Ru(bpy)_3^{2+}, \; Ru(bpy)_3^{3+} \longrightarrow Ru(bpy)_3^{3+}, \; Ru(bpy)_3^{2+}$$

Electropolymerization based on polymerizable vinyl groups has provided a general procedure for the preparation of a variety of films on electrodes (34). Polymeric films have been deposited on Pt, Au, SnO_2, TiO_2, and vitreous carbon electrodes, although most of the experiments described here have been carried out on Pt. Films have been prepared by electroreductions based on 4-methyl-4'-vinyl-2,2'-bipyridine (vbpy), trans-4'-X-stilbazoles, (trans-N$\bigcirc$-CH=CH-$\bigcirc$-X; X = Cl, OMe, CN, H), as well as 4-vinylpyridine (vpy) itself. Examples of compounds which have been electropolymerized include: $Ru(vbpy)_3^{2+}$, $Fe(vbpy)_3^{2+}$, $Ru(bpy)_2(vpy)(NO_2)^+$, Os-$(bpy)_2(vpy)_2^{2+}$, $Ru(trpy)(BPE)_3^{2+}$, $Ru(HC(pz)_3)(vpy)_3^{2+}$ $((HC(pz)_3)$ is tris-(pyrazolyl)methane), and $Ru(bpy)_2(4'-methoxystilbazole)_2^{2+}$. The extent of surface coverage and the stability of the resulting films can vary significantly. For example, thicker, more stable films result when multiple polymerizable groups are present in the monomers. Polymer films have been prepared which vary in thickness from a few layers to thousands of layers.

From the synthetic point of view, one of the interesting features about the electropolymerization procedure is the ability to carry out copolymerizations. For example, reduction at -1.37 V in 0.1M $[N(C_2H_5)_4](ClO_4)/CH_3CN$ causes the electropolymerization of $Ru(bpy)_2(vpy)_2^{2+}$. In the presence of added $Ru(bpy)_2(vpy)Cl^+$, Ru^{III}/II surface waves for both the bis-pyridyl (1.22V) and chloropyridyl (0.76V) couples appear in the resulting interfaces. A revealing fact is that at -1.37V only $Ru(bpy)_2(vpy)_2^{2+}$ is reduced, which suggests a chain propagation mechanism for electropolymerization with $Ru(bpy)(bpy)(vpy)_2^+$ acting as initiator. Similarly, it has proven possible to copolymerize $Ru(vbpy)_2Cl_2$ in the presence of $Ru(bpy)_2(vpy)_2^{2+}$ and to prepare mixed-metal films by the copolymerization of $Fe(vbpy)_3^{2+}$ or $Os(bpy)_2(vpy)_2^{2+}$ with Ru complexes containing vinyl groups. Although the mechanism of electropolymerization is not known in detail, a number of experimental observations are available based on rates of surface coverage which give some insight (34, 40). Mechanistically, the polymerizations are probably based on radical anion induced chain reactions. The surface poly-

$$\text{C=C} + e^- \longrightarrow [\text{C} \dot{=} \text{C}]^{-} \xrightarrow{+\text{C=C} \; (-)} :C-C-C-C \cdot \rightarrow \rightarrow$$

merization data are consistent with this view in that the rate of

appearance of surface polymer increases with more negative scan
potentials in the bpy$^{0/-}$ region. Because of steric constraints
imposed by the volumes of the monomers, linear chain growth based
on a single polymerizable ligand as in Ru(bpy)$_2$(vpy)NO$_2^+$ must occur
as a helical spire with little motional flexibility. With multiple
vinyl groups, more flexible structures are possible. Here, for
example, polymer growth could occur via tail to tail coupling and
the formation of linked dimeric pairs and both types of structures
may play a role.

The preparation and characterization of interfaces by electropolymerization have raised some important issues, but of more interest are the chemical properties of the resulting interfaces
from two different points of view: 1) Comparisons with chemically
related interfaces prepared by the two other techniques described
earlier. 2) Some remarkable observations arising from the ability
of the films to mediate charge transfer between the electrode and
a second film or between the electrode and a second redox couple
in the external solution.

Electropolymerization of Ru(bpy)$_2$(vpy)NO$_2^+$ gives films in
which the py/Ru ratio is necessarily 1:1 and the Ru-NO$_2$ sites are
held in close spatial proximity. Following oxidation to Ru^{III}-NO$_2$,
both nitrato and nitrosyl products are observed, but the Ru-ONO$_2$/
RuNO ratio is dependent on film thickness. At high coverages the
ratio approaches values obtained for the silane attached Ru-NO$_2$
group. At low coverages the ratio approaches the 1:1 value found
for the ligand-based reaction of Ru(bpy)$_2$(py)NO$_2^{2+}$ in solution.

The absence of free pyridyl groups in the films can have a
direct bearing on the net chemistry that occurs. Following oxidation of -(py)Ru(bpy)$_2$N$_3^+$, two subsequent processes occur. The
first involves oxidation of bound azide and its loss as N$_2$. With
no free pyridyl groups available, a competition for the open coordination site exists between solvent (CH$_3$CN) and counterion (Cl-
O$_4^-$).

$$-(py)Ru(bpy)_2N_3^+ \underset{+e^-}{\overset{-e^-}{\rightleftharpoons}} -(py)Ru(bpy)_2N_3^{2+} \begin{array}{c} \xrightarrow[\ \ -\frac{3}{2}N_2\ \ ]{+ClO_4^-} -(py)Ru(bpy)_2OClO_3^+ \\ \\ \xrightarrow[-\frac{3}{2}N_2]{+CH_3CN} -(py)Ru(bpy)_2(CH_3CN)^{2+} \end{array}$$

In the second, slower process, the perchlorato complex undergoes
solvolysis,

$$-(py)Ru(bpy)_2OClO_3^+ + CH_3CN \rightarrow -(py)Ru(bpy)_2(CH_3CN)^{2+} + ClO_4^-$$

The emphasis so far has been on the preparation and chemical
manipulation of the sites within polymers films on electrodes. Because of the spatial organization within the interface, the film
itself must play an important role in any electrochemical redox

event, since it is an intermediate phase between the electrode and the external environment. As a consequence, in properly designed systems the current-voltage-time response of the electrode will be dominated by the film and its interfacial characteristics at the film boundaries. The most direct example is the blocking of the oxidation or reduction of an external couple by diffusion to the electrode because of the presence of the film.

However, given the properties of the films, other pathways may exist for charge transfer where the films play a more active role. As an example, the polymers of concern here contain fixed cationic sites and, as noted before, can function as anion exchange membranes. At sufficiently thick films the usual electrode response for a cationic couple in the external solution can be quenched by the film. However, anionic couples like $Fe(CN)_6^{4-/3-}$ can enter the films, and within the films their response becomes that of an electrostatically-bound couple as noted above. In fact, the concentrating effect of the ion exchange membrane can lead to a very sensitive electroanalytical technique for anions.

However, more sophisticated pathways exist for charge transfer through the films, based on their redox properties. The first and a very dramatic example was observed at a spatially segregated bilayer structure prepared by electropolymerization on a Pt electrode (39, 40). The inner layer was prepared by electropolymerization of $Ru(bpy)_2(vpy)_2^{2+}$, giving a film having $E_{\frac{1}{2}}(Ru^{III}/II) = 1.23V$ vs. the SSCE. A second layer was then deposited on top of the inner layer by electropolymerization using a mixture of $Ru(bpy)_2(vpy)_2^{2+}$ and $Ru(bpy)_2(vpy)Cl^+$. Recall, as mentioned above, that copolymerization gave surface waves for both couples. In the spatially segregated bilayer a direct pathway to the electrode by electron hopping between like sites is no longer available to the $-(py)Ru(bpy)_2Cl^+$ sites if the inner layer is sufficiently thick. Because they are fixed sites, diffusion cannot occur and their charge transfer processes must be mediated by the inner layer.

With the inner layer in the Ru^{II} state, there is no basis for the film acting as anything other than an insulator in terms of electron transport. However, when the inner films are partially oxidized, $Ru^{II} \xrightarrow{-e^-} Ru^{III}$, or partially reduced, $Ru^{II}(bpy) \xrightarrow{+e^-} Ru^{II}(b\bar{p}y)$, they become mixed-valence in character and electron transport can occur by electron hopping, as in eq. 9.

$$-Ru^{III} - Ru^{II} - \longrightarrow - Ru^{II} - Ru^{III} - \qquad (9)$$

The situation is analogous to electron transfer in mixed-valence dimers and oligomers, e.g.,

$$[(bpy)_2ClRu^{II}N \bigcirc NRu^{III}Cl(bpy)_2]^{3+}$$

where the details of intersite charge transfer in solution are well understood (7, 9).

There are kinetic and energetic restraints on the electron

hopping pathway. In the $Ru(py)Cl^+/Ru(py)_2^{2+}$ bilayer, the potential for the $Ru(py)Cl^{2+/+}$ couple in the outer layer is lower by 0.46V, 1.22 vs. 0.76V. A positive, oxidative potential-time sweep positive of +0.76V leads to no perceptible current because of the insulating character of the inner layer in this potential range. As the potential for the $Ru(py)_2^{3+/2+}$ couple is approached, a few of the sites in the film are oxidized, and the inner layer is turned into a conducting medium with regard to the outer layer. The redox potential of the sites in the inner layer enter the problem through the Nernst equation, e.g., for solution couples,

$$E = E^{o'}(Ru^{III/II}) - \frac{nF}{RT} \log(a_{Ru^{III}}/a_{Ru^{II}})$$

which shows that the ratio of Ru^{III} to Ru^{II} sites is determined by the applied potential. When the inner film becomes partially mixed-valence, a conductivity channel is opened based on electron transfer at the film/film interface (eq. 10), followed by electron hopping to the electrode by eq. 9.   (10)

$$Pt \left\{ Ru^{III}(py)_2^{3+} \atop (inner) \right\} \left\{ Ru^{II}(py)Cl^+ \atop (outer) \right\} \xrightarrow[0.46V]{\Delta E =} \left\{ Ru^{II}(py)_2^{2+} \atop (inner) \right\} \left\{ Ru^{III}(py)Cl^{2+} \atop (outer) \right\}$$

In its operation as a conducting medium, the inner film could be described as a localized, narrow band semiconductor. What is observed experimentally is that in an oxidative potential-time sweep, oxidation of the outer layer is inhibited until the potential approaches $E_{\frac{1}{2}}$ for the couple in the inner layer. At that point, the outer layer is "discharged" as an oxidative spike preceding the usual surface wave for the electropolymerized $Ru(bpy)_2$-$(vpy)_2^{2+}$ couple in the inner layer.

Just as dramatic is the fact that once the outer layer has been oxidized, the $Ru^{III}(py)Cl^{2+}$ sites are trapped in the Ru^{III} state. Following an oxidative potential-time scan past 1.23V, a subsequent reductive scan shows the presence of the expected wave for the electropolymerized $(bpy)_2Ru(vpy)_2^{2+}$ couple in the inner layer, but no wave appears for the $(bpy)_2Ru(vpy)Cl^+$ couple in the outer layer. With regard to the outer layer, the inner layer has once again become an insulator. Reduction of the outer layer by the reverse of eq. 10 is slow because interfilm electron transfer is nonspontaneous by 0.46V. Discharge of the stored charge can occur by the reverse of eq. 10, which is a leakage pathway, but its rate depends on the potential difference between the couples in the inner and outer layers. In a bilayer made of an inner layer of electropolymerized $Ru(vbpy)_3^{2+}$ and an outer layer of $Fe(vbpy)_3^{2+}$ the difference in potentials between the $M^{III/II}$ couples is only 0.10V and charge from the outer layer leaks through the inner layer on a timescale of seconds to minutes.

In the $Ru(py)_2^{2+}/Ru(py)Cl^+$ bilayer, charge trapping in the outer layer is maintained regardless of the applied voltage at the

electrode until the first ligand-based reduction at -1.36V vs.
SSCE is approached. At this point the inner film undergoes another insulator-conductor transition. The film becomes conducting in
the reductive sense because, with the appearance of reduced sites
in the film, electron hopping can once again occur, but now based
on electron transfer between $b\bar{p}y$ and bpy sites.

$$—Ru^{II}(b\bar{p}y) —— Ru^{II}(bpy) - \longrightarrow —Ru^{II}(bpy)—Ru^{II}(b\bar{p}y)—$$

The opening of the reductive channel results in rapid reduction of
the outer layer because now the interfilm electron transfer process is favored by 2.12V.

$$Pt \left\| —Ru^{II}(b\bar{p}y)^{2+} \right\} Ru^{III}Cl^{2+} \right\} \xrightarrow{\Delta E \cong 2.12V} \left\| —Ru^{II}(bpy)^{2+} \right\} Ru^{II}Cl^{+} \right\}$$
$$\quad (inner) \quad\quad (outer) \quad\quad\quad\quad (inner) \quad\quad (outer)$$

In the net sense, the bilayers provide a means for directed
or unidirectional electron transfer from an external film to the
electrode and in that sense they impart a rectifying character to
the electrode-film interface.
    Similar effects can be observed at single layer interfaces
when they are exposed to appropriate redox couples in an external
solution (40, 45, 46). With a solution couple the possibility
exists for electron transfer either by diffusion through the film
or by electron hopping from the external solution to the electrode
using the conductivity properties of the film. In general, both
pathways exist and, as shown by a series of cyclic voltammetry experiments, they can coexist. The relative importance of the two
pathways is controllable by making variations in the film thickness or in the potential-time electrochemical scan rate (45).
    The responses of Pt electrodes coated by electropolymerized Ru-
$(bpy)_2(vpy)_2^{2+}$, of varying film thicknesses, were observed in the
presence of $Fe(\eta^5-C_5H_5)_2$ (Fc) or $Ru(bpy)_2(py)Cl^+$ in the external
solution $(0.1M [N(C_2H_5)_4](ClO_4)-CH_3CN)$. At low surface coverages
of polymer, the voltammetric waves for the $Ru^{III/II}$ and $Fc^{0/+}$ couples are diffusional in character at a scan rate of 200 mV/s. At
higher coverages, ~10 monolayers, the $Ru(bpy)_2(py)Cl^{2+/+}$ wave becomes significantly distorted and an oxidative spike appears which,
as in the bilayer experiment, occurs at the onset of the surface
wave for the $-(py)_2Ru(bpy)_2^{3+/2+}$ couple. At faster scan rates the
diffusional wave becomes increasingly distorted and decreases in
area at the expense of the oxidative spike. The appearance of two
waves shows the presence of both diffusional and electron hopping
pathways to the electrode. At a thicker film (~54 monolayers),
the diffusional pathway is entirely blocked on the timescale of
the experiment and only the oxidative spike characteristic of electron hopping is observed. The area of the spike is proportional
to the amount of added Ru^{II} and varies in a systematic way with

sweep rate. At the same electrode, but in a solution containing ferrocene, waves for both the diffusional and hopping pathways are observed for the $Fc^{+/0}$ couple. It seems clear that diffusion through the cationic polymer is more facile for ferrocene than for $Ru(bpy)_2(py)Cl^+$ and the differences in diffusional mobility provide a basis for carrying out selective oxidations at the interface. The diffusional wave for the $Fc^{+/0}$ couple can be completely blocked at 200 mV/s but only at even thicker films. A related experiment shows that the diffusional pathway for one component can be blocked by a second. At a film-coated electrode (~10 monolayers) where a diffusional wave is observed for the $Ru(bpy)_2(py)-Cl^{2+/+}$ couple, the addition of an equal amount of ferrocene leads to a complete disappearance of the Ru(III)/Ru(II) diffusional wave and the concomitant growth of the oxidative spike. The clear implication is that ferrocene can block the diffusion of the complex through the film.

The electron hopping pathway which is the dominant pathway at thick films is an example of directed charge transfer just as in the bilayer experiment. The sense of the direction of electron transfer from outside the inner film to the electrode is also the same. However, there are differences between the processes, per-

$$\text{Ru}^{III}(py)_2^{3+} \Big\{ \text{Ru}^{II}(bpy)_2(py)Cl^+ \xrightarrow{\Delta E = +0.46V} \text{(film)} \quad \text{(soln)}$$

$$\text{Ru}^{II}(py)_2^{2+} \Big\{ \text{Ru}^{III}(bpy)_2(py)Cl^{2+} \text{(soln)}$$

haps the most important being that in the solution experiment the trapped charge is in the external solution where it is freely mobile by diffusion, and that in the bilayer experiment the charge is trapped in a second, immobile polymer layer.

Between the bilayer and solution experiments it is possible to begin to show how to transfer the rectifying properties observed on photolysis at a semiconductor-solution interface to any electrode material. In a more general context, it seems clear that the single layer and bilayer interfaces have intrinsic characteristics usually associated with solid state electronics devices.

Conclusions and Final Comments

Thinking toward the future, it should be emphasized that the work described here is of a relatively recent origin. A number of interesting observations have been made which, hopefully, have provided a basis for a series of continued systematic developments. The key to our efforts has been the flexibility and the numerous positive characteristics inherent in the Ru-bpy systems chosen for study, and using them future developments will no doubt include: 1) A fuller exploitation of their available chemical properties for carrying out micromanipulations within the films, 2) An increasing emphasis on the excited state properties of Ru-bpy and Os-bpy excited states on polymers and within interfaces. 3) Application of surface sensitive techniques such as Resonance Raman and Scanning Electron Microscopy to questions of film structure and morphology. 4) Use of Ru-bpy films to establish fuller details of electron and ion transport within semiconducting polymer films.

The Ru-bpy chemistry has been revealing in establishing synthetic possibilities. In due course, they should provide a basis for the preparation of a series of new interfaces based on different metals and different ligands, and to new schemes for interface preparation.

Returning to the question posed in the title, it seems evident that solution reactivity properties can be transferred to an electrode surface but with certain caveats. From the results described here, individual Ru-bpy sites appear to retain their intrinsic redox characteristics and their ability to undergo facile electron transfer. In addition, some of the more complex chemical reactions known for Ru-bpy complexes, including ligand-based reactions like $RuNO \rightarrow RuNO_2 \rightarrow RuONO_2$, and oxidation of azide, also occur in the films. It is also notable that the catalytic abilities of the $Ru^{III}-NO_2$ or $Ru^{IV}=O$ groups can be transferred to the electrode-polymer interface.

However, it is also clear that the act of immobilization or attachment to an electrode surface leads unavoidably to changes. The changes arise from restricted mobility of the redox sites and from the different chemical environment imposed by the interface itself. From our results, the surrounding medium can enter the problem in several ways, including: 1) The chemical environment created by preparation of the interface (a silane link or polymer backbone) provides the structural basis for the interface, including the immobilization of individual sites, and the means for the preparation of complex assemblies including the inherent spatial character needed to prepare bilayers. 2) The properties of the interface can play a major role in determining local environment as shown by the pH properties of the $-(py)Ru(bpy)_2H_2O^{2+}$ films and the ion exchange properties of the polycationic films. 3) The chemical material at the interface can intervene directly to modify reactivity and/or the course of the reaction, as shown by the cross-linking reaction with $-(py)Ru(bpy)_2N_3^{2+}$ undergoes oxidative loss of azide in PVP, by the degradation of $Ru-OH_2^{2+}$ sites with extended oxidative cycling or, by the variations in the $RuNO_2 \rightarrow RuNO + RuONO_2$ chemistry observed under different conditions. 4) Even if the net chemistry is not changed, variations in reaction rates can and will occur, the most obvious example being diminished rates of electron and counterion transport in films dilute in redox sites.

Acknowledgements are made to the Department of Energy under Grant no. ER-78-S-05-6034 and the Army Research Office Durham under Grant no. DAAG29-79-C-0044 for support of this research and to the Solid State Research Department of the Sandia National Laboratory for support for TJM during the period that this account was written.

References Cited

1.   a) Oyama, N.; Anson, F. C. J. Am. Chem. Soc. 1979, 101, 3450-
        6.
     b) Kaufman, F. B.; Engler, E. M. Ibid. 1979, 101, 547-9.
        Kaufman, F. B.; Schroeder, A. H.; Engler, E. M.; Kramer,
        S. R.; Chambers, J. Q. Ibid. 1980, 102, 483-8.
     c) Kerr, J. B.; Miller, L. L.; Van de Mark, M. R. J. Am. Chem.
        Soc. 1980, 102, 3383-90.
     d) Merz, A.; Bard, A. J. Ibid. 1978, 100, 3222-3.
        Itaya, K.; Bard, A. J. Anal. Chem. 1978, 50, 1487-9.
     e) Daum, P.; Murray, R. W. J. Phys. Chem. 1981, 85, 389-96.
     f) Wrighton, M. S. Accts. Chem. Res. 1979, 12, 303-10.
     g) Abruña, H. D.; Denisevich, P.; Umaña, M.; Meyer, T. J.;
        Murray, R. W. J. Am. Chem. Soc. 1981, 103, 1-5.
        Ellis, D.; Neff, V. D. J. Phys. Chem. 1981, 85, 1225-31.
     i) Ellis, C. D.; Murphy, W. R.; Meyer, T. J. J. Am. Chem.
        Soc., in press.
     j) Denisevich, P.; Abruña, H. D.; Leidner, C. R.; Meyer, T.
        J.; Murray, R. W. Inorg. Chem., in press.
     k) Samuels, G. J.; Meyer, T. J. Ibid. 1981, 103, 307-13.
     m) Shigehara, K.; Oyama, N.; Anson, F. C. J. Am. Chem. Soc.
        1981, 103, 2552-8.
     n) Murray, R. W. Accts. Chem. Res. 1980, 13, 135-41.
     o) Calvert, J. M.; Meyer, T. J. Inorg. Chem. 1980, 20, 27-33.
2.   a) Salmon, D. J., Ph.D. Dissertation, University of North
        Carolina, 1978.
     b) Connor, J. A.; Meyer, T. J.; Sullivan, B. P. Inorg. Chem.
        1979, 18, 1388-91.
3.   a) Keene, F. R.; Young, R. C.; Meyer, T. J. J. Am. Chem. Soc.
        1977, 99, 2468.
     b) Brown, G. M.; Sutin, N. J. Am. Chem. Soc. 1979, 101, 883.
4.   Moyer, B. A.; Meyer, T. J. Inorg. Chem. 1981, 20, 436-44.
5.   a) Adeyemi, S. A.; Miller, F. J.; Meyer, T. J. Inorg. Chem.
        1972, 11, 994.
     b) Adeyemi, S. A.; Johnson, E. C.; Miller, F. J.; Meyer, T. J.
        Inorg. Chem. 1973, 12, 2371.
     c) Brown, G. M.; Callahan R. W.; Meyer, T. J. Inorg. Chem.
        1975, 14, 4440.
6.   Durham, B.; Walsh, J. L.; Carter, C. L.; Meyer, T. J. Inorg.
     Chem. 1980, 19, 860-5.
7.   Meyer, T. J. Ann. N.Y. Acad. Sci. 1978, 313, 496.
8.   Baumann, J. A.; Wilson, S. T.; Salmon, D. J.; Hood, P. L.;
     Meyer, T. J. J. Am. Chem. Soc. 1979, 101, 2916-20.
9.   Meyer, T. J. Accts. Chem. Res. 1978, 11, 94.
10. a) Keene, F. R.; Salmon, D. J.; Meyer, T. J. J. Am. Chem.
        Soc. 1976, 98, 1884.
     b) Brown, G. M.; Weaver, T. R.; Keene, F. R.; Meyer, T. J.
        Inorg. Chem. 1976, 15, 190.
11. Bowden, W. L.; Little, W. F.; Meyer, T. J. J. Am. Chem. Soc.

1977, 99, 4340; Powers, M. J.; Meyer, T. J. J. Am. Chem. Soc. 1980, 102, 1289-97.

12. Walsh, J. L.; Bullock, R. M.; Meyer, T. J. Inorg. Chem. 1980, 19, 865-9.

13. Moyer, B. A.; Meyer, T. J. J. Am. Chem. Soc. 1979, 101, 1326-8.

14. a) Keene, F. R.; Salmon, D. J.; Walsh, J. L.; Abruna, H. D.; Meyer, T. J. Inorg. Chem. 1980, 19, 1896-1903.
    b) Keene, F. R.; Salmon, D. J.; Meyer, T. J. J. Am. Chem. Soc. 1977, 99, 2384.

15. Moyer, B. A.; Sipe, B. K.; Meyer, T. J. Inorg. Chem. 1981, 20, 1475-80.

16. Sutin, N. J. Photochem. 1979, 10, 19.

17. Balzani, V.; Bolletta, F.; Gandolfi, M. T.; Maestri, M. Top. Curr. Chem. 1977, 75, 1.

18. Keene, F. R.; Salmon, D. J.; Meyer; T. J. J. Am. Chem. Soc. 1977, 99, 4821.

19. Moyer, B. A.; Thompson, M. S.; Meyer, T. J. J. Am. Chem. Soc. 1980, 102, 2310-2.

20. a) Moses, P. R.; Murray, R. W. J. Am. Chem. Soc. 1976, 98, 7435. b) Moses, P. R.; Wier, L. M.; Lennox, J. C.; Finklea, H. O.; Lenhard, J. R.; Murray, R. W. Anal. Chem. 1978, 50, 576. c) Lenhard, J. R.; Rocklin, R.; Abruna, H. D.; Willman, K.; Kuo, K.; Nowak, R.; Murray, R. W. J. Am. Chem. Soc. 1978, 100, 5213. d) Koval, C. A.; Anson, F. C. Ibid. 1978, 50, 223. e) Fujihara, M.; Osa, T.; Hursh, D.; Kuwana, T. J. Electroanal. Chem. 1978, 88, 285.

21. Abruña, H. D.; Meyer, T. J.; Murray, R. W. Inorg. Chem. 1979, 18, 3233-40.

22. Callahan, R. W.; Meyer, T. J. Inorg. Chem. 1977, 16, 574.

23. a) Abruña, H. D.; Walsh, J. L.; Meyer, T. J.; Murray, R. W. Inorg. Chem. 1981, 20, 1481-6.
    b) Abruña, H. D.; Walsh, J. L.; Meyer, T. J.; Murray, R. W. J. Am. Chem. Soc. 1980, 102, 3272-4.

24. Lane, R. F.; Hubbard, A. T. J. Phys. Chem. 1973, 77, 140.

25. Katchalsky, A.; Rosenheck, K.; Altmann, B. J. Polym. Sci. 1957, 23, 955.

26. a) Clear, J. M.; Kelly, J. M.; Pepper, D. C.; Vos, J. G. Inorg. Chim. Acta 1979, 33, L 139. b) Sullivan, B. P.; Browning, I. B.; Curtis, J.; Meyer, T. J. "Abstracts of Papers: 175th Natl. Meeting of the American Chemical Soc.; Anaheim, Cal.; March 1978; American Chemical Society, Washington, DC 1978, Inor. 213.

27. Calvert, J. M.; Meyer, T. J. Inorg. Chem. 1981, 20, 27-33.

28. a) Laviron, E. J. Electroanal. Chem. 1974, 52, 395.
    b) Brown, A. P.; Anson, F. C. Anal. Chem. 1977, 49, 1589.
    c) Laviron, E. J. Electroanal. Chem. 1981, 112, 1.

29. Binstead, R. A.; Moyer, B. A.; Samuels, G. J.; Meyer, T. J. J. Am. Chem. Soc. 1981, 103, 2897-9.

30. Thompson, M. S.; Meyer, T. J. J. Am. Chem. Soc. 1981, 103, 5577-9.

31. Samuels, G. J.; Meyer, T. J. J. Am. Chem. Soc. 1981, 103, 307-12.
32. Calvert, J. M., work in progress.
33. Thompson, M. S.; Meyer, T. J., submitted.
34. Calvert, J. M.; Sullivan, B. P.; Meyer, T. J.; this volume.
35. Haas, A.; Kriens, M.; Vos, J. G. J. Am. Chem. Soc. 1981, 103, 1318-9.
36. Durham, B.; Caspar, J. V.; Nagle, J. K.; Meyer, T. J., J. Am. Chem. Soc., submitted.
37. Westmoreland, T. D.; Calvert, J. M.; unpublished results.
38. Kalir, R.; Zilkha, A. Eur. Polym. J. 1978, 14, 557.
39. Abruña, H. D.; Denisevich, P.; Umaña, M.; Meyer, T. J.; Murray, R. W. J. Am. Chem. Soc. 1981, 103, 1-5.
40. Denisevich, P.; Abruña, H. D.; Leidner, C. R.; Meyer, T. J.; Murray; R. W. Inorg. Chem., in press.
41. Daum, P.; Lenhard, J. R.; Rolison, D. R.; Murray, R. W. J. Am. Chem. Soc. 1980, 102, 315.
42. Chan, M. S.; Wahl, A. C. J. Phys. Chem. 1978, 82, 2543.
43. Kanazawa, K. K.; Diaz, A. F.; Geiss, R. H.; Gill, W. D.; Kwak, J. F.; Logan, J. A.; Rabolt, J. F.; Streit, J. B. J. C. S. Chem. Comm. 1979, 854.
44. Powers, M. J.; Meyer, T. J. J. Am. Chem. Soc. 1980, 102, 1289-97.
45. Ellis, C. D.; Murphy, W. R.; Meyer, T. J. J. Am. Chem. Soc., in press.
46. Oyama, N.; Anson, F. C. Anal. Chem. 1980, 52, 1192.

RECEIVED January 13, 1982.

Reductive Chloride Ion Loss and Electropolymerization Techniques in Preparing Metallopolymer Films on Electrode Surfaces

J. M. CALVERT, B. P. SULLIVAN, and T. J. MEYER

University of North Carolina, Department of Chemistry, Chapel Hill, NC 27514

Two approaches for modifying electrode surfaces with a variety of metal complexes will be discussed. In the first method, reductive chloride loss from a complex in a non-coordinating solvent near or within a previously deposited polymer film is coupled with capture by ligating groups of the polymer to form a covalently bound species. This procedure has been used to create multimetallic films containing rhenium and osmium. The second approach involves electro-reductive polymerization of metal complexes with vinyl-containing ligands. This technique has now been generalized to include complexes of other metals, e.g., $Os(bpy)_2(vpy)_2^{2+}$ (bpy = 2,2'-bipyridine; vpy = 4-vinylpyridine) and different ligands such as BPE and substituted stilbazoles. The reactivity and properties of these complexes will be compared in a quantitative manner with regard to the type and quantity of polymerizable ligands.

Surface chemistry, in general, is an area in which the ability to selectively modify the chemical and physical properties of an interface is highly desirable. The synthetic chemistry of surfaces is now in a developing stage, particularly with respect to the attachment of electroactive redox sites to metal or semi-conductor surfaces (1-3). Single component and bilayer (4) electroactive films have been a field of intense research activity since their applications are apparent in catalysis, solar energy conversion, directed charge transfer, electrochromic devices, and trace analysis.

There are four broad methods of forming electroactive surface films:

1) Surface linkage of preformed electroactive sites to reactive groupings on the surface. An example of this procedure involves silanization of a metal oxide and subsequent reaction with an electroactive molecule

bonded to a nucleophile-containing side chain; For
example, see ref. 2.

2) Deposition of preformed electroactive polymers. An
example of this approach is found in refs. 3 and 1d.

3) Deposition of thin layers of insulating polymer on
a metal or semiconductor surface followed by attachment
of the electroactive sites to polymer functionalities;
see, for example, ref. 1a.

4) Formation of a growing polymer at the electrode surface
by an electroinitiated process, as demonstrated in ref.
1g.

In this paper we wish to discuss new synthetic advances in
methods of preparation of electroactive polymer-coated electrodes
which fall into categories 3 and 4 listed above.

The technique which we will discuss in the opening section of
this paper is referred to as reductive Cl⁻ ion loss, which
involves using a preformed polymer coating as a "pseudo-solvent"
for performing an electroreduction of a transition metal complex
that undergoes a facile loss of chloride ion. The reactive intermediate generated upon reduction then reacts with ligating groups
within the polymer film, producing surface-bound electroactive
transition metal complexes. Examples of this type of reaction
have been found in Os, Re, and Ru chemistry and appear to be
relatively general phenomena (5).

The second section of this paper deals with the synthesis of
new Ru and Os derivatives of 4-vinylpyridine (vpy) trans-4-stil-
bazole (stilb) and trans-1,2-bis-(4-pyridyl)-ethylene (BPE) and
their electroinitiated polymerization reactions. The electropolymerization (EP) reactions of the BPE and stilb complexes
represent graphic examples of the broad scope of this surface
derivatization technique that is available with substituted vinylpyridine ligands (6). These studies have provided considerable
insight into structural and electronic influences on thin film
formation.

Experimental

Chemicals and Solvents. Acetonitrile (Burdick and Jackson)
and dichloromethane (Fisher) were stored over Davisson 3Å molecular sieves for at least 24 h. before use. Tetra-n-ethylammonium
hexafluorophosphate (TEAH) was purchased from Alfa and used without further purification. Tetra-n-ethylammonium perchlorate
(TEAP) was prepared from the corresponding bromide salt (Eastman)
with the use of a previously published procedure (7). Tetra-n-
butylammonium hexafluorophosphate (TBAH) was prepared by dissolv-
ing the iodide salt (Eastman) in a hot, equivolume water/ethanol/
acetone mixture followed by addition of HPF_6 (Alfa). The solution
was reduced to approximately half its original volume, then cooled
to room temperature. The resulting white solid was filtered off

and recrystallized three times from boiling ethanol. Following preparation, both TEAP and TBAH were dried in a vacuum oven at 70°C for 10 h., then stored in a dessicator. Electrolyte solutions were either 0.2 $\underline{M}$ TBAH/CH$_2$Cl$_2$ or 0.1 $\underline{M}$ in electrolyte if CH$_3$CN was used as the solvent.

Poly-(4-vinylpyridine) was purchased from Polysciences. Analysis by membrane osmometry (Arro Laboratories; Joliet, Ill.) yielded a molecular weight of 33,000.

The following polymerizable ligands were employed in the synthesis of the ruthenium and osmium complexes: 4-vinylpyridine (vpy) purchased from Aldrich Chemical Co. was distilled at reduced pressure (77°C (31 torr)) and stored tightly capped in the freezer. BPE was used as received from Aldrich. The ligands trans-4-stilbazole (stilb), various 4'-substituted 4-stilbazoles and the complex [Ru(bpy)$_2$(stilb)$_2$](PF$_6$)$_2$ (8) were generously provided by Dr. David G. Whitten. (The stilbazole ligands will henceforth be abbreviated as "4'-X-stilb" where X will be replaced by the appropriate functional group such as Cl, OCH$_3$ or CN. If X = "H" the ligand is stilbazole itself and may be represented by the abbreviation "stilb".)

Preparations for the complexes [Ru(bpy)$_2$(vpy)$_2$](PF$_6$)$_2$ (1g), mer-Os(Me$_2$PhP)$_3$Cl$_3$ (9), mer-Ru(Me$_2$PhP)$_3$Cl$_3$ (10), Os^{IV}(bpy)Cl$_4$ (11), and [Ru(bpy)$_2$(vpy)Cl]PF$_6$ (1g) (bpy = 2,2'-bipyridine; vpy = 4-vinylpyridine; Me = methyl; Ph = phenyl) have been described in the literature. Samples of these particular vpy complexes were generously provided by W. R. Murphy. The remaining ruthenium complexes were synthesized according to the following general procedure. The appropriate starting material, i.e., cis-Ru(bpy)$_2$-Cl$_2$ (12), cis-Ru(phen)$_2$Cl$_2$ (13), Ru(trpy)Cl$_3$ (14), Ru(HC(pz)$_3$)Cl$_3$ (15), and [Ru(trpy)(bpy)Cl]PF$_6$ (3) (trpy = 2,2',2"-terpyridine; HC(pz)$_3$ = tris-(pyrazolyl)-methane) was combined with an excess of the desired polymerizable ligand in 1:1 ethanol/water (v/v). The mixture was then heated at reflux until spectral changes were no longer evident. The product was precipitated as a PF$_6^-$ salt and separated from the accompanying insoluble polymeric material by extraction using CH$_2$Cl$_2$ or CH$_3$CN. The resulting solid was purified by chromatography on a column of alumina with CH$_3$CN/toluene or CH$_3$OH/CH$_2$Cl$_2$ mixtures as eluants.

Osmium complexes were also prepared according to the above procedure with the exception of ethylene glycol being used in place of ethanol in the reflux step.

<u>Electrodes and Instrumentation</u>. Electrodes were mechanically polished with one micron diamond paste (Buehler) until satisfactory background voltammograms were obtained. A disposable, 20 ml scintillation vial served as a convenient, one-compartment electrochemical cell.

Electrochemical instrumentation included a PAR model 174A Polarographic Analyzer and a homebuilt waveform generator (16). All measurements were recorded versus the saturated sodium chloride electrode (SSCE) at $25 \pm 2°C$ and are uncorrected for junction potential effects. No IR compensation was employed regardless of whether or not the surface of the working electrode was coated by a polymeric film. A platinum wire served as the counter electrode.

General Procedure for Cl$^-$ Ion Loss Experiments. Methanolic PVP solutions (1.86 mgs/50 mls CH$_3$OH) were prepared so that a 10μl aliquot applied to a vertically mounted glassy carbon disk delivered 5×10^{-8} moles of pyridyl sites per square cm of electrode area. The solution was allowed to air-dry, forming a visible film on the electrode surface. The film-covered electrode was then rinsed in stirring methanol for five minutes to swell the polymer and re-dried.

Introduction of the desired metal complex into the polymer film was accomplished by performing electrochemistry in an 0.2 M TBAH/CH$_2$Cl$_2$ electrolyte solution which was 5 mM in complex. Solutions of the osmium and rhenium phosphines were protected from light due to their photolytic instability. All solutions were degassed using a stream of CH$_2$Cl$_2$-saturated nitrogen. An N$_2$ blanket was maintained during the course of the experiment to prevent subsequent aeration.

Potential limits were set so that the cycle encompassed both the reduction of the solution species and the couple produced by polymer adduct formation. Cycling was continued until the size of the product couple no longer increased--typically thirty minutes duration. The working electrode was removed from the cell, rinsed with CH$_3$CN and air-dried. Further experiments on the coated electrode were performed in fresh electrolyte. Surface coverages, Γ, were determined by graphical integration of the area encompassed by the voltammetric wave due to the electroactive material of interest.

General Procedure of the Electropolymerization (EP) Experiments. Electrodes were Teflon-shrouded platinum disks (Engelhard) of known area. Otherwise, the electrochemical instrumentation and materials are identical to those described in the chloride-loss section.

The concentration of electropolymerizable complex used in an experiment varied from approximately 1 to 3 mM. In general, the complex concentration was inversely related to the number of polymerizable groups. For three groups, [complex] $\approx$ 1 mM; for two groups, [complex] $\approx$ 1-2 mM; for one group, [complex] $\approx$ 2-3 mM.

Prior to the electrochemical experiment, solutions were degassed using a stream of CH$_3$CN-saturated nitrogen, then protected by an N$_2$ blanket. Solutions containing bis-bipyridine complexes were protected from light to prevent the facile photosubstitution reaction known for complexes of this type (17).

Potential limits for the EP process were chosen so that the cathodic limit of the cycle was ca. 150 mV negative of the $E_{\frac{1}{2}}$ for the reductive couple of interest. In cases where the anodic component of a couple is not well-defined, the cathodic limit was set at a potential sufficiently past $E_{p,c}$ (18) ($\sim$ 100 mV) so that the reduction process would not be inhibited. The anodic limit of the cycle was chosen to be at a convenient potential in the range -0.8 to -1.0 V. The number of cycles used in a particular polymerization depended upon the nature and concentration of the complex involved as well as the potential settings and therefore was determined separately for each reaction. The scan rate employed in all experiments was 200 mV/s, except as noted otherwise.

After completion of the EP procedure the working electrode was removed from the cell, rinsed with acetone and allowed to air-dry. The coated electrode was then examined in a solution of fresh TEAP/CH$_3$CN electrolyte.

Results and Discussion

<u>Reductive Chloride Ion Loss as a Preparative Technique for Electroactive Thin Films. Chloride Loss from Transition Metal Complexes Upon Reduction.</u> Recently we have investigated the electrochemistry of a number of mixed polypyridyl and phosphine osmium complexes that contain halides as ancillary ligands (5). Representative complexes span three different oxidation states of osmium, $Os^{IV}(bpy)Cl_4$, mer-$Os^{III}(PMe_2Ph)_3Cl_3$ and cis-$Os^{II}(bpy)_2Cl_2$ (bpy = 2,2'-bipyridine). In addition, the perhalo species $[Os^{IV}Cl_6]^{2-}$, also was found to undergo facile Cl^- ion loss upon reduction to Os(III). Figure 1 shows the cyclic voltammetry of three of these complexes in CH$_3$CN solution with 0.1 M TBAH as supporting electrolyte, all at a scan rate of 200 mV/sec. Under these conditions all complexes exhibit an ECE-coupled mechanism which is associated with the initial chemically irreversible osmium-localized reduction. For $[Os^{IV}Cl_6]^{2-}$, the Os^{III} complex produced in the first reductive step is the labile product. (eq. 1-3)

$$[Os^{IV}Cl_6]^{2-} + e^- \xrightarrow{E_{p,c}} [Os^{III}Cl_6]^{3-} \tag{1}$$

$$[Os^{III}Cl_6]^{3-} + CH_3CN \xrightarrow{fast} [Os^{III}(CH_3CN)Cl_5]^{2-} + Cl^- \tag{2}$$

$$[Os^{III}(CH_3CN)Cl_5]^{2-} \xrightleftharpoons{E_{\frac{1}{2}}} [Os^{IV}(CH_3CN)Cl_5]^- + e^- \tag{3}$$

For both $[Os^{III}(bpy)Cl_4]^-$ and $Os^{III}(PMe_2Ph)_3Cl_3$, reduction to Os^{II} results in rapid Cl^- ion loss. (eq. 4-6)

$$[Os^{III}(bpy)Cl_4]^- + e^- \longrightarrow [Os^{II}(bpy)Cl_4]^{2-} \tag{4}$$

$$[Os^{II}(bpy)Cl_4]^{2-} + CH_3CN \longrightarrow [Os^{II}(bpy)(CH_3CN)Cl_3]^- \tag{5}$$

$$[Os^{II}(bpy)(CH_3CN)Cl_3]^- \xrightleftharpoons{} [Os^{III}(bpy)(CH_3CN)Cl_3]^0 + e^- \tag{6}$$

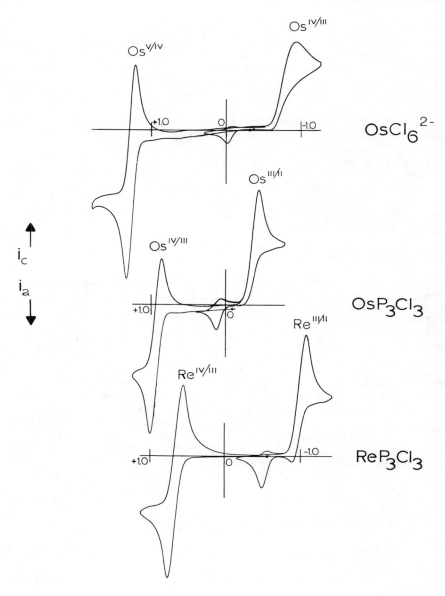

Figure 1. *Reductive Cl⁻ loss processes in Re(III), Os(IV), and Os(III) complexes in CH₃CN solution. Key: bottom, mer–Re(III)(Me₂PhP)₃Cl₃; middle, mer–Os(III)- (Me₂PhP)₃Cl₃; and top, [Os(IV)Cl₆]²⁻.*

Labeled couples are due to parent complex specified in figure. Middle couple is from product (acetonitrile) complex. A second product couple (not shown) occurs at potentials positive of the more oxidizing parent couple. Cyclic voltammograms were taken with 0.1 M TBAH as supporting electrolyte at a sweep rate of 200 mV/s.

The labilization of Cl^- upon reduction can be understood as a simple effect of putting electron density on the metal atom, thereby reducing the need for π-donation from the Cl^- ligands, which weakens the Os-Cl bond resulting in greater substitutional lability.

This effect is most dramatically illustrated in the case of $Os^{II}(bpy)_2Cl_2$ where labilization of Cl^- occurs not upon *metal* reduction but on the *second bpy* reduction. (eq. 7-11)

$$[Os^{II}(bpy)_2Cl_2]^0 + e^- \rightleftharpoons [Os^{II}(bpy)(b\bar{p}y)Cl_2]^- \qquad (7)$$

$$[Os^{II}(bpy)(b\bar{p}y)Cl_2]^- \longrightarrow [Os^{II}(b\bar{p}y)_2Cl_2]^{2-} \qquad (8)$$

$$[Os^{II}(b\bar{p}y)_2Cl_2]^{2-} + CH_3CN \longrightarrow [Os^{II}(b\bar{p}y)_2(CH_3CN)Cl]^- + Cl^- \qquad (9)$$

$$[Os^{II}(b\bar{p}y)_2(CH_3CN)Cl]^- \rightleftharpoons [Os^{II}(bpy)(b\bar{p}y)(CH_3CN)Cl]^0 + e^- \qquad (10)$$

$$[Os^{II}(bpy)(b\bar{p}y)(CH_3CN)Cl]^0 \rightleftharpoons [Os^{II}(bpy)_2(CH_3CN)Cl]^+ + e^- \qquad (11)$$

The ligand-reduced complex in eq. 8, $[Os^{II}(b\bar{p}y)_2Cl_2]^{2-}$, can be viewed as a formal analog of $[Os^{II}(bpy)Cl_4]^{2-}$, where both the Cl^- and bipyridine radical anion $(b\bar{p}y)$ strongly donate electron density to the metal center resulting in facile loss of the unidentate Cl^- ligand. This chloride ion loss chemistry appears to be reasonably general (5), further examples being $[Ru^{II}(trpy)-(PPh_3)_2Cl]^+$ (14), $Ru^{II}(bpy)_2Cl_2$ and $Re^{III}(PMe_2Ph)_3Cl_3$.

Formation of Surface Complexes from PVP Coated Electrodes by Reductive Cl^- Loss.

Preparation of thin, electroactive metallopolymer films on glassy carbon electrode surfaces was accomplished by performing the fast Cl^- loss process illustrated in equation 2, for example, at an electrode surface which had been previously modified with a coating of PVP. In a typical experiment a 5 mM solution of mer-Os(Me$_2$PhP)$_3$Cl$_3$ in CH_2Cl_2 with 0.1 M TBAH as supporting electrolyte was deoxygenated with an N_2 stream and then the PVP-coated electrode was used as the working electrode in a usual three electrode cyclic voltammetric configuration.

During multiple scans (ca. 10-50) into the Os^{III}/Os^{II} reduction the chloride ion loss and pyridine coordination reaction occurred as schematically illustrated in Figure 2. The re-oxidation of surface-bound osmium (eq. 12) proved to be a convenient method to monitor the amount of metal incorporation by the pyridine coordination sites.

$$Os^{II}(Me_2PhP)_3Cl_2N\bigcirc \rightleftharpoons [Os^{III}(Me_2PhP)_3Cl_2N\bigcirc]^+ + e^- \qquad (12)$$

Control of the rate of deposition could be achieved by scanning through only part of the reductive wave.

Table 1 compares $E°'$, $E_{\frac{1}{2}}$, and ΔE_p (18) values for several electrodes with the corresponding values for the non-polymer

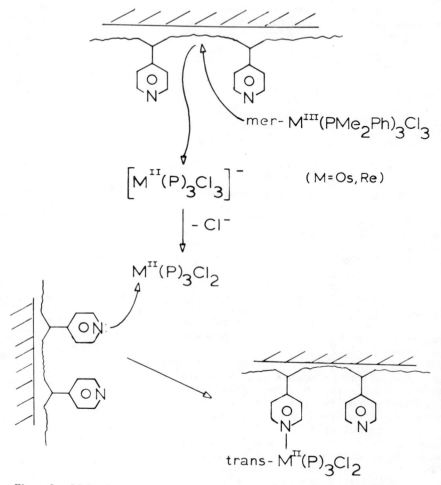

Figure 2. Molecular events in the preparation of trans-M(II)(Me₂PhP)₃(PVP)Cl₂-coated electrodes (M(II) = Re, Os) in CH₂Cl₂ solution with 0.1 M TBAH as supporting electrolyte.

Table 1. Surface and Solution Potentials of Re and Os Pyridine Complexes.

Complex or Electrode[a]	$E_{1/2}$ or $E^{\circ\prime}$ (V)	ΔE_p (mV)	Assignment and Comments
trans-$Os^{II}(Me_2PhP)_3(py)Cl_2$	+1.28	60	Os^{IV}/Os^{III} couple
	+0.01	60	Os^{III}/Os^{II} couple
trans-$Os^{II}(Me_2PhP)_3(PVP)Cl_2$	+1.30	20	Os^{IV}/Os^{III} couple
	+0.03	15	Os^{III}/Os^{II} couple
trans-$Re^{II}(Me_2PhP)_3(py)Cl_2$	+1.15	70	Re^{IV}/Re^{III} couple
	+0.61	60	Re^{III}/Re^{II} couple
trans-$Re^{II}(Me_2PhP)_3(PVP)Cl_2$	+1.17	20	Re^{IV}/Re^{III} couple
	-0.58	5	Re^{III}/Re^{II} couple
trans-$Re^{II}(Me_2PhP)_3(PVP)Cl_2$[b]	+1.32	50	Os^{IV}/Os^{III} couple
	+1.21	50	Re^{IV}/Re^{III} couple
trans-$Os^{II}(Me_2PhP)_3(PVP)Cl_2$[b]	+0.01	50	Os^{III}/Os^{II} couple
	-0.64	50	Re^{III}/Re^{II} couple

Table 1 continued on next page.

Table 1 continued.

Complex or Electrode[a]	$E_{1/2}$ or $E^{\circ'}$ (V)	ΔE_p (mV)	Assignment and Comments
mer-Os^{III}(Me$_2$PhP)$_3$Cl$_3$	+1.35	100	[trans-Os^{IV}(Me$_2$PhP)$_3$(CH$_3$CN)Cl$_2$]$^{2+}$ + e$^-$ $\rightleftharpoons$ [trans-Os^{III}(Me$_2$PhP)$_3$(CH$_3$CN)Cl$_2$]$^+$
	+0.94	70	[mer-Os^{IV}(Me$_2$PhP)$_3$Cl$_3$]$^+$ + e$^-$ $\rightleftharpoons$ mer-Os^{III}(Me$_2$PhP)$_3$Cl$_3$
	+0.13	60	[trans-Os^{III}(Me$_2$PhP)$_2$(CH$_3$CN)Cl$_2$]$^+$ $\rightleftharpoons$ trans-Os^{II}(Me$_2$PhP)$_3$(CH$_3$CN)Cl$_2$
	-0.38	---	irreversible reduction of Os^{III}(Me$_2$PhP)$_3$Cl$_3$
mer-Re^{III}(Me$_2$PhP)$_3$Cl$_3$	+1.00	120	same scheme as Os^{III} analog (see above)
	+0.64	60	
	-0.56	65	
	-0.96	---	

a) Potentials were measured vs. SSCE in 0.2M TBAH/CH$_2$Cl$_2$ or CH$_3$CN solution with 0.1M supporting electrolyte (TEAP or TBAH). Solution couples ($E_{1/2}$) were determined using a Pt disk electrode. Surface couples (E°') were measured as thin films mounted on glassy carbon disks. Sweep rate was 200 mV/s.

b) This material was one component of a bimetallic osmium/rhenium, surface-bound metallopolymer film.

analogs. The potentials for both the solution and surface-immobilized couples are very similar as has been observed by Murray et. al. for a wide variety of surface bound species [19].

Surface coverage values for trans-$Os^{II}(Me_2Ph\overline{P})_3(PVP)Cl_2$ varied from 10^{-9} to ca. 2×10^{-8} mol/cm^2 which, depending upon the PVP film thickness, indicated that up to 50% of the pyridine groups were metallated. This value is considered to be a lower limit since the pre-soaking technique (see experimental section) probably removes a fraction of the PVP coating from the surface.

Figure 3 shows the Os^{III}/Os^{II} surface couple at scan rates ranging from 1-500 mV/sec; the lower portion of the figure demonstrates the diffusional character of the surface couple at fast scan rates ($v \geq 50$ mV/sec) since a linear relationship between i_p and $v^{\frac{1}{2}}$ is observed. [20]

The origin of the diffusional response may arise from either: 1) an intrinsically slow rate of electron transfer between redox sites (self-exchange) or 2) fast electron transfer limited by the existence of a structural barrier due to incorporation of the sites into a polymeric film. The latter effect could be brought about in one of two ways: a) effective isolation of redox sites because of polymer network rigidity, or b) inability of the film to incorporate or expel a sufficient quantity of charge-compensating counterions during the redox process.

The first explanation is the least likely because in cases where comparisons have been made between homogeneous solution self-exchange data (k_{ex}) and charge transport rates (D_{CT}) for analogous complexes immobilized in redox polymer films ([1j], [1m]) it has been generally found that k_{ex} substantially exceeds D_{CT}, implying that electron exchange between redox sites is not the limiting factor in the overall rate at which charge is transported through the film. A crude calculation reveals that the redox site concentration in our films is in the molar region and Anson has shown ([1k]) that D_{CT} values in similar (although oppositely charged) metallopolymer films are unaffected even at redox site concentrations 100 times more dilute than those used here. These results argue against explanation 2a and, by default, point to 2b, restricted counterion diffusion, as the cause of the observed electrochemistry. However, Murray has determined the rate of diffusion of bromide ion through an electropolymerized metallopolymer film to be more than 10^3 times greater than D_{CT} ([1j]). Making the assumption that perchlorate (the counterion used in his and our experiments as well) has a similar mobility to Br^- he concludes that polymer lattice mobility (explanation 2a), not 2b, sets the upper limit for D_{CT}. With the knowledge of these two conflicting results we cannot, on the basis of our data, make an informed choice between explanation 2a and 2b but we can be reasonably certain that the diffusional response at faster sweep rates of our surface-bound polymer film has its origin in a structural barrier rather than an intrinsically slow electron transfer rate.

At slower sweep rates ($v \leq 20$ mV/s) i_p follows a linear

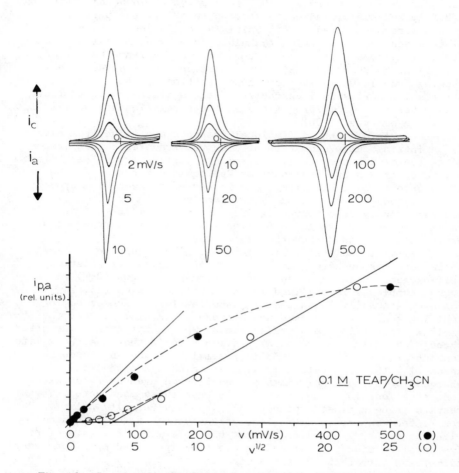

Figure 3. Scan rate dependence of the Os(III)/Os(II) surface couple for a typical Os(II)(Me₂PhP)(PVP)Cl₂ glassy carbon electrode (top) and iₚ versus v½ and iₚ versus v plots for the anodic wave of this couple (bottom). Cyclic voltammograms were recorded with 0.1 M TEAP as supporting electrolyte.

relationship with v which indicates that there are no longer kinetic limitations to the rate of charge transport through the polymer film.

We have also observed that there is a dramatic dependence of the electrochemical response on the *nature* of the electrolyte—in particular, the existence of a specific anion effect. Figure 4 shows the effect on the *same* polymer film of changing only the electrolyte anion from perchlorate to hexafluorophosphate. Not only is there a significant reduction in the size of both waves in the PF_6^- medium (note change in current sensitivity), but there is also a profound effect on the shapes of the waves. In particular, the extreme sharpness of the anodic Os^{III}/Os^{II} wave may be due, in part, to the phaselike behavior of crystalline elements in the film which form in the presence of PF_6^- as opposed to ClO_4^-. Similar behavior has been observed in the effect of electrolyte cations on the response of an anionic film of Prussian blue (1h) and also the effect of various solvents on a plasma-polymerized vinylferrocene film (1e).

Synthesis of Multimetallic Thin Films. The Cl^- loss technique can be extended to give films that have two or more metals and as many as five separate electrochemically metal-centered redox processes. An example of this is shown in Figure 5 where an $Os(Me_2PhP)_3(PVP)Cl_2$ film, prepared as previously described, was cycled in a solution of mer-$Re^{III}(Me_2PhP)_3Cl_3$. The resultant film has four redox processes corresponding to the M^{IV}/M^{III} and M^{III}/M^{II} couples. In 0.1 M TBAH/CH_3CN solution this film was reasonably stable on repeated cycling through the M^{III}/M^{II} couples, but ca. 10 cycles through the M^{IV}/M^{III} couples resulted in the characteristic cyclic voltammogram (Fig. 5B) of trans-$[Os^{II}(Me_2PhP)_3-(PVP)Cl_2]$, indicating that rapid solvation of $[Re^{IV}(Me_2PhP)_3(PVP)-Cl]^{2+}$ had occurred.

Under current investigation are the synthesis and properties of multimetallic thin films containing Ru^{II}, Os^{II}, and Re^{III} in a wide variety of coordination environments. Judicious choice of such materials may lead to creation of an electroactive polymer film which would exhibit a bandlike spectrum of reversible, metal-centered redox processes extending from ca. -0.6 to +1.5 V.

Electropolymerization of 4-Vinylpyridine Complexes. Investigations of Structural and Electronic Influences on Thin Film Formation. The recent discovery of the reductive polymerization of complexes containing vinylpyridyl ligands (1g), such as $Ru^{II}-(bpy)_2(vpy)_2^{2+}$, has led to the preparation of homogeneous thin layers of very stable electroactive polymers. This method has been extended to 4-vinyl-4'-methyl-2,2'-bipyridine (1g, 21a) and 4-vinyl-1,10-phenanthroline (21b) on both ruthenium and iron. In the following section we discuss our results on thin films derived from the polymerizable ligands BPE and the trans-4'-X-stilbazoles, (4'-X-stilb; X = Cl, OMe, CN and H).

In addition, we have prepared the first electropolymerizable

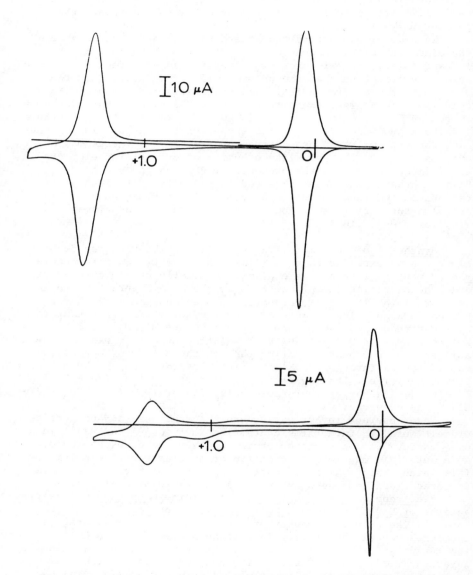

Figure 4. Changes in surface wave shape of the Os(IV)/Os(III) and Os(III)/ Os(II) surface couples for trans-Os(II)(Me₂PhP)₃(PVP)Cl₂ *as a function of support- ing electrolyte (anion), which was 0.1 M TEAP (top), and 0.1 M TEAH (bottom).*

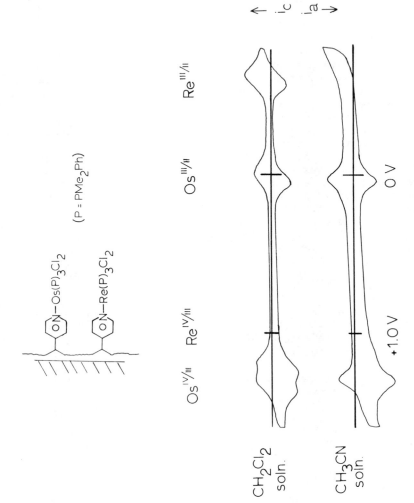

Figure 5. A bimetallic polymer film containing the trans-M(II)(Me₂PhP)₃(PVP)Cl₂ (M = Re, Os) complexes. Cyclic voltammograms were recorded in CH₂Cl₂ with 0.1 M TBAH as supporting electrolyte (top), and in CH₃CN with 0.1 M TBAH as supporting electrolyte after 10 scans through the M(IV)/M(III) couples (bottom).

Os^{II} complexes and several novel complexes of Ru^{II} which contain ancillary ligands other than pyridine or bipyridine, e.g., Ru-(trpy)(vpy)$_3$$^{2+}$ and Ru(HC(pz)$_3$)(vpy)$_3$$^{2+}$.

These rather extensive synthetic studies have allowed us to assess the following factors concerning the formation of transition metal films prepared by EP techniques:

1) The role of the direct ligand localized reduction of the vinyl-containing ligand in the polymerization process.

2) The effect of the number of vinyl-containing ligands upon surface coverage.

3) How surface coverage depends upon switching potential.

4) Apparent steric and adsorption effects on surface coverage.

In Table 2 is shown the surface coverages of all the electropolymerized complexes relative to Ru(bpy)$_2$(vpy)$_2$$^{2+}$. The experiments were conducted with solutions of complex varying in concentration from 1 to 3 m$\underline{M}$ and with the number of cycles ranging from 1 to 300. This data was then normalized with respect to the surface coverage obtained as a result of ten reductive cycles through the first reduction of Ru(bpy)$_2$(vpy)$_2$$^{2+}$. In this manner an approximate comparison of intrinsic polymerizability of the new complexes shown in Table 2 can be made.

<u>Direct Reduction of 4-Vinylpyridyl-Containing Ligands</u>. Comparison of the first scan cyclic voltammetry of the complexes Ru-(HC(pz)$_3$)(vpy)$_3$$^{2+}$, Ru(trpy)(vpy)$_3$$^{2+}$ and Ru(trpy)(py)$_3$$^{2+}$ shown in Fig. 6 reveals an irreversible reduction process located in the potential region -1.6 to -1.9V.

For Ru(trpy)(py)$_3$$^{2+}$ this process can be assigned to the pyridine localized reduction (E$_{p,c}$ = -1.96V) by analogy with that in Ru(py)$_6$$^{2+}$ (E$_{p,c}$ = -1.93V) (22). Both Ru(HC(pz)$_3$)(vpy)$_3$$^{2+}$ and Ru-(trpy)(vpy)$_3$$^{2+}$ show an irreversible reductive wave at potentials 400 and 200 mV more positive, respectively, which can reasonably be assigned to the direct reduction of coordinated 4-vinylpyridine. In the case of complexes such as Ru(bpy)$_2$(vpy)$_2$$^{2+}$ or Ru-(bpy)$_2$(stilb)$_2$$^{2+}$, however, the vinyl ligand reduction is intensely masked by a second bpy→bp$\bar{y}$ reduction process.

An indication that the intramolecular redox equilibrium between the first polypyridine reduction and the more negative vinyl ligand reduction is responsible for the radical initiation and subsequent film formation reaction of Ru(bpy)$_2$(vinyl-ligand)$_2$$^{2+}$ complexes is demonstrated in Figure 7. From the data for the various Ru(bpy)$_2$(4'-X-stilb)$_2$$^{2+}$ complexes in Table 2 it is seen that the first bipyridine reductions [E$_{\frac{1}{2}}$(red,1)] all occur at approximately the same potential (-1.22+0.03V). Thus, a disproportionation equilibrium will exist (eq. 13) which depends upon the reduction potential of the coordinated vinyl ligand.

$$2 \ [Ru^{II}(bpy)(b\bar{p}y)(vpy)_2]^+ \xrightleftharpoons{K_{dis}} [Ru^{II}(bpy)(b\bar{p}y)(vpy)(v\bar{p}y)]^0$$

$$+ \ [Ru^{II}(bpy)_2(vpy)_2]^{2+} \ (13)$$

Table 2. Solution potentials, Surface potentials and Normalized Surface Coverages for the Electropolymerized Complexes.

Complex[a]	$E(ox)$[b,c]	$E°'(ox)$[b,d]	$E(red,1)$[c,e]	$(\Gamma/\Gamma_o)_1$[g,h]	$E(red,2)$[c,f]	$(\Gamma/\Gamma_o)_2$[g,i]
$Ru(bpy)_2(vpy)_2{}^{2+}$	1.25	1.22	-1.36	1.0	-1.54	5.5
$Os(bpy)_2(vpy)_2{}^{2+}$	0.77	0.74	-1.33	3.5	-1.53	38
$Ru(phen)_2(vpy)_2{}^{2+}$	1.25	1.24	-1.37	0.4	-1.51	20
$Ru(trpy)(vpy)_3{}^{2+}$	1.23	1.22	-1.24	3.9-5.3	-1.76[j]	52-164
$Ru(trpy)(bpy)(vpy)^{2+}$	1.21	1.20	-1.26	0.02	-1.59	0.13
$Ru(HC(pz)_3)(vpy)_3{}^{2+}$	1.17	1.16	---[k]	--	-1.58[j]	2.4-220
$Ru(trpy)(bpy)(BPE)^{2+}$	1.21	1.20	-1.26	0.12	-1.58	0.10
$Ru(bpy)_2(BPE)_2{}^{2+}$	1.30	1.23	-1.35	0.40-0.58	-1.53	0.34-0.83
$Ru(trpy)(BPE)_3{}^{2+}$	1.26	1.27	-1.23	5.6-6.6	-1.51[j]	120-164
$Ru(bpy)(stilb)_2{}^{2+}$	1.23	1.22	-1.36	0.04	-1.54	2.6
$Ru(trpy)(stilb)_3{}^{2+}$	1.20	1.23	-1.25	0.004	-1.68[j]	17-45
$Ru(trpy)(bpy)(4'-Cl-stilb)^{2+}$	1.21	1.20	-1.35	0.005	-1.55	0.035
$Ru(bpy)_2(4'-Cl-stilb)_2{}^{2+}$	1.22	1.24	-1.38	0.24	-1.54	5.25
$Ru(trpy)(4'-Cl-stilb)_3{}^{2+}$	1.20	1.22	-1.25	0.03-0.06	-1.60[j]	125-269
$Ru(bpy)_2(4'-OMe-stilb)_2{}^{2+}$	1.19	1.25[m]	-1.39	0.007	-1.59	0.21-0.58
$Ru(bpy)_2(4'-CN-stilb)_2{}^{2+}$	1.25	1.23	-1.40	0.95	-1.64	0.32-0.37

Footnotes on next page.

Footnotes to Table 2.

[a] Electrolyte was 1.0M TEAP or TBAH in acetonitrile. All measurements are reported in volts.

[b] $M^{3+/2+}$ couple; metal oxidation

[c] Value for complex in solution

[d] Value for surface-bound complex

[e] First polypyridyl ligand reduction

[f] Second ligand-localized reduction

[g] Surface coverages of complex obtained, relative to that produced by cycling through the first reduction of $Ru(bpy)_2(vpy)_2^{2+}$. Normalized for concentration of complex in solution and number of scans.

[h] Cycled through first reduction only

[i] Cycled through both reductions

[j] Reduction irreversible; value of $E_{p,c}$

[k] No reductive couple in the -1.2 to -1.5 V region

[l] Irreversible oxidation of methoxystilbazole group at $E_{p,a} = +1.47V$

[m] Irreversible oxidation of methoxystilbazole group at $E_{p,a} = +1.57V$.

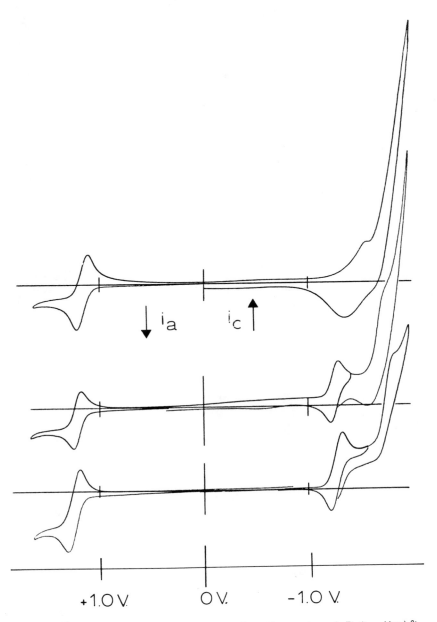

Figure 6. Comparison of the solution cyclic voltammetry of Ru(trpy)(py)$_3^{2+}$, Ru(trpy)(vpy)$_3^{2+}$, and Ru(HC(pz)$_3$)(vpy)$_3^{2+}$ showing the reductions assignable to the pyridine or vinylpyridine ligand. Cyclic voltammograms were recorded in CH$_3$CN solution with 0.1 M TEAP as supporting electrolyte at a scan rate of 200 mV/s.

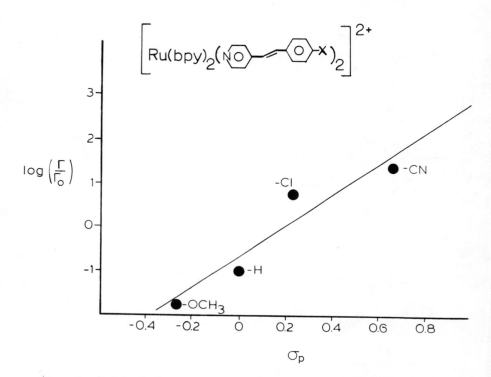

Figure 7. Relation between σ_p and the logarithm of normalized surface coverage for the complexes $Ru(bpy)_2(L)_2^{2+}$ (L = trans-4'-substituted-4-stilbazole). See Table 2.

The linear plot in Figure 7 of $\log(\frac{\Gamma}{\Gamma_0})$ (see Table 2, foot-
note g) and the Taft-Hammett (23) σ_p parameter for these complexes
Ru(bpy)$_2$(4'-X-stilb)$_2^{2+}$ arises because the increasing σ_p parameter
reflects the more anodic redox potential for the vinyl ligand,
which results in a greater concentration of initiator, a more
rapid polymerization reaction, and hence a greater amount of polymer deposition on the electrode surface. Such a correlation is
indeed remarkable because it implies a greater surface coverage
per unit time only if factors such as steric bulk, polymer conformation and rate of polymer precipitation remain relatively constant for the substituted <u>trans</u>-stilbazole series.

The Effect of the Number of Vinyl Groups Upon the Effective
Surface Coverage. It seems reasonable that statistical considerations such as the number of polymerizable groups and their relative disposition at the metal center can be directly related to
the surface coverage obtained if the EP experiment is performed
under a set of standardized conditions (see Table 2). This hypo-
thesis was tested with data on the series Ru(trpy)(bpy)(L)$^{2+}$, Ru-
(bpy)$_2$(L)$_2^{2+}$ and Ru(trpy)(L)$_3^{2+}$ shown in Table 2 and shown pictorially in Figure 8 (L = vpy, stilb and 4'-Cl-stilb). It is easily
seen that for both vpy and BPE there is a general trend of greater
surface coverage with increasing number of vinyl groups. 4'-Chlo-
rostilbazole, however, is anomalous in that it yields very low
surface coverages and even exhibits a decreased coverage when comparing polymers containing two and three polymerizable groups.
This probably cannot be accounted for on the basis of steric
effects, but may have its origin in greater solubility in the case
of the stilbazole as opposed to vpy or BPE-containing polymeric
metal complex chains, which results in much lower surface coverages.

The Effect of Switching Potential on Surface Coverage. We
have previously discussed thin film formation that results from
controlled initiation by selective reduction of the first polypyridyl reduction. The general scheme shown in equations 14-16 can
be proposed to account for the film-forming EP reactions.

$$[\text{Ru}^{II}(\text{bpy})_2(\text{vpy})_2]^{2+} + e^- \rightleftharpoons [\text{Ru}(\text{bpy})(\text{b}\bar{\text{p}}\text{y})(\text{vpy})_2]^+ \qquad (14)$$

$$2\ [\text{Ru}(\text{bpy})(\text{b}\bar{\text{p}}\text{y})(\text{vpy})_2]^+ \rightleftharpoons [\text{Ru}(\text{bpy})_2(\text{vpy})_2]^{2+}$$

$$+ [\text{Ru}(\text{bpy})(\text{b}\bar{\text{p}}\text{y})(\text{vpy})(\text{v}\bar{\text{p}}\text{y})]^0 \qquad (15)$$

$$[\text{Ru}(\text{bpy})(\text{b}\bar{\text{p}}\text{y})(\text{vpy})(\text{v}\bar{\text{p}}\text{y})]^0 + [\text{Ru}(\text{bpy})(\text{b}\bar{\text{p}}\text{y})(\text{vpy})_2]^+ \longrightarrow \text{dimer}$$

$$\longrightarrow \text{polymer} \qquad (16)$$

As has been noted previously (1g) and is also demonstrated by
the data in Table 2, setting the cathodic potential limit in the

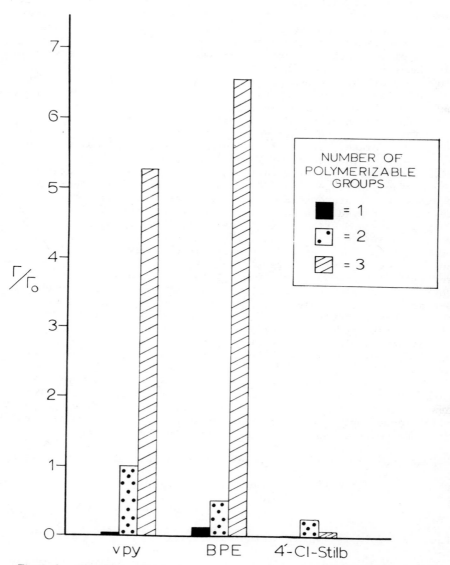

Figure 8. The relationship between normalized surface coverage and number of polymerizable groups for the Ru(bpy)$_2$(L)$_2^{2+}$ complexes (L = vpy, BPE, or 4'-Cl-stilb).

region of ca. −1.7 to −1.9 V which corresponds to the approximate potential of the coordinated vinyl ligand found, for example, in $Ru(trpy)(vpy)_3^{2+}$, results in dramatically greater surface coverages than when the negative limit of the potential cycle is constrained to traverse only the first polypyridine reduction.

Steric and Adsorption Effects on Surface Coverage. The data in Table 2 demonstrate, somewhat surprisingly, the lack of any significant inhibition of film formation due to greater steric bulk of the vinyl-containing ligand. For example, the surface coverages of $Ru(bpy)_2(vpy)_2^{2+}$ are similar to $Ru(bpy)_2(BPE)_2^{2+}$ even though the latter is obviously larger.

An interesting comparison is that of $Ru(phen)_2(vpy)_2^{2+}$ and $Ru(bpy)_2(vpy)_2^{2+}$, the former exhibiting surface coverages 4 times that of the latter complex upon cycling into the second polypyridine reduction (see Table 2). The major qualitative difference in the solution electrochemistry of the analogous monomeric complexes lies in the observation that the phen monomer, $Ru(phen)_2(py)_2^{2+}$ shows a sharp oxidative spike following the second polypyridyl reduction whereas the corresponding bpy complex, $Ru(bpy)_2(py)_2^{2+}$ does not exhibit a similar effect for the doubly-reduced, neutral complex (24). This observation strongly implicates an adsorption process which results in enhanced surface coverages of vinyl-ligand containing phen complexes relative to bpy.

Acknowledgements are made to the Army Research Office-Durham under Grant no. DAAG29-79-C-0044 for support of this research. The authors would also like to thank Dr. Royce W. Murray for his insightful comments and suggestions.

Literature Cited
1) A listing of key references in this rapidly expanding area is the following:
   a) Oyama, N.; Anson, F.C. Anal. Chem. 1980, 52, 1192–8.
      Oyama, N.; Anson, F.C. J. Am. Chem. Soc. 1979, 101, 3450–6.
   b) Kaufman, F.B.; Engler, E.M. Ibid. 1979, 101, 547–9.
      Kaufman, F.B.; Schroeder, A.H.; Engler, E.M.; Kramer, S.R.; Chambers, J.Q. Ibid. 1980, 102, 483–8.
   c) Kerr, J.B.; Miller, L.L.; Van de Mark, M.R. J. Am. Chem. Soc. 1980, 102, 3383–90.
   d) Merz, A.; Bard, A.J. Ibid. 1978, 100, 3222–3.
      Itaya, K.; Bard, A.J. Anal. Chem. 1978, 50, 1487–9.
   e) Daum, P.; Murray, R.W. J. Phys. Chem. 1981, 85, 389–96.
   f) Wrighton, M.S. Acc. Chem. Res. 1979, 12, 303–10.
   g) Abruña, H.D.; Denisevich, P.; Umaña, M.; Meyer, T.J.; Murray, R.W. J. Am. Chem. Soc. 1981, 103, 1–5.
   h) Ellis, D.; Neff, V.D. J. Phys. Chem. 1981, 85, 1225–31.
   i) Ellis, C.D.; Murphy, W.R.; Meyer, T.J. J. Am. Chem. Soc., in press.
   j) Ikeda, T.; Schmehl, R.; Denisevich, P.; Willman, K.; Murray, R.W. J. Am. Chem. Soc., submitted.
   k) Shigehara, K.; Oyama, N.; Anson, F.C. J. Am. Chem. Soc.

1981, 103, 2552-8.

l) Samuels, G.J.; Meyer, T.J. Ibid. 1981, 103, 307-12.

m) Shigehara, K.; Oyama, N.; Anson, F.C. Inorg. Chem. 1981, 20, 518-22.

2) Murray, R.W. Accts. Chem. Res. 1980, 13, 135-41.

3) Calvert, J.M.; Meyer, T.J. Inorg. Chem. 1981, 20, 27-33.

4) The term "bilayer" means two spatially segregated macromolecular layers. Examples of applications of single component and bilayer electrodes to interesting chemical processes can be found in the individual references found in ref. 1.

5) Sullivan, B.P.; Kober, E.M.; Caspar, J.V.; Calvert, J.M., unpublished results.

6) Calvert, J.M.; Sullivan, B.P.; Meyer, T.J., manuscript in preparation.
   Schmehl, R.H.; Murray, R.W. manuscript in preparation.

7) Sawyer, D.T.; Roberts, J.L. "Experimental Electrochemistry for Chemists"; Wiley-Interscience: New York, 1974, p. 212.

8) Wildes, Ph.D. Thesis, University of North Carolina, Chapel Hill, NC, 1970.

9) Chatt, J.; Leigh, G.J.; Mingos, D.M.P.; Paske, R.J. J. Chem. Soc.(A) 1968, 2636-41.

10) Douglas, P.G.; Shaw, B.L. Ibid. 1969, 1491-4.

11) Buckingham, D.A.; Dwyer, F.P.; Goodwin, H.A.; Sargeson, A.M. Aust. J. Chem. 1964, 17, 315-24.

12) Sullivan, B.P.; Salmon, D.J.; Meyer, T.J. Inorg. Chem. 1978, 17, 3334-41.

13) These complexes were prepared in an analogous manner to the bis-bipyridine complex described in ref. 12.

14) For preparation of this complex, see: Sullivan, B.P.; Calvert J.M.; Meyer, T.J. Inorg. Chem. 1980, 19, 1404-7.

15) This complex was prepared by an analogous reaction scheme to that used for mer-Ru(trpy)Cl$_3$ cited in ref. 14. A sample of the material was generously provided by Dr. M.S. Thompson.

16) Woodward, W.S.; Rocklin, R.D.; Murray, R.W. Chem. Biomed. Environ. Instrum. 1979, 9, 95-105.

17) Durham, B.; Walsh, J.L.; Carter, C.L.; Meyer, T.J. Inorg. Chem. 1980, 19, 860-5.

18) $E_{p,c}$ = cathodic peak potential; conversely, $E_{p,a}$ = anodic peak potential; $\Delta E_p = E_{p,a} - E_{p,c}$

19) Lenhard, J.R.; Rocklin, R.; Abruña, H.; Willman, K.; Kuo, K.; Nowak, R.; Murray, R.W. J. Am. Chem. Soc. 1978, 100, 5213-5.
    Abruña, H.D.; Meyer, T.J.; Murray. R.W. Inorg. Chem. 1979, 18, 3233-40.

20) Laviron, E.; J. Electroanal. Chem. 1980, 112, 1-10.
    Laviron, E.; Rouiller, L.; Degrand, C. Ibid. 1980, 112, 11-23

21) a) Ghosh, P.K.; Spiro, T.G. J. Am. Chem. Soc. 1980, 102, 5543-9
    b) Ghosh, P.K.; Spiro, T.G., manuscript in preparation.

22) For preparation and oxidative electrochemistry of this complex, see: Templeton, J.L. J. Am. Chem. Soc. 1979, 101, 4906-4917.

23) Lowry, T.H.; Richardson, K.S. "Mechanism and Theory in Organic Chemistry", Harper and Row: New York, 1976, p. 62.

24) The electrochemistry of the bipyridine complex has been reported in: Salmon, D.J., Ph.D. Thesis, University of North Carolina, Chapel Hill, NC, 1976. Data for the phenanthroline complex is from: Salmon, D.J., unpublished results. Cyclic voltammetry of the complex $Ru(phen)_3^{2+}$ has been described in: a) Kahl, J.K.; Hanck, K.W.; DeArmond, K. J. Phys. Chem. 1979, 83, 2611-5. b) Tokel-Takvoryan, N.E.; Hemingway, R.E.; Bard, A.J. J. Am. Chem. Soc. 1973, 95, 6582-9.

RECEIVED November 4, 1981.

Chemical Modification of TiO₂ Surfaces with Methylsilanes and Characterization by IR Absorption Spectroscopy

HARRY O. FINKLEA and R. VITHANAGE

Virginia Polytechnic Institute and State University, Chemistry Department, Blacksburg, VA 24061

Infrared absorption spectra have been obtained of methylsilanes bonded to a TiO$_2$ powder. The reacting silanes include Me$_{4-n}$SiX$_n$ (n=1-4; X=Cl, OMe) and hexamethyldisilazane (HMDS). Reactions were performed on hydroxylated-but-anhydrous TiO$_2$ surfaces in the gas phase. IR spectra confirm the presence of a bonded silane layer. Terminal surface OH groups are found to react more readily than bridging OH groups. By-products of the modification adsorb tenaciously to the surface. The various silanes show only small differences in their ability to sequester surface OH groups. Following hydrolysis in moist air, Si-OH groups are only observed for the tetrafunctional silanes.

We are investigating the effects of binding non-electroactive molecules to electrode surfaces. The attached layer will be sufficiently thin (ca. 1 monolayer) that electron transfer across the electrode/electrolyte interface will not be inhibited. However, other surface properties may be advantageously modified. For semiconductor electrodes, desirable changes include suppression of the photo-activated surface corrosion and shifts in the flatband potential. We are seeking to improve the performance of semiconductor liquid-junction solar cells by these means.

One highly successful form of surface modification is silanization (1) (equation 1). A silane containing a hydrolytically

$$\text{Ti}-\text{O-H} + \text{X}-\overset{|}{\underset{|}{\text{Si}}}- \longrightarrow \text{Ti}-\text{O}-\overset{|}{\underset{|}{\text{Si}}}- + \text{HX} \quad (1)$$

unstable bond will react with a surface O-H group to form a silyl ether bond to the substrate. Commercially available silanes offer a selection of leaving groups such as chlorides (X=Cl), alcohols (X=OR), and amines (X=NHR). They also provide the possibility of forming one-to-three bonds between the silicon atom and the surface. We have systematically investigated a series of methylsilanes which span the three leaving groups mentioned and one-to-four hydrolytically unstable bonds ($Me_{4-n}SiX_n$; n=1-4; X=Cl, OMe; and hexamethyldisilazane - HMDS). These silanes were used to modify a TiO_2 substrate.

Knowledge of the composition and coverage of the attached layer is vitally important to our investigations. Previous work on monolayers of silanes have employed x-ray photoelectron spectroscopy (XPS) as a probe (2-7). XPS confirms the presence of silicon after the reaction and also allows an estimation of the layer thickness. We have used an infrared spectroscopic technique (8, 9, 10) which provides complementary information on the nature of the surface layer.

Experimental

TiO_2 powder (Degussa P-25) was used in all experiments. It consists of anastase particles with a mean diameter of 0.03 microns and a surface area of approximately 50 m^2/g. The powder was heated in air to 500°C for several hours and then stored in moist air. Approximately 50 mg of powder was pressed into a translucent pellet using a 13 mm diameter die and a hydraulic laboratory press. The pellet was mounted in a vacuum IR cell (CaF_2 windows) which could be sealed, detached from the vacuum line, and inserted in the spectrometer. All spectra were recorded on a Perkin-Elmer 283B Infrared Spectrophotometer with a P-E computer data station.

Pellets were predried by heating to 150°C for 2 hours under vacuum (<1 micron). Silanization was performed by exposing the pellet to silane vapor for 1 hour and then pumping away the excess reactant. Silane vapor pressure was controlled by thermostatting the degassed liquid reagent. This procedure was designed to prevent polymer formation of the bound silane.

Silane reagents were purchased from Petrarch Systems, Inc., and distilled prior to use.

Results and Discussion

Figure 1A illustrates the characteristic spectrum of a clean, dry TiO_2 pellet. Bulk TiO_2 is effectively transparent from bandgap energies (3 eV; 24,400 cm^{-1}) down to 1200 cm^{-1}. Below 1200 cm^{-1} lattice vibrations absorb the photons strongly. The peaks above 1200 cm^{-1} originate from absorptions by surface species. Three sharp peaks at 3730, 3650, and 3420 cm^{-1} are assigned to isolated surface O-H groups. They reside on a broad

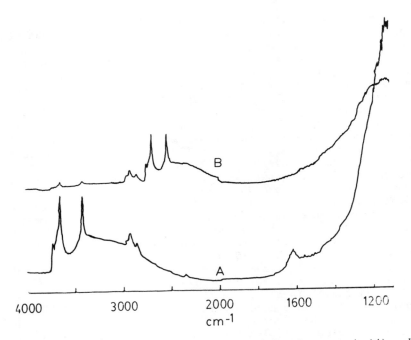

Figure 1.   Pellet # TI 67 after drying (150° for 2 h under vacuum) (A), and after exposure to D₂O vapor (6 torr) for 1 h at room temperature, followed by drying (B).

envelope of absorption caused by hydrogen bonding interactions
between surface O-H groups. We adopt the assignments of Griffiths
and Rochester (11); the bands at 3730 and 3650 cm^{-1} correspond to
terminal O-H groups, while the 3420 cm^{-1} band corresponds to a
bridging O-H group ((Ti)$_2$-OH). Absorptions due to residual hydrocarbons and molecular water appear at 3000-2800 cm^{-1} and 1620 cm^{-1}
respectively.

All surface O-H groups are accessible to gaseous reagents.
When the pellet of Figure 1A is exposed to D$_2$O vapor, Figure 1B
results. Surface O-H groups are quantitatively exchanged to O-D
groups. The exchange process is reversible.

When a TiO$_2$ substrate is exposed to a methylchlorosilane
(Figure 2), new peaks appear in the IR spectrum. The peaks at
2960 and 2910 cm^{-1} are assigned to C-H stretches of the methyl
groups on the silane; a C-H bend appears at 1410 cm^{-1}. An intense
Si-C stretching band is observed at 1260 cm^{-1}. These peaks confirm the presence of the methylsilane on the surface. The peak
positions match well the solution spectrum of the reagent silane.
We conclude that the silanization has proceeded as expected
(equation 1). Likewise, the O-H bond intensities are attenuated
as O-H is replaced with O-Si. A new peak appears at 3540 cm^{-1};
this peak is reproduced if a clean TiO$_2$ pellet is exposed to the
byproduct of the silanization, HCl. Based on its deuterium shift,
we postulate that this peak arises from a Ti-O-H moiety forming a
hydrogen-bond to adsorbed HCl. Increased hydrogen-bonding is
evident from the increase in the absorption envelope at 3700-2700
cm^{-1}. The molecular water peak disappears.

Reactions with methoxysilanes (Figure 3) and HMDS (Figure 4)
produce similar results to the chlorosilanes. The methoxy function, either as Ti-O-Me, Si-O-Me, or MeOH (see below), generates
bands at 2840 and 1450 cm^{-1}. Ammonia, the byproduct from HMDS,
produces new peaks at 3390, 3345, 3240, 3150, and 1600 cm^{-1}.

In all cases, IR spectra are consistent with the attachment
of a methylsilane in accordance to equation 1. Proof of chemical
bonding lies in the thermal stability of the modified surfaces;
prolonged heating (150°C) under vacuum causes little to no
decrease of the methyl C-H or Si-C bands.

In Figure 2B, the terminal O-H groups have disappeared quantitatively. It is tempting to conclude that all of the terminal
groups have bonded to silanes. Consequently, the bonded silane
layer must be homogeneous. However, several side reactions also
cause attenuation of O-H intensity (vide infra), and the conclusion is invalid.

A surprising aspect revealed by IR is the selective reactivity of the two different types of surface O-H groups. In all
cases, the loss of the terminal O-H bands greatly exceeds the loss
of the bridging O-H band. If we equate the loss in O-H intensity
with the formation of a silyl ether bond, then we must account for
the low reactivity of the bridging O-H group. We suggest that
reaction between the bridging O-H group and a silane is sterically

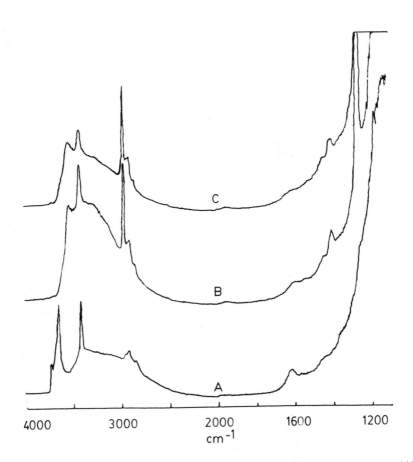

Figure 2.   Pellet # TI 34 after drying (A); after exposure to Me₂SiCl₂ vapor (41 torr) for 1 h at room temperature (B); and after heating to 150° for 2 h under vacuum (C).

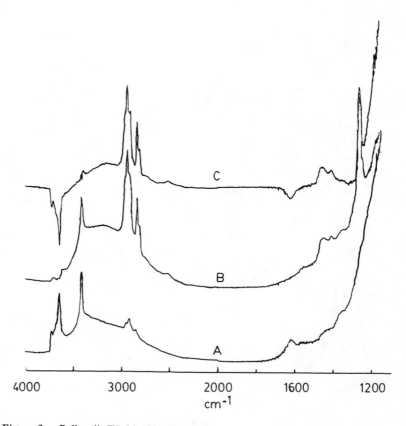

Figure 3.   *Pellet # TI 54 after drying (A); after exposure to MeSi(OMe)₃ vapor (7 torr) for 1 h at room temperature (B); and the difference spectrum B–A (C).*

hindered; a bridging O-H lies closer to a surface plane of titanium atoms (such as the 110 plane) than does a terminal O-H.

Byproduct adsorption and/or reaction is an ubiquitous feature in vapor phase silanizations. We include the possibility of reaction because of the following experiments. Exposure of clean pellet to byproducts (HCl, CH_3OH, or NH_3) generates the respective absorption bands cited above, but it also causes gross attenuation of the O-H bands. Such a result is consistent with equation 2:

$$Ti-\!\!\!\equiv\!\!\!-O\text{-}H + HX \longrightarrow Ti-\!\!\!\equiv\!\!\!-X + H_2O \qquad (2)$$

Following silanization, some byproduct molecules are merely adsorbed. Heating the pellet after a reaction at room temperature (Figure 2B and 2C), or heating the pellet during the course of the reaction (Figure 4B and 4C) reduces the intensity of the byproduct absorptions. Complete removal is difficult; only days of exposure to the atmosphere eliminates all byproduct absorption bands.

We would like to equate the attenuation of the sharp O-H peaks with the yield of the reaction i.e. what percentage of the surface O-H groups have formed silyl ether bonds? Several problems invalidate the comparison. Reaction with byproducts (equation 2) and de-hydroxylation (equation 3) are both side reactions

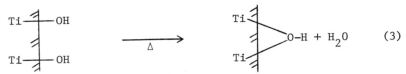

$$(3)$$

that decrease O-H absorption intensity. Also, an unknown amount of O-H absorption intensity is diffused through the broad envelope ascribed to hydrogen-bonding interactions. With these caveats in mind, we have measured terminal and bridging peak areas before and after silanization. The respective percentage losses in O-H peak areas are shown in Table I, along with the reaction conditions. Using these numbers as a guide to the coverage obtained by various silanes, we find surprisingly small differences. Chlorosilanes appear to be the most effective reagents; quantitative loss of the terminal O-H bonds is usually observed. Methoxysilanes are slightly less effective, with monomethoxysilane yielding the lowest coverage. HMDS exhibits good coverage despite its low vapor pressure. Neither increasing the temperature (room temperature to 150°C) nor doubling the vapor pressure produce significant increases in the coverage.

Polyfunctional silanes can form multiple bonds to the substrate; how many bonds they actually form is a question of interest. Previous work suggests that $-SiX_2$ and $-SiX_3$ silanes form on the average two bonds to the substrate (3, 5, 12). Thus, unreacted Si-X bonds should exist following silanization with a

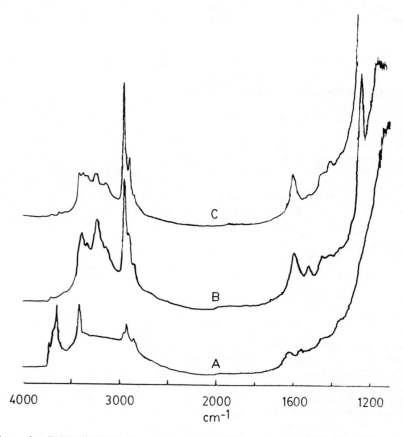

Figure 4. Pellet # TI 31 after drying (A); after exposure to HMDS vapor (1 torr) for 1 h at room temperature (B); and after drying, followed by exposure to HMDS vapor (6 torr) for 1 h at 150° (C).

Table I

Percentage Loss of Ti-O-H Intensity after Chemical Modification

Silane	(b.p.)[a]	Silane[a] Temperature	Silane[b] Vapor Pressure	Pellet[a] Temperature	Pellet Number	% Terminal[c] O-H Loss	% Bridging O-H Loss
Me₃SiCl	(58°)	0°	63	RT[d]	TI 24	100%	47%
		0°	63	RT	TI 26	100%	38%
		0°	63	150°	TI 27	100%	40%
		0°	63	150°	TI 30	100%	41%
		15°	143	150°	TI 66	100%	21%
Me₂SiCl₂	(71°)	0°	41	RT	TI 23	100%	7%
		0°	41	RT	TI 34	100%	2%
		0°	41	150°	TI 35	100%	44%
		15°	84	150°	TI 38	100%	61%
MeSiCl₃	(67°)	0°	54	RT	TI 44	100%	32%
		0°	54	150°	TI 45	100%	25%
		0°	54	150°	TI 68	100%	42%
		15°	101	150°	TI 46	100%	65%
SiCl₄	(52°)	0°	82	RT	TI 39	75%	2%
		0°	83	150°	TI 40	66%	1%
		15°	152	150°	TI 41	100%	100%
Me₃SiOMe	(58°)	0°	70	RT	TI 47	73%	0%
		0°	70	150°	TI 48	84%	0%
		15°	140	150°	TI 49	77%	0%
Me₂Si(OMe)₂	(82°)	0°	24	RT	TI 51	86%	31%
		0°	24	150°	TI 52	94%	3%
		15°	50	150°	TI 53	91%	34%

Table I continued on next page.

Table I continued.

Silane	(b.p.)[a]	Silane[a] Temperature	Silane[b] Vapor Pressure	Pellet[a] Temperature	Pellet Number	% Terminal[c] O-H Loss	% Bridging O-H Loss
MeSi(OMe)$_3$	(103°)	0°	7	RT	TI 54	83%	0%
		0°	7	150°	TI 55	95%	23%
		0°	7	150°	TI 69	100%	32%
		15°	16	150°	TI 54	96%	27%
Si(OMe)$_4$	(122°)	0°	1	RT	TI 59	100%	40%
		0°	1	150°	TI 58	98%	0%
		15°	6	150°	TI 57	100%	27%
HMDS	(127°)	0°	1	RT	TI 31	86%	e
		0°	1	150°	TI 32	96%	e
		15°	6	150°	TI 33	98%	e
HCl		--	85	RT	TI 62	62%	69%
		--	152	150°	TI 61	100%	100%
MeOH	(65°)	0°	36	RT	TI 50	68%	0%
		0°	75	150°	TI 60	81%	f
		15°	50	150°	TI 63	90%	f
NH$_3$		--	5	RT	TI 64	59%	e
		--	5	150°	TI 65	57%	e

(a) All temperatures in °C; (b) vapor pressures in torr; (c) peak areas above the absorption envelope due to hydrogen-bonding; (d) RT = room temperature, typically 20-25°C; (e) peak area not available due to strong overlap with a byproduct peak (NH$_3$); (f) peak area actually <u>increased slightly</u>. Reaction times were one hour.

trifunctional silane. Since the Si-X absorption is inaccessible
on TiO₂ substrates, the reacted pellets were exposed to water
vapor (humid air) to effect the hydrolysis of the Si-X bond. The
resulting Si-OH should appear at a sharp peak at 3740 cm⁻¹.
Mono-, di-, and trifunctional silanes do <u>not</u> produce any observ-
able silanol peak; only the tetrafunctional silanes yield the
anticipated peak (Figure 5). Since each pellet is dried at 150°C
under vacuum following exposure to moist air, silanols might con-
dense with adjacent O-H groups during the drying step. Consequently, we examined the pellets modified with trifunctional
silanes <u>before</u> the drying step (Figure 5C). Again no Si-O-H peaks
are observed. <u>We conclude that unreacted Si-X bonds are not
present after modification with MeSiX₃ or Me₂SiX₂, by our procedure.</u> By implication multiple bonds are formed between the
silicon and either the surface and/or adjacent silanes.

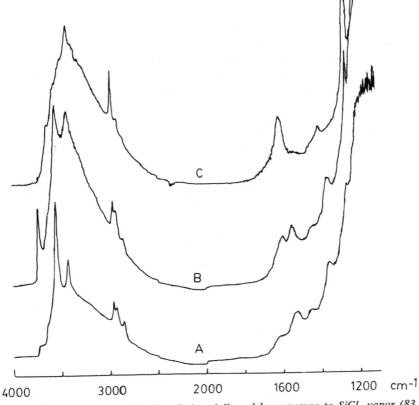

*Figure 5. Pellet # TI 40 after drying, followed by exposure to SiCl₄ vapor (83
torr) for 1 h at 150°(followed by heating to 150° for 2 h under vacuum (A); after
exposure to moist air for 3 h at room temperature, followed by drying (150° for
2 h under vacuum) (B); and after drying, followed by exposure to MeSiCl₃ vapor
(54 torr) for 1 h at 150°, followed by exposure to moist air for 2½ d at room temperature, followed by evacuation at room temperature for 2 h (C).*

An interesting question is whether these results are characteristic of vapor-phase silanizations or whether they extend to
liquid-phase reaction conditions. Silanizations are most commonly
performed in solutions. We are pursuing this question currently.

Acknowledgements

This work was supported by the NASA Langley Research Center
under grant # NAG-1-89.

Literature Cited

1. Murray, R. W. Acc. Chem. Res. 1980, 13, 135.
2. Untereker, D. F.; Lennox, J. C.; Wier, L. M.; Moses, P. R.;
    Murray, R. W. J. Electroanal. Chem. 1977, 81, 309.
3. Moses, P. R.; Wier, L.; Murray, R. W. Anal. Chem. 1975, 47,
    1882.
4. Elliott, C. M.; Murray, R. W. ibid. 1976, 48, 1247.
5. Moses, P. R.; Wier, L. M.; Lennox, T. C.; Finklea, H. O.;
    Lenhard, J. R.; Murray, R. W. ibid. 1978, 50, 576.
6. Finklea, H. O.; Murray, R. W. J. Phys. Chem. 1979, 83, 353.
7. Finklea, H. O.; Abruna, H.; Murray, R. W. "Interfacial
    Photoprocesses: Energy Conversion and Synthesis"; Adv. Chem.
    Ser. #184; Wrighton, M. S., Ed.; 1980; p 253.
8. Kiselev, A. V.; Lygin, V. I. "Infrared Spectra of Surface
    Compounds"; Wiley and Sons, New York, NY, 1975.
9. Hair, M. L. "Infrared Spectroscopy in Surface Chemistry";
    Marcel Dekker, New York, NY, 1967.
10. Little, L. H. "Infrared Spectra of Adsorbed Species";
    Academic Press, London, 1966.
11. Griffiths, D. M.; Rochester, C. H. J. C. S. Far. Trans. I.
    1977, 73, 1510.
12. Gilpin, R. K.; Burke, M. F. Anal. Chem. 1973, 45, 1383.

RECEIVED January 22, 1982.

Electrochemistry of Silane-Derivatized Iridium

C. A. LUNDGREN and C. E. RICE

Bell Laboratories, Holmdel, NJ 07733

The properties of silane-derivatized iridium and anodic iridium oxide (AIROF) electrodes have been studied by cyclic voltammetry in tetraethylammonium perchlorate/acetonitrile solutions. Both electrodes react with silanes such as dichlorosilylferrocene (DCSF) to give persistently bonded silylferrocene monolayers based on geometric area. This contrasts with the behavior of anodized platinum (Pt/PtO), which gives considerable polymerization with DCSF, resulting in layers of variable and unpredictable thickness. The electrochemical behavior of these three derivatized electrodes, and the information this provides about the nature of their oxide films are discussed.

In the course of our studies of electrochromic iridium oxide in nonaqueous electrolytes (1,2,3), we recognized that it has unique properties which might make it an interesting and useful electrode for the study of the electrochemistry of surface-bound molecules. This electronically conducting oxide can be grown anodically in films of accurately known thickness (4). It is a hydrous oxide, with ample acidic protons available for reaction with chloro- and alkoxysilanes. Yet it is quite electrochemically inert in nonaqueous electrolytes lacking small ions. In addition, we anticipated that the reaction of anodic iridium oxide with silanes might provide useful information about the surface chemistry of this unusual material, which is not only a good electrochromic but also an excellent electrocatalyst for oxygen evolution (5).

Subsequently we found that iridium reacts easily with silanes even without preanodization, giving persistent films of monolayer coverage with reproducible electrochemical properties (6). By contrast, the more widely studied Pt/PtO electrode requires a lengthy anodization pretreatment before derivatization, and gives films of variable and unpredictable coverage (7,8,9).

0097-6156/82/0192-0197 $6.00/0
© 1982 American Chemical Society

In a previous communication, we gave a detailed description of the electrochemical properties of silylferrocene on iridium (6). In this paper we briefly review this work, and compare derivatized iridium, Pt/PtO, and anodic iridium oxide electrodes. We show that the results of derivatization can give useful and sometimes unexpected information about the nature of the oxides on these electrodes.

Experimental

Dichlorosilylferrocene($FeC_{10}H_8SiCl_2$) (DCSF) was synthesized by a published procedure (10). Other silanes (as described below) were used as received from Petrarch Chemicals. The synthesis and derivatizations were performed in a dry box under a nitrogen atmosphere.

Electrodes were made of 0.25 mm. Pt and Ir sheet, and each had a total geometric area of 0.8 cm^2. Electrode cleaning procedures are detailed elsewhere (6). Pt was anodized on 0.5 M H_2SO_4 by potential cycling between the hydrogen and oxygen evolution potentials until the cyclic voltammogram was constant ($\approx$2–3 hours) and then held at +1.1 V versus SCE until the current decayed to a small value (11). Anodic iridium oxide film (AIROF) electrodes with thicknesses from 10 to 135 nm. were grown by potential cycling of Ir in 0.5 M H_2SO_4 from −0.25 to +1.25 V versus SCE (4); growth times for the thickest films were 10–15 minutes. The prepared Ir, Pt/PtO, and AIROF electrodes were kept under vacuum for several hours at room temperature to eliminate surface water. They were then reacted with 0.01 M silane solutions in toluene or ether for times varying from 1–27 hours at room temperature.

Cyclic voltammetric studies were performed using a three electrode cell consisting of the derivatized working electrode, a platinum counter electrode, and a Ag/Ag$^+$ nonaqueous reference electrode (+0.182+0.002 V versus SCE) (6). Tetraethylammonium perchlorate (TEAP) in acetonitrile was used as the electrolyte throughout. Care was taken for the strict exclusion of water and oxygen during solution preparation and electrochemical measurements.

Results and Discussion

The cyclic voltammograms of underivatized Ir and Pt/PtO electrodes in 0.2 M TEAP/acetonitrile are shown in Figure 1. A comparison of the two electrodes shows that Ir has a 200 mv. wider potential window between the points where electrolyte breakdown occurs, and 30 percent less residual (capacitive) current than Pt/PtO. The cyclic voltammogram of an underivatized AIROF electrode is shown in Figure 2. It differs from "clean" iridium in having a slightly smaller potential window and considerably greater (and thickness dependent) capacitive current (for example, a 125 nm. film had approximately six times more residual current than bare Ir).

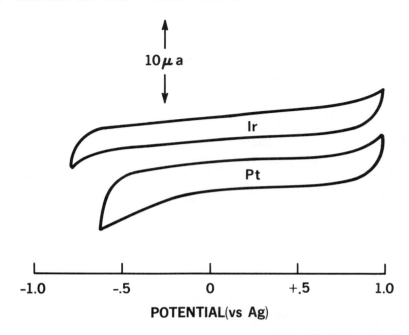

Figure 1.   Comparison of residual current for underivatized Pt/PtO and Ir electrodes having the same area. Scan speed 0.05 V/s.

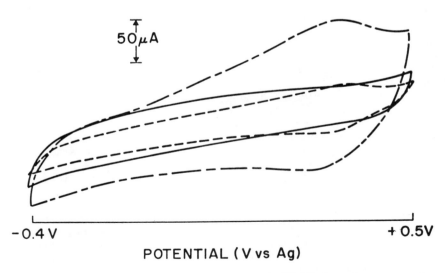

Figure 2.   Cyclic voltammograms of underivatized AIROF electrode, scan speed 0.05 V/s (solid line); silylferrocene-derivatized AIROF, scan speeds 0.05 V/s (– – –) and 0.2 V/s (—— — ——). AIROF thickness 120 nm.

Halo- and alkoxysilanes react with acidic protons on oxide surfaces according to reaction (1),

$$R_3SiX + \sigma\text{-OH} \rightarrow HX + \sigma\text{-O-SiR}_3 \qquad (1)$$

where X is a halide or alkoxide and σ represents the oxide surface. Silanes with a single X group can only form monolayer films of surface-bound molecules, while silanes with two or three Xs can polymerize to form thicker films if water is present in the reaction solution or within the oxide itself.

Both Ir and anodized Pt (Pt/PtO) are reactive toward silanes. However, the extent of reaction is different in the two cases in ways that give information about the nature of the oxide films on these electrodes. For example, at reaction times greater than about four hours, iridium always reacts with the same amount of dichlorosilylferrocene. Integration of the ferrocene-fericinium redox wave in the cyclic voltammogram (Figure 3) gives a coverage approximately what one would expect for a closely packed monolayer ($5-7\times10^{-10}$mol/cm^2 geometric area). This must mean that the native oxide on Ir is rather "dry", with a uniformly hydroxylated surface. By contrast, Pt/PtO always gives greater than monolayer coverage when reacted with DCSF (see Figure 3), and this coverage varies rather unpredictably from electrode to electrode. Reported coverage ranged from $4-280\times10^{-10}$mol/cm^2 (10). Thus, the anodic oxide on platinum must contain adsorbed water; it is also plain that the amount of oxide formed by the anodization process is not very reproducible. Many electrochemical parameters (such as E_0 of the ferrocene-fericinium couple which ranged from +0.47 to +0.55 V versus SCE for E_{oxid} (8)), the width at half height of the redox peak, ΔE_p (the difference between anodic and cathodic peak potentials, which ranged from 30 to 80 mv. (8)) of silylferrocene-derivatized Pt/PtO also show a fair amount of variability, again, we think, due to variations in oxide thickness and water content. While the electrochemical properties of silylferrocene on iridium deviate from those expected for an ideal surface-attached electroactive species (E_{oxid} ranged from +0.329 to +0.353 V versus Ag/Ag$^+$; ΔE_p ranged from 48 to 87 mv. (6)), they are somewhat more reproducible than those of Pt/PtO.

In general, however, the two derivatized electrodes are quite similar. E_0 values are comparable, coverage is persistent, and the redox process is reversible (equal anodic and cathodic integrated charge) in both cases (6).

Before discussing derivatization of anodic iridium oxide films (AIROFs), we will briefly review what is known about this material. The AIROF has been extensively studied as an electrochromic and electrocatalyst (1-5), however its exact composition and structure are still not known. It is amorphous, low density film which can be formed on Ir by potential cycling in aqueous acids. It exists in two oxidation states: a reduced, colorless form containing Ir^{3+} and an oxidized, blue-black form containing

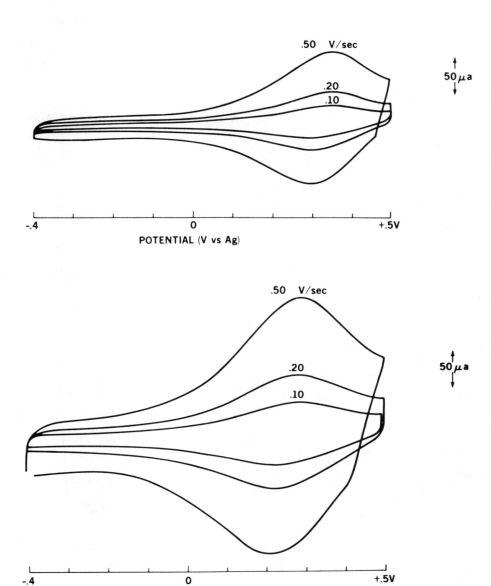

Figure 3. Cyclic voltammograms of silylferrocene-derivatized Ir (monolayer coverage) (top); and derivatized Pt/PtO (greater than monolayer coverage) (bottom).

Ir^{4+} (all our derivatizations were carried out on the oxidized form, which is air-stable). It is understood to contain large quantities of water and to be very porous, with a large surface area (13,14).

Since the AIROF is known to contain water, even after vacuum drying, we expected it to give extensive polymerization when treated with highly reactive DCSF. We hoped that the degree of polymerization could be controlled by regulating the AIROF thickness. We were quite surprised to find no evidence of polymerization in the reaction of DCSF with AIROFs, regardless of oxide thickness, especially since the much thinner, vacuum-dried Pt/PtO did polymerize this silane.

Calculation of the silylferrocene coverage on AIROF electrodes was complicated by the fact that the silane caused a reduction in the capacitive contribution to the current in the cyclic voltammogram (Figure 2). Thus, coverage could not be computed by simply taking the difference in integrated charge between derivatized and underivatized AIROF voltammograms; in fact, sometimes this gave a negative answer. This current reduction was not due to any change in the nature of the AIROF, but rather was caused by a simple reduction of capacitance by the interposition of an insulating layer between electrode and electrolyte. The capacitive current of derivatized AIROFs was still greater than that of derivatized iridium, and increased with increasing on oxide thickness. We assumed that only the amount of capacitive current, not the shape of the non-Faradaic volammogram, was affected by the presence of the insulating silane. (These assumptions will be justified in the discussion of the behavior of insulating silane films, below.) By making these corrections we found the silylferrocene coverage on AIROFs to be slightly greater on average than that seen on iridium and with more variation from electrode to electrode ($5-15 \times 10^{-10}$ mol/cm^2 geometric area). However, this coverage was not dependent on oxide thickness or reaction time. We feel these values still correspond to monolayer coverage, with the variation being due to small differences in surface area. This coverage is quite small when compared with the observation of up to 60 molecular layers in the reaction of Pt/PtO with DCSF (10).

Two rather surprising conclusions can be drawn from these results: first, that the water in the AIROF must be very strongly bound if it does not react with highly reactive chlorosilanes; second, that the AIROF may not be very porous at all. Some previous studies suggested that this oxide has a rather open structure consisting of both macro ($\approx 25 \mu$m) and micro (a few Å) pores, providing the interior of the film with access to the electrolyte (13,14). These low silane coverage values imply that the AIROF may actually have a relatively smooth surface (no evidence of macropores).

Other than the higher background current, we found the electrochemistry of silylferrocene on anodic iridium oxide to be similar in most respects to its behavior on "clean" iridium. However, some interesting trends in electrochemical parameters were noticed. ΔE_p decreased as the oxide thickness increased; the ratio of peak redox currents i_{pa}/i_{pc} changed from 1.14 for iridium to 1.01 for a 135 nm. AIROF. In both cases the parameters tend toward more ideal values (ΔE_p of zero, i_{pa}/i_{pc} of 1.0) (15) as oxide thickness increases. The reason for this more ideal behavior as the electroactive molecules are moved farther from the iridium metal surface is not clear to us.

We were somewhat surprised by the magnitude of the capacitive current suppression caused by a silylferrocene monolayer on the AIROF (as much as 50 percent). No other study of silane-derivatized electrodes has reported a similar decrease in capacitive current. In order to determine whether this decrease could be attributed to insulation by the silane, rather than some change in the AIROF, we investigated the effects of derivatization with a variety of nonelectroactive silanes on the cyclic voltammogram of iridium in TEAP/acetonitrile. For this study we chose silanes with from one to three X groups, with X = Cl or OEt, and with R groups of different sizes and chemical properties. We found that all silanes reduced the capacitive current, with the decrease dependent on the bulkiness of the R groups (thus the thickness of the insulating layer) and not on any other factors. The shape of the cyclic voltammogram was not affected by silanization. The decreases ranged from 30 percent for relatively small silanes such as isocyanatopropyltriethoxysilane, to 90 percent for the long chain triethoxysilylpropyldiethylenetriamine. Thus, the 50 percent capacitive current reduction seen for silylferrocene on AIROF electrodes is not unreasonable.

Conclusions

A comparison of iridium, anodized platinum (Pt/PtO), and anodized iridium (AIROF) as derivatizable electrodes shows iridium to be the most useful for the study of surface-bound molecules. It requires minimal surface preparation, and has the most favorable electrochemical properties. Iridium and the AIROF are unique among derivatizable electrodes yet reported in that they give no more than monolayer coverage when reacted with chloro- or alkoxysilanes. The reaction of silanes with AIROF electrodes gives interesting insights into the nature of this oxide, however, the large capacitive background current of this electrode makes it unsuitable for general use in derivatization studies. We show that the insulating properties of silane layers may need to be considered in computing the coverage on modified electrodes.

Literature Cited

1. Rice, C. E. Appl. Phys. Lett., 1979, 35, 563.
2. Rice, C. E., in Proceedings, Intl. Conf. on Fast Ion
    Transport in Solids, (North-Holland, Amsterdam, 1979),
    p. 103.
3. Beni, G.; Rice, C. E.; Shay, J. L. J. Electrochem.
    Soc., 1980, 127, 1342.
4. Gottesfeld, S.; McIntyre, J. D. E.; Beni, G.; Shay, J.
    L. Appl. Phys. Lett., 1978, 33, 208.
5. Gottesfeld, S.; Srinivasan, S. J. Electroanal. Chem.,
    1978, 86, 89.
6. Lundgren, C. A.; Rice, C. E., to be published.
7. Wrighton, M. S.; Austin, R. G.; Bocarsly, A. B.;
    Bolts, J. M.; Haas, O.; Legg, K. D.; Nadjo, L.;
    Palazzotto, M. C. J. Electroanal. Chem., 1978, 87
    429.
8. Wrighton, M. S.; Palazotto, M. C.; Bocarsly, A. B.;
    Bolts, J. M.; Fisher, A. B.; Nadjo, L. J. Am. Chem.
    Soc., 1978, 100, 7264.
9. Lenhard, J. R.; Murray, R. W. J. Am. Chem. Soc.,
    1978, 100, 7870.
10. Fisher, A. B.; Wrighton, M. S.; Umana, M.; Murray,
    R. W. J. Am. Chem. Soc., 1979, 101, 3442.
11. Angerstein-Kozlowska, H.; Conway, B.; Sharp, W. B.,
    Jr. J. Electroanal. Chem., 1973, 43, 9.
12. Sawyer, D. T.; Roberts, J. L., Jr. "Experimental
    Electrochemistry for Chemists;" John Wiley and Sons:
    N. Y., 1974: p. 55.
13. McIntyre, J. D. E.; Peck, W. F.; Nakahara, S. J.
    Electrochem. Soc., 1980, 127, 1264.
14. Michell, D.; Rand, D. A. J.; Woods, R. J.
    Electroanal. Chem., 1977, 84, 117.
15. Bard, A. J.; Faulkner, L. R. "Electrochemical
    Methods;" J. Wiley and Sons: N. Y.: 1980.

RECEIVED January 29, 1982.

Improvements in Photoelectrochemical and Electrochromic Reactions at Chemically Modified Electrodes

N. R. ARMSTRONG, T. MEZZA, C. L. LINKOUS, B. THACKER, T. KLOFTA, and R. CIESLINSKI

University of Arizona, Department of Chemistry, Tucson, AZ 85721

Chemical and physical modification of semiconductor, metal and metal oxide electrodes has been carried out for the purpose of improvement of the visible light response of these surfaces, or for the enhancement of the kinetics of the deposition of the n-heptyl viologen cation radical. Phthalocyanine aggregates have been sublimed to the surfaces of either SnO_2 or gold metallized-plastic film electrodes and reactions observed which correspond to either photosensitization and energy conversion and/or photoelectrocatalysis -- both with unusually high quantum efficiencies of 2-9%. Metal oxide electrodes can be chemically or ion-beam modified to enhance the rate of nucleation of the n-heptyl viologen cation radical ($n-HV^{++} + e^- \rightleftarrows n-HV^{+\cdot}$). The $n-HV^{++}$ reduction follows an instantaneous nucleation mechanism and the nucleation site density, N_o, can be increased through the addition of a silane layer to the surface, or after the bombardment with 1-10 molecular layers of 0.5-1.5 KeV, argon ions.

As shown in this symposium, interest in chemical modification of electrode surfaces has been extended in many directions, including the study of light-assisted redox reactions, and the use of modified electrodes in electrochromic devices (1,2). Our own studies have centered on the study of metal and metal oxide electrodes modified with very thin films of phthalocyanines (PC) and on the electrochromic reaction of n-heptyl viologen on metal oxide electrodes, and on the effect on these reactions of changing substrate chemical and physical composition (4,5).

In the case of the photoelectrochemical reactions, dye-modified electrodes may participate in two types of photon-stimulated reaction: a) photosensitization of the semiconductor substrate (leading to energy conversion) and b) a photoassisted catalytic response (leading simply to an enhanced reaction rate

0097-6156/82/0192-0205 $6.00/0

(3). The rate of charge transfer at the PC-electrolyte interface and the rate of charge transfer at the substrate-PC interface are both photocurrent-determining processes.

In the case of the n-heptyl viologen deposition, nucleation
rates of the first molecular layers of this molecule control the
deposition rates of subsequent layers. The nucleation reaction
follows the instantaneous nucleation model -- and is found to
be highly sensitive to the chemical and physical nature of the
electrode surface prior to deposition. RF-plasma of ion-beam
etched surfaces generally show greatly enhanced nucleation and
bulk deposition rates.

Light-Assisted Electrochemical Reactions at Phthalocyanine
Modified Surfaces.

If solar energy conversion devices are the objective, in
the use of photoactive electrodes, three basic requirements must
be met:

a) The electrode must be receptive, and show its maximum
efficiency, to light in the red-visible and near-
infrared regions of the spectrum, since most solar
energy is concentrated in this region.

b) The power conversion efficiency of solar photons to
electrochemical energy must be high (in excess of 10%
is desirable). This condition requires that the electrode material be optically opaque, the electron-hole
pair recombination events be minimized in the solid,
and that the conduction and valence band edges of
the electrode be favorably placed with respect to both
the oxidation and reduction reaction e.m.f. of solution
species so as to promote rapid rates of electron transfer.

c) The electrode must be stable to the photoelectrochemical process.

Unfortunately, many of the semiconductor materials which
would satisfy requirement (a) and (b) are not stable and undergo
light-assisted corrosion instead of driving the desired redox
reaction. Several important methods have been devised to
chemically protect the surfaces of such materials as Si, CdS or
CdSe, and the GaAs with the result however that the redox reactions that can be light-assisted are dictated by the redox e.m.f.
of the surface-attached species (6).

Modification of semiconductor electrode response with adsorbed or attached dye molecules is an attractive alternative to
other photoelectrochemical systems (7-13). Metal oxides which
are stable or have very low corrosion rates but are transparent
to visible wavelength light can be used in light-assisted electrochemical reactions when modified with monolayers and multilayers of a wide variety of chromophores interposed between the
electrode and electrolyte. With one exception, the initial reports of energy conversion efficiencies of electrodes with
adsorbed dyes was disappointingly low. Recently however,

Tsubomura and coworkers have reported on high-surface area, ZnO electrodes with adsorbed rose bengal, which show an energy (power) conversion efficiency of 2.5% (14).

Research in our laboratory and by Osa and Fujihira showed that it is possible to covalently attach monolayers of chromophores to metal-oxide semiconductor surfaces -- with no compromise in quantum efficiency to energy conversion compared with dyes adsorbed from solution (9-11). The quantum efficiency for these systems (ratio of photo-generated current to photons adsorbed in the dye layer, n_e/n_p) is quite low, in the range of 10^{-5} to 10^{-4} and argues against device applications of these simple modified electrodes without further improvements, such as linear, multielectrode stacks of dye-modified, semi-transparent electrodes (10).

An electrode covered with several molecular layers of dye could be made to adsorb all of the visible light, and obviate the need for the multielectrode stack. Very thick dye layers have tended not to be conductive or highly photoconductive so that their photoelectrochemical efficiencies are no better and perhaps worse than those seen on electrodes modified with very thin dye films. Molecular disorder of the dye appears to be the dominant reason for lack of conductivity in thick films of fluorescein-type, cyanine-type, and phthalocyanine-type dyes (12). It has been shown however that ordered molecular systems (mainly conjugated, highly unsaturated hydrocarbons) have considerable potential as conductive media, and that these ordered systems may be used to chemically modify electrode surfaces (12, 15).

Our attention has been directed to modifying SnO_2 electrodes and later, metal electrodes with very thin films (10-100 molecular layers) of phthalocyanines which appear to aggregate when sublimed. The oriented phthalocyanine phase or phases sensitize the response of the SnO_2 electrodes with efficiencies many times greater than monomolecular layers of covalently attached chromophores or randomly oriented multilayer dye films (9). Our initial studies have been conducted with phthalocyanines which we expected would orient in a linear "pancake-stack," by virtue of the interaction between the central metal atoms -- either a covalent bond or a strong electrostatic interaction. The synthesis, by Professor Malcolm Kenny at Case Western Reserve University, of a series of silicon phthalocyanine polymers (SiPc) (aggregates of the monomer of this series, m-SiPc, are discussed here) and of a series of aluminum and gallium, fluoro and chloro phthalocyanines (AlPc-Cl, GaPc-Cl, AlPc-Cl, GaPc-F) allowed us to study several oriented systems (16). Some concepts of orientation possible with <u>all</u> Pc films are shown in Figure 1. We now understand that these types of chromophore orientations are only some of several which are present on our electrode surfaces and which may lead to increased photoelectrochemical efficiencies. Those phthalocyanines

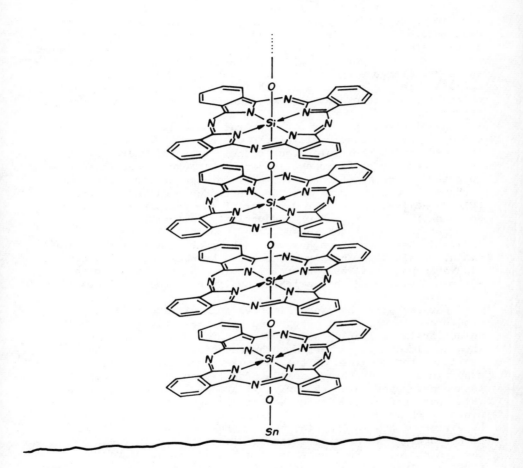

Figure 1a.   Silicon phthalocyanine polymer shown attached to SnO₂ surface.

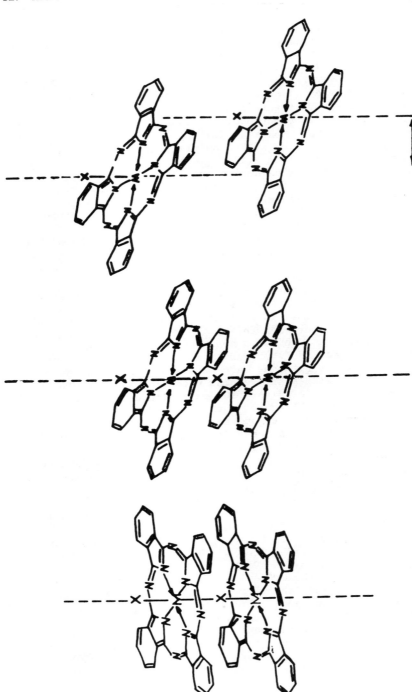

Figure 1b. Metal phthalocyanine polymorphs obtainable in thin sublimed layers.

which lead to high photoelectrochemical efficiencies share the ability to form aggregates on the electrode surface which leads to a visible spectrum which is broadened and red-shifted from that of the monomeric form (9).

Figure 2 shows the dark versus illuminated current/voltage response of two types of phthalocyanine-modified SnO_2 (m-SiPc-SnO_2 and GaPc-Cl-SnO_2) electrodes, and the current/voltage response of a platinum electrode, all in a pH = 4, 10^{-3} M hydroquinone (H_2Q) solution. Several features of these curves deserve discussion. The oxidation of H_2Q on platinum is kinetically slow in pH = 4 aqueous media (17). On the illuminated Pc-SnO_2 electrodes, however, the oxidation process is considerably enhanced, the onset potential for the oxidation process is actually negative of the potential observed on the Pt electrode. A closed-cycle photovoltaic cell is possible using a Pt cathode ($Q + 2e^- + 2H^+ \rightleftarrows H_2Q$) and an illuminated Pc-$SnO_2$ electrode ($H_2Q \rightleftarrows Q + 2H^+ + 2e^-$). Preliminary experiments have shown that an open circuit photovoltage, $V_{o.c.} = -0.20$ volts vs. Pt is obtained using the SiPc-SnO_2 electrode system under the conditions described in Figure 2.

The shape of the photocurrent/voltage curves on the Pc-SnO_2 electrodes suggests some strong similarities and differences between the two systems. In both cases, the photoelectrochemical efficiency (n_e/n_p) increases sharply in the potential range near +0.2 volts vs. Ag/AgCl which is near the E^o for the quinone/hydroquinone redox couple (18). The maximum quantum efficiency increases up to 2% for both the GaPc-Cl and SiPc modified electrodes with increasing positive bias potential (9). The photoassisted reaction is definitely the oxidation of hydroquinone, and does not irreversibly consume the phthalocyanine on the electrode surface. As with many semiconductor photoelectrolysis reactions, the oxidation process is not mass transport controlled at bias potentials negative of +0.6 volts (where the dark current process begins). The raction rate on both electrodes is linearly controlled by photon flux up to 400-500 watts/cm^2 at which point, continuous-wave (cw) laser light or pulsed-dye laser light begins to saturate the dye, resulting in degradation of the dye layer. The difference between the two electrode materials is seen in that on the m-SiPc-SnO_2 electrodes only the oxidation of $H_2Q \rightarrow Q$ is enhanced, and on the GaPc-Cl-SnO_2 electrodes, both the oxidation and the reduction, $Q \rightarrow H_2Q$, show enhanced rates upon illumination.

This ability of the GaPc-Cl modified electrodes to photoenhance both the oxidation and reduction redox processes has been further explored using gold, metallized plastic films (Au-MPOTE, Sierracin Corporation) modified with 10-100 molecular layer thicknesses of this phthalocyanine. Figure 3 shows the light and dark i/V behavior of such an electrode modified with a non-porous film of GaPc-Cl. The dark i/V behavior of an unmodified gold electrode in the same solution is shown for comparison.

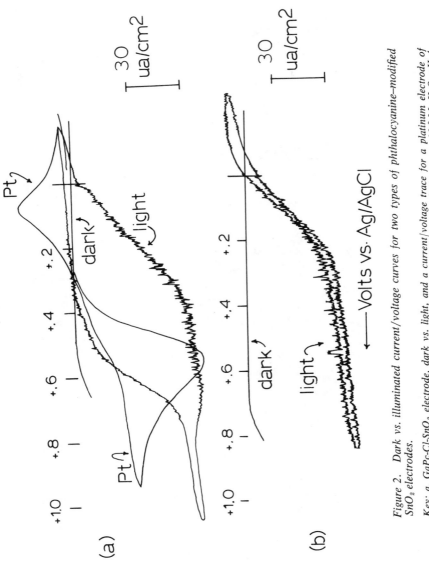

Figure 2. Dark vs. illuminated current/voltage curves for two types of phthalocyanine–modified SnO₂ electrodes.

Key: a, GaPc-Cl-SnO₂ electrode, dark vs. light, and a current/voltage trace for a platinum electrode of the same area; and b, SiPc-Cl-SnO₂ electrode, dark vs. light. All solutions were 10^{-3} M, H_2O, pH 4, illumination with polychromatic light (470–900 nm), ca. 100 mW/cm². Potential scan rates were 10 mV/s. Reproduced with permission from Journal of Electroanalytical Chemistry.

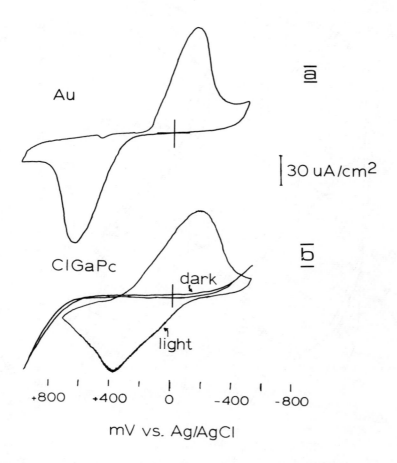

Au

ClGaPc

dark

light

|30 uA/cm2

+800   +400   0   -400   -800

mV vs. Ag/AgCl

Figure 3.   Dark vs. illuminated current/voltage curves for thin-layer voltammetry on plain and GaPc-Cl-modified Au-MPOTE's. Conditions as for Figure 2, except the potential scan was carried out at 2 mV/s.

Since these voltammograms were obtained in a thin layer electro-chemical cell, considerable displacement of the voltammetric peaks can be seen because of the uncompensatable solution resistance. It is nevertheless apparent that in the dark both the $H_2Q \to Q$ and the $Q \to H_2Q$ electrolysis are suppressed, while under illumination the rate of oxidation and reduction is enhanced over that observed on the plain gold substrate. In addition, the extent of this kinetic enhancement is controlled by the flux of photons delivered to the electrode surface! For this type of modified gold substrate, no apparent photopotential is observed for the quinone/hydroquinone couple.

We have previously shown that it is possible to form a gold oxide layer on the Au-MPOTE, using an O_2-RF plasma, and/or electrochemical oxidation (5). We undertook the study of GaPc-Cl modified Au-MPOTE's which had 1-5 molecular layers of oxide placed on their surfaces, prior to Pc-modification. The resultant i/V curves under illumination are similar to those in Figure 3, with the onset potential for oxidation pushed successively positive with increasing coverage of the non-conductive oxide layer. In contrast, when the RF-plasma is used in a substrate cleaning procedure, prior to Pc deposition, the photoelectrochemical efficiency is seen to increase. m-SiPc-modified SnO_2 electrodes as described in Figure 2 show photoelectrochemical quantum efficiencies which improve from ca. 1% to ca. 9% when the SnO_2 surface is cleaned in an O_2-RF plasma prior to Pc deposition. These experiments demonstrated the importance of good electrical communication between the Pc and the underlying substrate.

It is clear that some distinction needs to be made between the photoelectrochemical reactions on the Pc-modified semiconductor substrate, where true energy conversion may be observed -- and on the Pc-modified metal substrate where kinetic enhancement may be the dominant photoelectrochemical process. Figure 4 summarizes the energetics of photosensitization of an n-type semiconductor electrode by monolayer or thin multilayer coverages of a phthalocyanine such as m-SiPc. Dark equilibrium is obtained for both monolayer and a continuous multilayer film by equalizing of the a) Fermi potential of the semiconductor, b) the ground state E^0 of the dye (monolayer) or the Fermi potential of the p-type dye layer (multilayer) and c) the e.m.f. of the solution redox species. The energetics of the equilibrium case shown in Figure 3 are possible provided that the electrochemical potentials of the Fermi-level of the SnO_2 ($E_F(SnO_2)$), the Fermi-level of the phthalocyanine ($E_F(Pc)$) and the $E^0_{R/Ox}$ were arranged before contact according to: $E_F(SnO_2) < E_F(Pc) < E^0_{R/Ox}$. Irradiation of the modified electrode surface causes: 1): the monolayer dye to achieve an excited state with new redox levels capable of donating an electron to the conduction band of the semiconductor substrate or 2) the formation of electron/hole pairs in the phthalocyanine layer which separate and react at

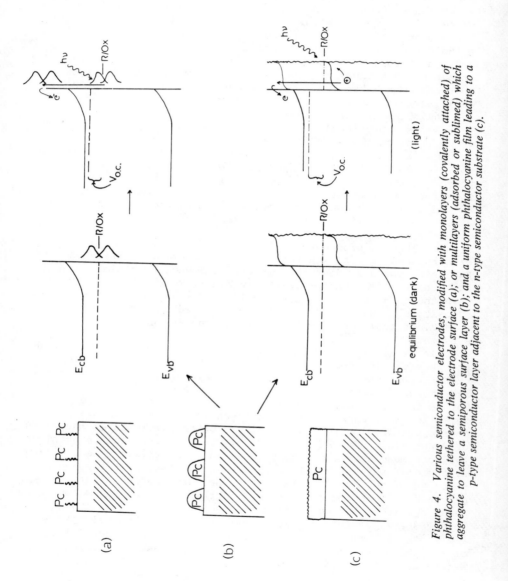

Figure 4. Various semiconductor electrodes, modified with monolayers (covalently attached) of phthalocyanine tethered to the electrode surface (a); or multilayers (adsorbed or sublimed) which aggregate to leave a semiporous surface layer (b); and a uniform phthalocyanine film leading to a p-type semiconductor layer adjacent to the n-type semiconductor substrate (c).

the semiconductor/Pc interface and the Pc/solution interface respectively. The change in population of charge carriers causes a shift in the Fermi level of the semiconductor and the formation of an open circuit photo-potential, $V_{o.c.}$ The semiconductor substrate has been deemed necessary for monolayers of dye molecules to suppress the back-electron donation and maintain the photoelectrochemical energy conversion process (6,7). Examination of the details in the photoelectrochemical process however may clarify the extent to which that requirement must be met.

The photoelectrochemical process can be divided into the four reactions (Equations 1-4) involving photon excitation and charge separation in the Pc film (Equation 1) recombination events (Equation 2), charge transfer at the electrode substrate-Pc interface (Equation 3) and charge transfer at the Pc-solution interface (Equation 4). The net process is the oxidation of hydroquinone with O to form quinone and R. If this is normally a thermodynamically uphill process where the dye is superimposed on a semiconductor substrate, then true photosensitized energy conversion has occurred.

Reaction Scheme of Quinone Electrolysis at Phthalocyanine-Modified Electrodes

$$h\nu \rightsquigarrow (Pc)_{surf} \longrightarrow Pc^{\oplus} + Pc^{\ominus} \qquad \text{Eq. 1}$$

$$Pc^{\oplus} + Pc^{\ominus} \longrightarrow Pc + h\nu, \text{ heat} \qquad \text{Eq. 2}$$

$$Pc^{\ominus} \underset{?}{\overset{substrate}{\rightleftharpoons}} Pc + e^{-}{}_{(to\ cathode)} \qquad \text{Eq. 3}$$

$$2Pc^{\oplus} + H_2Q \rightleftharpoons ? \rightleftharpoons Pc + Q + 2H^{+} \qquad \text{Eq. 4.}$$

net:
$$H_2Q + 2O \overset{h\nu}{\rightleftharpoons} 2R + Q + 2H^{+} \qquad \text{Eq. 5}$$

$$E_{Q/H_2Q} > E_{O/R} \longrightarrow \text{p.s.} \qquad \text{Eq. 6}$$

$$E_{Q/H_2Q} \leq E_{O/R} \longrightarrow \text{p.e.c.} \qquad \text{Eq. 7}$$

If this is a thermodynamically favored process as seen where the dye is placed on a metal substrate, then the dye-modified electrode may serve only to enhance (photoelectrocatalyze the reaction rate. Precedent for both types of processes has been summarized by Bard (6). Figure 5 shows the difference in i/V response at the dye-modified electrode when photosensitization occurs vs. photoelectrocatalysis. No photo-potential is expected in the photoelectrocatalytic case, but a significant

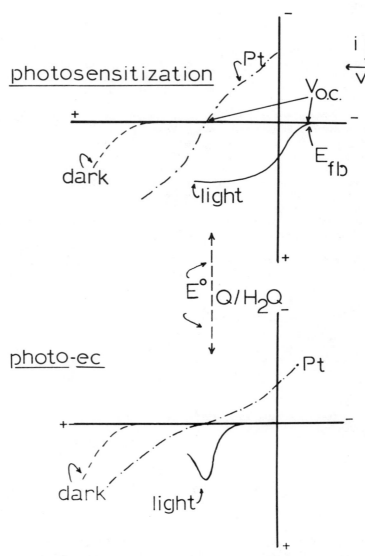

*Figure 5.   Photosensitization vs. photoelectrocatalytic reactions. At top, the illu-
minated current/voltage curve is placed negative of the current/voltage response on
bare Pt in the dark.   At bottom the current/voltage curve indicates an increase in
reaction rate, but no change in the apparent emf of the reaction.*

lowering of overpotential for kinetically inhibited reactions is possible--similar to the catalytic effects for other modified electrodes surfaces described in this symposium and elsewhere (2, 18-21). We are currently exploring whether it is possible on Pc-modified Au substrates to achieve both photoelectrocatalytic response and energy conversion (observation of a true photopotential), if the phthalocyanine layer has the correct thickness, porosity and molecular order. In all cases it is clear that electron transfer at the Pc/substrate interface (semiconductor or metal) is as critical to the overall photoelectrochemical efficiency as the Pc/electrolyte interface. Control of the substrate surface chemistry and morphology, by RF-plasma or ion-beam etching is important in the optimization of efficiencies of these processes.

Electrochromic Reactions at Chemically Modified and Ion-Beam Modified Electrode Surfaces.

Modification of electrode substrates with highly energetic argon or nitrogen ions (from plasmas or ion-guns) changes the nature of the current/potential response of many electrochemical reactions, where the product is adsorbed or somehow attached to the electrode surface. Our interest in these types of surface modifications was initiated by the observation that thin films of gold or indium-tin oxide MPOTE's could show easily detectable changes in current/potential response after delivery of 10^{14} to 10^{16} argon ions/cm^2 to their surfaces (0.1-10 molecular layers of damage to substrate atoms) (5). In the ion-beam modification experiment the electrode is exposed to a defocussed ion-beam, surface composition is assayed by Auger electron spectroscopy (AES) and the electrode then examined voltammetrically in an aqueous electrolyte. Surface analysis studies of the Au-MPOTE and ITO-MPOTE showed a larger than expected concentration of carbon and carbon oxides admixed with the conductive film. Ion-beam activation of the Au-MPOTE produced an electrode with increased electrochemical surface area, and a new, reversible surface redox species which was correlatable with the increased surface concentration of carbon oxides (5).

More recently we have extrapolated these surface activation experiments to the examination of the reduction of n-heptyl viologen dication to its insoluble cation radical $(n\text{-}HV^{++} + e^- \longrightarrow n\text{-}HV^{+\cdot})$ on unmodified and ion-beam activated indium-tin oxide MPOTE surfaces. Previous work in this laboratory has shown that the addition of one molecular layer of silane to a SnO_2 or an ITO MPOTE surface considerably enhanced the mass-transport controlled reduction of n-heptyl viologen (4) and the oxidation of fluorescein-type dyes such as erythrosin (8). We reasoned that the ion-beam, especially if it exposed the underlying polymer on the MPOTE surfaces, would produce a similar enhancement.

Linear sweep voltammetry delineates several regions in the current/potential relationships for the n-heptyl viologen

reduction. At potentials 25-50 millivolts negative of the true
E^o, deposition of the product occurs by nucleation at individual
surface sites (22-24). Chronoamperometric experiments, where
the electrode potential is stepped to this domain, shows a
current-time response like that in Figure 6a. Following decay
of the charging current, the current increased with $(time)^{1/2}$,
in relation to the rate of the nucleation process (Figure 7c).
Once 1-2 complete molecular layers are deposited, further film
growth occurs at rates controlled by electron transfer through
the film, and by mass-transport. The rate of nucleation is
strongly dictated by the type of anion present in the electo-
lyte. Solutions of KBr promote nucleation at a rate at least 10
times faster than for potassium hydrogen phthalate (KHP). The
Br^- ion optimizes film growth of the heptyl viologen cation
radical (HV^+) at all stages including nucleation probably by
the formation of dimers or higher aggregates which further
crystallize following deposition (22, 23). These rates of nucleation can be further enhanced up to 50% or more by: a) the
addition of a monolayer of a low molecular weight silane to the
electrode surface (Figure 7a) or b) the damaging of that surface
with an argon ion dose of 10^{15} to 10^{17} ions/cm^2 (Figures 6b and
7b). In both cases new nucleation sites are formed, which contribute to the increase in driving force for adsorption.

The slope of the current versus $(time)^{1/2}$ plots (Figures
7a-c) is proportional to the number of nucleation sites,
according to the model of Hills and coworkers (24) and Fletcher,
et al., (22).

$$i = 1.04 \; nF\pi (2DC^o)^{3/2} \; (M^{1/2}/\rho^{1/2}) N_o t^{1/2}$$

where n, F, and π have their usual significance, and D = the
bulk diffusion coefficient of $n-HV^{++}$; C^o = the instantaneous
surface soncentration of $n-HV^{++}$ prior to nucleation (nominally
the bulk concentration); M = Molecular weight of $n-HV^{++}$;
ρ = density of $n-HV^{++}$; N_o = number of nucleation sites (a potential dependent parameter). The number of nucleation sites, N_o,
observed at a particular overpotential varys from $N_o=7\times10^{-6}$cm^{-2}
to $N_o=8\times10^{-6}$cm^{-2} to $N_o=11\times10^{-6}$cm^{-2} for the unmodified, ion-beam
modified and silane modified ITO sufaces respectively. In the
case of the silane-modified surfaces, electrochemical adsorption
studies indicate that the viologen is partitioning into the
silane surface layer prior to electrochemical reduction (both N_o
and C^o increase). The increased nucleation rate is due in part
to the pre-concentration of reactant in the electrode surface
layer (25). In the case of the ion-beam modified surfaces,
removal of contaminants from the electrode surface contribute to
increased nucleation sites (5). Ion beam treatment of metal
oxides with the types of ion doses described also leads to some
reduction of the oxide as indicated by electron spectroscopies

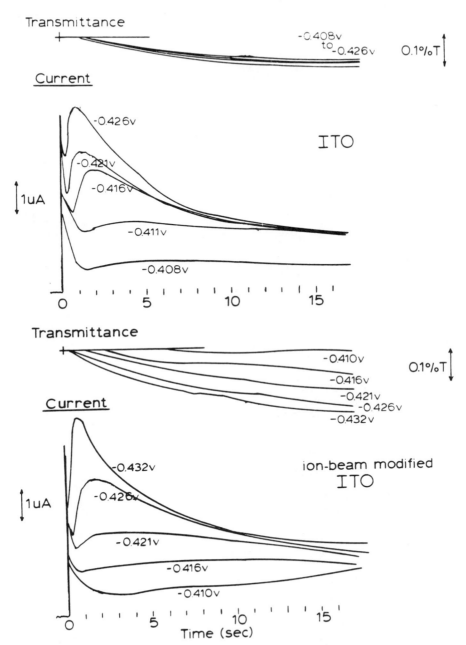

Figure 6. Current vs. time, and transmittance–decrease vs. time plots for n-heptyl-viologen reduction obtained on a clean (top) and ion-beam modified (bottom) ITO, MPOTE. Current increases with (time)½ in the nucleation region, and then decreases, while the absorbance changes linearly. Rates of nucleation are enhanced on the modified surface. [n-HV⁺⁺] = 10⁻³M, 0.1 M KHP. Potential steps are indicated with each plot.

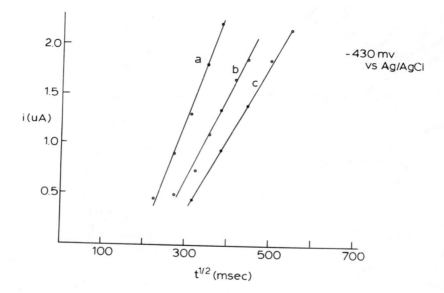

*Figure 7.   Current vs. (time)½ plots for the nucleation of n-HV⁺˙ at various elec-
trode surfaces. Dimethyldiethoxysilane (DMDE) modified ITO, MPOTE surface
(a); ion-beam modified ITO, MPOTE, 10¹⁶ ions/cm² (as in Figures 5 and 6) (b);
and clean ITO, MPOTE surface (c). Conditions as in Figure 7.*

(25). The substoichiometric oxide surface may provide better electron transfer rates to the solutions species, preferred adsorption sites for the cation radical, or especially the anion (as in the case of Br⁻ adsorption on tin metal (22)), both of these effects leading to increased nucleation rates.

Further studies of the n-heptyl viologen reaction on modified surfaces are reported elsewhere (25). It is clear that the interaction of ion-beams or plasmas with the electrode surface can be a powerful modification tool, complementary to chemical modification procedures for application to either photoelectrochemical or electrochromic reactions.

Acknowledgements

This research has been supported by grants from the National Science Foundation, CHE80-17571 and from the Sierracin Corporation.

Literature Cited

1. See papers by Van Duyne, Kaufman, Diaz, Kuwana, Meyer, Wrighton, Finklea, and Lundgren in this symposium.
2. A comprehensive review of this area up through 1980 is available by R. W. Murray, Accts. Chem. Res., 1980, 12, 135.
3. Kuwana, T., this symposium, paper #96.
4. Cieslinski, R.; Armstrong, N. J. Electrochem. Soc. 1980, 127, 2606.
5. Armstrong, N. R.; White, J. R. J. Electroanal. Chem. 1982, 131, 121.
6. See recent reviews by Bard, A. J. Science 1980, 207, 139 and J. Photochem. 1970, 10, 59; Wrighton, M. S. Accts. Chem. Res. 1970, 12, 303, and paper #98, this symposium.
7. Gerischer, H., Topics in Applied Physics, Vol. 31, "Solar Energy Conversion," Seraphin, B. O., Ed.; Springer-Verlay: New York; 1979; pp. 115-169.
8. Hawn, D.; Armstrong, N. R. J. Phys. Chem. 1978, 82, 1288; Shepard, V. R.; Armstrong, N. R. J. Phys. Chem. 1989, 83, 1268.
9. Mezza, T.; Linkous, C.; Shepard, V. R.; Armstrong, N. R.; Nohr, R.; Kenney, M. J. Electroanal. Chem. 1981, 124, 311.
10. Armstrong, N. R.; Shepard, V. R. J. Electroanal. Chem. 1982, 131, 113.
11. Osa, T.; Fujihira, M. Nature, 1976, 264, 349.
12. Dähne, S. Photographic Sci. and Eng. 1979, 23, 219; Saunders, V. I; Lovell, S. P. Ibid, 1970, 24, 171, 176.
13. Iwasaki, T.; Sumi, S.; Fujishima, A.; Honda, K. Ibid. 1979, 23, 17.
14. Matsumura, M.; Matsudaira, S.; Tsubomura, H.; Takata, M.; Yanagida, H. I and EC Prod. Res. and Dev. 1980, 19, 415.
15. Schoch, K. F., Jr.; Kundulkar, B. R.; Marks, T. J. J. Amer. Chem. Soc. 1979, 101, 7071.

16. Janson, T. R.; Kane, A. R.; Sullivan, T. F.; Knox, K.;
    Kenney, M. J. Amer. Chem. Soc. 1969, 91, 5210; Kusnesol,
    R. M.; Wynne, K.; Nohr, R.; and Kenney, M. J. Chem. Soc.
    Chem. Comm. 1980, 121.

17. Vetter, K. J. Zeit. Elektrochimie, 1952, 56, 797.

18. Oyama, N.; Anson, F. Anal. Chem. 1980, 52, 1192.

19. Collman, J. P.; Denisevich, P.; Konai, Y.; Marrocco, M.;
    Koval, K.; Anson, F. J. Amer. Chem. Soc. 1980, 102, 6027.

20. Tse, D. C. S.; Kuwana, T. Anal. Chem. 1979, 51, 2257;
    Bettelheim, A.; Chan, R. J. H.; Kuwana, T. J. Electroanal.
    Chem. 1979, 99, 39.

21. Andrieus, C. P.; Dumas-Bouchiat, J. M.; Saveant, J. M.
    J. Electroanal. Chem., 1978, 87, 39; 1978, 93, 163,; 1980,
    114, 159; and in press.

22. Fletcher, S.; Duff, L.; Barradas, R. G. J. Electroanal.
    Chem. 1979, 100, 759.

23. Bruinink, J.; Kregting, C. G. A.; Ponjee, J. J. J. Electro-
    chem. Soc. 1977, 124, 1854; Jasinski, R. Ibid. 1978, 125,
    1619; Ibid. 1979, 126, 167.

24. Bunawardena, B.; Hills, G.; Montenegro, I. Chem. Soc.
    Faraday Symp. 1977, #12, pp. 90-100.

25. Cieslinski, R.; Armstrong, N. R. J. Electroanal. Chem.
    submitted for publication.

RECEIVED April 8, 1982.

Derivatized Layered M(IV) Phosphonates

MARTIN B. DINES, PETER M. DIGIACOMO, KENNETH P. CALLAHAN,
PETER C. GRIFFITH, ROBERT H. LANE, and RICCI E. COOKSEY

Occidental Research Corporation, Irvine, CA 92713

In contrast to the conventional approach whereby various organic groups are subsequently bound to a previously prepared surface, we have been synthesizing a broad series of anchored, layered-structure solids by precipitating the pre-derived phosphonate salts with tetravalent metal ions. The two-dimensional backbone has the zirconium phosphate structure; however, substituted for hydroxylic groups are the desired organics, oriented away from the basal surfaces in a bilayered fashion in the interlayer region. These crystals can act as packets of modified surface, accessible by intercalation. Our focus has been aimed at the characterization and behavior of these compounds in various ion-exchange, sorption and catalytic reactions which will be described. Of particular interest are the mixed component products, in which two or more different groups are present within the interlayer.

The modification of surface properties by covalent bonding of various organic groups is by now a well-established procedure for a broad range of solids. The use of inorganic layered compounds as substrates for such chemistry is, however, quite limited in its known scope, particularly when the "surface" is meant to include both external and internal basal sites. The primary motivation for preparing covalently anchored layered compounds should be apparent: not only would such products enjoy the very significant advantages of other immobilized systems (ease of separations, stability, concentration of sites, etc.), but in addition they should have the potential for enhanced selectivity effects in their interactions with other molecules, and they present the possibility of trans- or cis-chelation, both as a direct consequence of the two-dimensional situation of the termini of the affixed organics (see Figure 1). Of course, there may be a trade-off in accessing the internal (bulk) sites to reactants, since this will

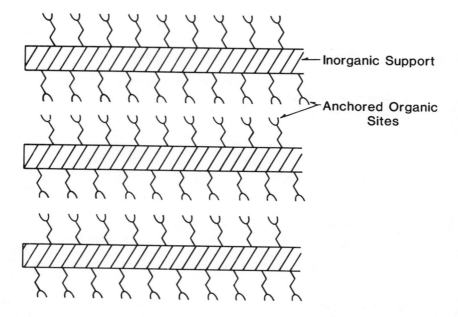

Figure 1.   Ordered array of covalently anchored organic groups on a stable inorganic support with a layered structure.

have to occur by an intercalation process, whereby the diffusion implied could have significant rate impedence.

The first challenge in this endeavor was the choice of an appropriate layered substrate. A brief process of elimination led us to the class of tetravalent metal phosphates, typified by the zirconium salt, whose α-phase structure was solved by Clearfield and his group (1). Yamanaka (2) had described a method of preparing anchored alcohols by treating the γ-variation of this salt with ethylene oxide, but we found this route to be far too limited in its scope. However, the structure of the phosphate was exactly suited for our purposes (Figure 2) and an alternative approach toward anchoring on the pendant hydroxyl groups based on chlorosilanes (as had been described with silica surfaces (3)) was undertaken. This method proved to be fraught with preparative difficulties which, though not intractable, quickly yielded to a far superior alternative in which phosphonic acids, having the desired organic group already present prior to precipitative polymerization of the solid (equation 1), were used.

$$(1) \quad Zr^{+4}(soln) + 2\ H_2O_3PR \longrightarrow Zr(O_3PR)_2(solid)$$

As hoped for, the products of this very general and simple reaction were found to have the same layered backbone structure as the parent phosphate, only with the organic group (-R) substituted for the hydroxyl. This is amply borne out by the x-ray diffraction powder data on the products, which yield the expected layer-layer distances directly, and by a plot of molecular density vs. interlayer distance, which gives a straight line dependence whose slope corresponds to the common site area, 24Å (Figure 3). In the midst of our investigation, Alberti published some similar work leading to the same conclusions (4). Many of our early results on the properties of this new class of hybrid inorganic-organic materials were recently disclosed, and experimental details may be found therein (5, 6). In this symposium it is our intention to report on some recent progress made in the areas of surface area and crystallinity manipulation, catalysis, mixed component products and the effects of "pillaring" in the layered phosphonates. In separate papers we will describe results on the preparation and ion-exchange behavior of anchored sulfonic acids, and on the "magic angle" nmr techniques for characterizing the phosphonates.

Surface Area and Crystallinity

Depending on the conditions of the precipitation reaction, including the utility of sequestrants such as HF, products of varying crystallinity (as assessed by breadth of the x-ray diffraction reflections) can be obtained. Similar effects have been found with the phosphates (7, 8). We were primarily interested in

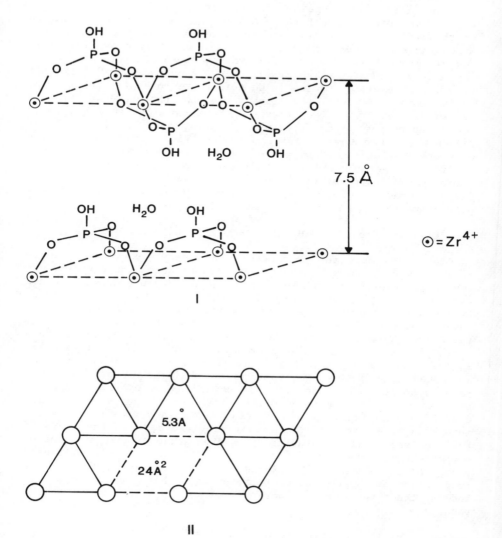

Figure 2.   *The structure of α-zirconium phosphate. The area per site on the basal
surface is about 24 Å².*

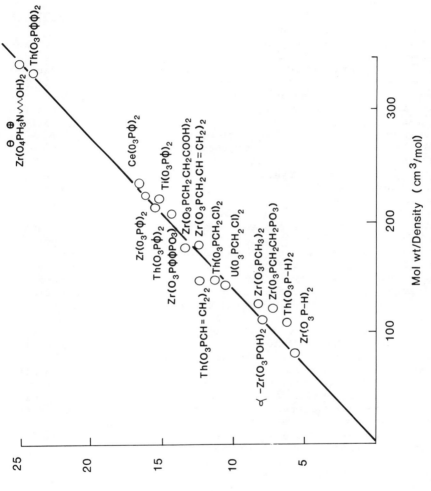

Figure 3. *Molecular volume vs. interlayer spacing, revealing that the various compounds share a common site area (about 24 Å² from the slope) and are essentially isostructural.*

the structure of the more "amorphous" products -- those with rather broad or even absent powder x-ray lines -- since these are generally more active, having higher surface areas. The two alternative explanations for this characterization are 1) the formation of glassy, or dried gel structures with complete or nearly so loss of order within the composite particles; or 2) substantial maintenance of the unit cell structure and order with very small (<100 Å) crystallites.

Using the methyl compound $Zr(O_3PCH_3)_2$ as a prototype, we prepared a series of products whose apparent particle sizes varied from 0.3 microns (as measured by scanning electron microscopy) down to below the limit of resolvability (about 100 Å). The higher crystallinity was achieved using HF or concentrated methylphosphonic acid reflux to slowly precipitate a product, while the more amorphous products were made by carrying out the preparation in relatively dilute solutions with or without refluxing. We measured the surface areas of the products thus obtained and found that they varied from about 16 m^2/g (using a standard BET N_2 method) for the more crystalline up to about 600 m^2/g for the least. Beyond about 200m^2/g, the scanning electron microscopy revealed only lumpy chunks, that is, no clearly delineated particles (Figure 4). There was, however, a clearly evident inverse relationship between the surface area and crystallinity as gauged both by SEM and XRD line broadening. In Figure 5, some representative powder patterns and the corresponding surface areas are shown. The data discussed to this point, however, do not clearly allow a distinction between the choices proposed above, since one could argue that a disorderd structure, if it contains nitrogen accessible pores, might be expected to manifest high surface areas just the same as ever decreasing sized particles would.

Some credence was given the latter of these alternatives by the observation that densities measured by displacement of helium in a gas pycnometry cell were essentially identical for the highest and lowest surface area products. The difference was less than 2%. It is suggested that an intrinsically amorphous structure should have a range of void spaces due to inefficient filling of its volume, the net result of which should be a significantly diminished density compared to the highly crystalline form. Thus, we favor the view that the more amorphous products are composed of smaller, but essentially ordered, particles.

Mixed Component Phases

Two of the most exciting and versatile methods of manipulating the chemical and geometrical properties of the interlamellar region of these substances are the co-inclusion of two (or more) different organic groups, and employment of terminal bis-phosphonic acids as "pillaring" constituents, groups which can both fix the interlayer distance and prop the layers apart. The use

Figure 4. Scanning electron micrographs of low (A and B) and high (C) crystal-linity Zr(O₃PCH₃)₂. The magnification of A is about 50; B and C are about 20,000.

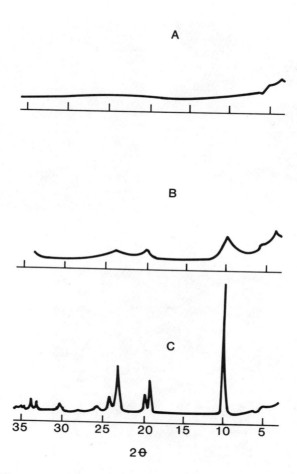

Figure 5.   X-ray diffraction patterns for high surface area (A, 600 m²/g), intermediate (B, 288 m²/g) and low surface area (C, 16 m²/g) Zr(O₃PCH₃)₂. A and C
correspond to the materials A (and B), and C in Figure 4.

of mixed components has several very compelling consequences: it allows for the preparation of solids having very bulky groups (those having a cross section greater than the 24 Å^2 limit given by the rigid framework) by including compensatory small groups, such as $-H$, $-CH_3$ or $-OH$; bifunctionality can be tailored into the material (this can take on many forms, such as Lewis and Bronstead acidity, redox couples of transition metals, compatibility with hydrophilic or lipophilic guests, etc.); control of the concentration of an active agent, such as a catalytic site; and the ability to architect microporosity in the solids. The extent to which these features can indeed be controlled will undoubtedly have a critical bearing on the performance of these compounds in nearly any envisioned application. And the flexibility promised gives many of the characteristics of the formidable synthetic zeolites.

It was implied in the previous discussion on crystallinity that the precipitation reaction is quite rapid, leading to very small particle powders. Therefore, in attempting to prepare a multicomponent product one must be aware that the composition and distribution of the different organic groups used in the precipitation may not be directly reflected in the product as a homogeneous solid solution. That is, if two phosphonic acids are used in the precipitation in a given ratio, there is no guarantee that this proportion will be evenly maintained within each crystallite. If the relative rates of precipitation of the two is very different, or if the two groups are not compatible for either chemical or geometrical reasons, then the product may be phase segregated either within crystallites or into separate crystallites. Since these initial products are actually kinetically determined, there may be some hope in preparing more ordered, crystalline phases by the use of HF, as was described earlier; however, phase segregation is even more likely in this case. These conjectures are summarized in Scheme 1. An illustrative example follows:

$$Zr^{+4} + a\ H_2O_3PR + b\ H_2O_3PR' \longrightarrow Zr(O_3PR)_x(O_3PR')_{2-x}$$

(Single phase, ordered or disordered)

$$\frac{a}{2}\ Zr(O_3PR)_2 + \frac{b}{2}\ Zr(O_3PR')_2$$

(Segregation into separate phases)

Scheme 1. Possible pathways in multicomponent reactions. The ratio of a/b need not equal x/2-x.

We have chosen as a simple model system the situation for which R=H and R'=phenyl. They both separately react very fast, and form single phase products easy to identify both by infrared spectroscopy (ν_{p-H} at 2470 cm^{-1}; phenyl C-H fingerprint in the 700–800 cm^{-1} region) and by their very different layer repeat

distances (5.6 Å for the P-H analog vs. 15 Å for the phenyl).
Starting with a solution in which the hydride to phenyl ratio was
3:1 (and the combined amount was in two-fold excess over zirconium), a product was isolated after 2 hrs reflux which contained
nearly 1:1 phenyl to hydride. The XRD indicated a poorly crystalline phase with a d-spacing of about 11.3 Å. This value is
most consistent with a structure in which the most prevalent
interaction across the interlayer is phenyl/hydrogen, that is, the
approximate average value of the two pure phases. In its infrared
spectrum, this material exhibited a broad P-H band centered at
2455 cm^{-1} as well as the distinct phenyl fingerprint. On redis-
solving this product in dilute HF and recrystallizing by partial
evaporation, there is a quantitative recovery of material having
sharp XRD reflections attributable to both pure phase products (at
5.6 and 15 Å) as well as a small peak corresponding to a 10.6 Å
spacing. The infrared has a sharp doublet in the P-H region at
2440 and 2470 cm^{-1}. It appears that on recrystallization the
material forms three phases: both of the pure single component
phases as well as a mixed product, possibly ordered. This sequence is illustrated in Figure 6. The results are consistent
with a picture in which an initial kinetic product is formed, most
likely a disordered structure in the sense that the appended
groups are randomly distributed in approximately equal amounts.
The most likely interlayer distance will be dictated by phenyl-
hydrogen interactions (simplistically, this is twice as likely as
either phenyl/phenyl or hydrogen/hydrogen abutments), thus the
11 Å spacing. On recrystallization, a thermodynamic product --
the pure phase segregated materials -- results. The presence of
some mixed component product (with a sharper infrared band and XRD
reflection than the initial) implies that it may be a stable
ordered structure.

If the above reaction is carried out with an initial Zr^{+4}/H/
phenyl mole ratio of 1:1:1, a product of composition Zr(O$_3$PH)$_{3/4}$
(O$_3$PC$_6$H$_5$)$_{5/4}$ is afforded. Once again, the ability of the phenyl
to incorporate somewhat preferentially is seen. This material
gives a d-spacing of 15.5 Å only, suggesting that in this case
the phenyl-phenyl interactions seem to dictate the interlayer
distance.

Pillared Phases

The use of terminal bis-phosphonic acids to crosslink layers
adds the ability to fix the interlayer distance to the picture.
We have prepared several of these compounds as pure phases --
Zr(O$_3$PRPO$_3$) in which R is either a straight chain hydrocarbon,
aralkyl, or a phenyl, diphenyl or terphenyl linkage. In all cases
the layer repeat distance found was equal to that expected based
on CPK models (Table I).

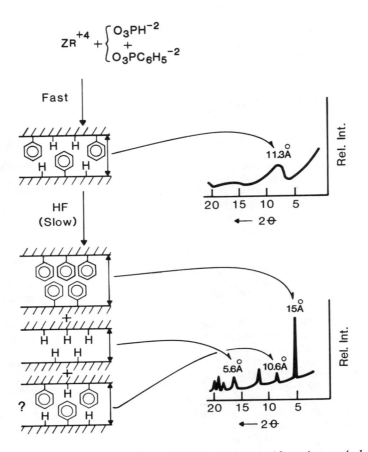

Figure 6. Sequence of events in reacting zirconium ions with a mixture of phenyl-phosphonic and phosphorous acids.

Table I. Interlayer Distances Found for Crosslinking Groups.

Compound	d-Spacing from XRD
$Zr(O_3PCH_2CH_2PO_3)$	7.8 Å
$Zr(O_3PCH_2CH_2CH_2PO_3)$	no reflection observed
$Zr(O_3P(CH_2)_{10}PO_3)$	17.2 Å
$Zr(O_3P\text{-}C_6H_4\text{-}PO_3)$	9.6 Å
$Zr(O_3P\text{-}C_6H_4\text{-}C_6H_4\text{-}PO_3)$	13.9 Å
$Zr(O_3P\text{-}C_6H_4\text{-}C_6H_4\text{-}C_6H_4\text{-}PO_3)$	18.5 Å
$Zr(O_3PCH_2\text{-}C_6H_4\text{-}CH_2PO_3)$	10.8 Å

The only anomaly we encountered, apparent in the Table, was the finding that the three-carbon bis-phosphonic acid product, which had a good elemental analysis, did not exhibit any XRD lines. We conjecture that this apparent inability to form a crystalline product results from the fact that there is no obvious way to force a conformation on a three carbon chain so that the terminal phoshonates will be in a parallel configuration, as required by a layered structure. This, then, may be an example of an intrinsically amorphous product.

It should be apparent that a particularly desirable class of layered phosphonates is the mixed composition crosslinked products. In these structures, there would be present some (preferably) small groups such as -H, -OH or alkyl, together with a bis-phosphonic acid which can serve to "pillar" the layers so as to form microporous voids in the structure which would allow for the possibility of molecular sieving, as seen with the well-known zeolites. A schematic of the structure desired is shown in Figure 7, where it can be seen that the dimensions of the micropores produced can be hopefully controlled by the length of the pillaring groups, and their concentration. Even if they are randomly distributed, they should be able to manifest a size exclusion for incoming molecules based mainly on the basal surface separation. Of course, if the pillaring groups are too dilute, one might expect some sort of "roof collapse" to occur, resulting in a partial closing off of the internal volume.

In the preparation of such mixed component pillared compounds, a simple method of estabishing that single phase products having structures such as that given in Figure 7 was required. We chose to use the surface area measurement (nitrogen one point BET) as a means of verifying pillaring. This was necessitated by the observation that very poor XRD patterns were usually obtained, thus obviating this method, and furthermore, that the surface area can give a direct measurement of the new surface which should be opened up in the process of pillaring. The argument adopted was that in a series of mixed component products, substantial deviations from a straight line connecting the surface areas of the end members was most likely attributable to opening up of the microstructure, whereas lack of such could either mean that no enhanced access results from forming the mixed component phase, or that phase separation was occurring. The critical assumption implicit in this logic is that there is a monotonic variation in particle size throughout the series; that is, that any deviation from the straight line was not attributable to changes in the particle size induced by the presence of the coreacting phosphonate.

In Figure 8 is presented the results for a small series of such products whose end members are $Zr(O_3PH)_2$ and $Zr(O_3P-$ –Ⓞ-Ⓞ-$PO_3)$. Note that we have designated the specific surface areas in units of M^2/mmole, so that the mole fraction axis is linear. SEM revealed no substantial change in particle size in the series (particles about 0.06 microns in diameter, appearance non-crystalline). The surface area observed for the intermediate compositions is about double that expected if no consequential interaction occurs. An estimate of how much increase could be expected if each –H site allows one N_2 molecule to incorporate for the 0.5 mole fraction case is about 100 M^2 (6.02×10^{20} molecules x 16.2 A^2/molecule). The value observed was 80 additional M^2/mmol. Additional evidence for the presence of micropores was obtained by pre-treating the 0.33 mole fraction product in nonane and rerunning the surface area measurement after exhaustive pumping to remove any residual liquid. This method is described (9) to effectively "plug" microporous surface area. We found a diminution of about 75% in the surface area measured, roughly placing the point on the non-interaction line (Figure 8). On subsequent heating in a flow of helium, the original area was nearly completely restored. An estimate of the dimension of the pores thought to result is about 8.3 Å by 5 Å, based simply on the spacing difference between the diphenyl and hydrogen compounds, and an assumption that an average of one –H site separates neighboring pillars.

We have prepared other mixed composition pillared compounds which have as their non-pillaring group the hydroxyl moiety, and thus are simply relatives of zirconium phosphate in which the layers are spread at a fixed distance apart. These products behave as expected in titration and ion-exchange experiments, and will not be further discussed here.

Anchored Catalysts

One of the most intriguing possible applications of the derivatized layered phosphonates is in the area of heterogenized

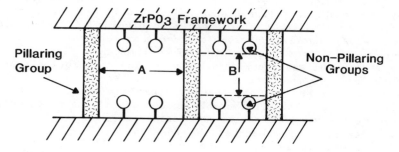

Figure 7. *Architecture of micropores in layered phosphonate compounds. Distance A is dictated by the density of pillars; B is determined by the length of the pillar, relative to the size of the nonpillar groups.*

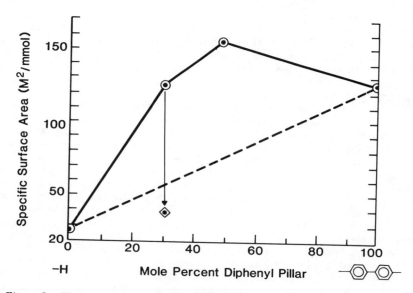

Figure 8. *Variation of the specific surface area of mixed component pillared compounds, whose end members are the hydride and the diphenyl bisphosphonate. The point denoted with a diamond corresponds to the area measured after nonane treatment.*

transition metal catalysts. Generally, the idea here is to prepare a product containing appended organic groups which can then
function as ligands for the subsequent complexation of suitable
metal species which can, in turn, serve to catalyze reactions of
intercalated molecules. We have chosen as a prototype support for
this chemistry the anchored pyridine compound (broad XRD reflection corresponding to an 18.6Å spacing), prepared by precipitation of 2-ethyl(4-pyridyl)phosphonic acid (Equation 2), which can
then be used as a substrate for palladium(II).

$$(2) \quad Zr^{+4} + 2 \ (HO)_2\overset{O}{\overset{\|}{P}}CH_2CH_2\text{-}\underset{\bigcirc}{}N \longrightarrow Zr(O_3PCH_2CH_2\underset{\bigcirc}{}N)_2$$

$$\xrightarrow{Pd(II)} Zr(O_3PCH_2CH_2\text{-}\underset{\bigcirc}{}N)_2Pd(II)_x$$

Using bis(benzonitrile)palladium dichloride, and stirring in a
tetrahydrofuran slurry of the pyridyl anchored compound for
several days, a product having a value for x, after exhaustive
extraction, of about 0.2 (corresponding to 3% Pd loading by
weight) was afforded. This catalyst was found to be very active
for the hydrogenation of cyclohexene at 80°C with 375 psi hydrogen. Under these conditions, the conversion to cyclohexane was
complete in less than 20 min. There was evidence, based at first
on color changes of the catalyst (from tan to black) that reduction of the Pd(II) had occurred. Later, this was confirmed by
ESCA spectra run on the used and fresh catalyst (Figure 9). We
cannot be certain whether the Pd(II) or Pd(0) is the catalytically
active species, nor do we yet understand how the Pd(0) is bound to
the solid.

The catalyst was also found to be very active for the hydrogenation of benzonitrile to benzylamine, nitrobenzene to aniline,
diphenylacetylene to stilbenes, and benzene to cyclohexane.

We are investigating the incorporation of other metals into
similarly anchored solids, and examining other catalytic reactions. In particular, we are interested in attacking the problem
of catalyst leaching from the solid. This work is in progress and
will be reported on in the future.

Transmission Electron Microscopy

There is no more compelling evidence of the microscopic
morphology of layered compounds than a direct image as can be
afforded only by transmission electron micrography. The current
state of the art allows for routine limits of resolution on the
order of 5 - 10 Å as opposed to about 70 Å for scanning
electron methods. We turned to the hexyl rather than the methyl
analog for our prototype compound -- $Zr(O_3PC_6H_{13})_2$ -- to gain a
factor of about two in the layer-layer distance (19 vs. 9 Å).

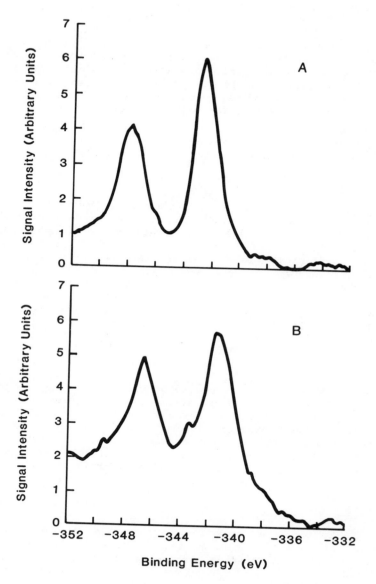

Figure 9.   ESCA spectra of Pd-loaded pyridyl compounds before (A) and after (B) use in catalytic hydrogenation. Note the decrease in Pd3d$_{5/2}$ binding energy: 342.6 eV in A, 341.2 eV in B, consistent with Pd(II) in A, Pd(0) in B.

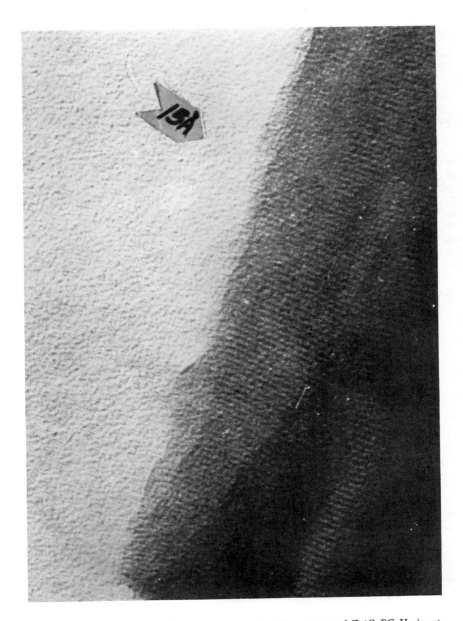

Figure 10. Transmission electron micrograph of the compound $Zr(O_3PC_6H_{13})_2$, at 540,000 power. The layer–layer stacking is apparent in profile, with a repeat distance of about 15Å.

The material used was prepared by a simple precipitation and overnight heating. It had a single point BET surface area of 17.8
m^2/g. Shown in Figure 10 is a microcrystal in profile, in which
the layer stacking is clearly apparent. The repeat distance estimated from the photographic and instrumental magnification was
15 Å, in satisfactory agreement with the powder diffraction
result.

Summary and Conclusions

The derivatized layered tetravalent metal phosphonates have
proven to be a particularly apt example on which to test many of
our hypotheses regarding planar bulk arrays of anchored organics.
They are relatively easily prepared, providing the phosphonic acid
or ester is available, and they provide for a site area which is
perfect for nearly close-packed coverage. We have made substantial progress in the detailed characterization of their physical
and chemical properties, especially in the areas of crystallinity,
surface area and micropore behavior, mixed component phases, and
in heterogenization of catalytic sites.

Literature Cited

1. Clearfield, A.; G. D. Smith, Inorg. Chem. 1969, 8, 431.
2. Yamanaka, S., Inorg. Chem. 1976, 15, 2811.
3. Boucher, L. J.; A. A. Oswald; L. L. Murrell, Preprints Petro-
    leum Div. A.C.S. Meeting, Los Angeles, CA, March, 1974, 162.
4. Alberti, G; U. Costantino; S. Alluli; N. Tomassini; J. Inorg.
    Nucl. Chem. 1978, 40, 1113.
5. Dines, M. B.; P. M. DiGiacomo; Abstract of Papers, 179th
    A.C.S. National Meeting, Houston, TX, March, 1980, Inorg. Div.
    paper no. 168.
6. Dines, M. B.; P. M. DiGiacomo, Inorg. Chem. 1981, 20, 92.
7. Alberti, G.; E. J. Torracca, Inorg. Nucl. Chem. 1968, 30, 317.
8. Clearfield, A.; A. Oskarsson; C. Oskarsson, Ion Exchange and
    Membranes 1972, 1, 91.
9. Gregg, S. J.; J. F. Langford, Trans. Faraday Soc. 1969, 65,
    1394.

RECEIVED November 4, 1981.

Intercalation of Molecular Catalysts in Layered Silicates

T. J. PINNAVAIA

Michigan State University, Department of Chemistry, East Lansing, MI 48824

A variety of cationic catalysts species can be intercalated in swelling layered silicate clay minerals such as hectorite. Under appropriate conditions of interlayer swelling by a polar solvent, the immobilized catalyst is accessible for reaction with reagents from solution. Intercalated rhodium phosphine complexes have been found to be active for the hydrogenation of olefins, alkynes, dienes, and prochiral α-enamides and for the hydroformylation of olefins. Since the reactions occur in solvated interlayers of more-or-less uniform thickness, spacial factors and polarization effects can lead to significant enhancement in substrate selectivity or product distribution. The ability to control interlayer swelling offers the possibility of inducing size selectivity which may not be realized for the metal complex catalysts in homogeneous solution. Large enzyme molecules can also be intercalated in layered silicates. With glucose oxidase as the intercalant, loadings up to 50 wt% can be achieved. The versatility of layered silicates as matrices for the immobilization of molecular catalysts is emphasized.

The immobilization of metal complex catalysts on polymers and inorganic oxides has received considerable attention as a means of combining the best advantages of homogeneous and heterogeneous catalysis (1-6). The swelling layer lattice silicates known as smectite clay minerals have added an important new dimension to metal complex immobilization. These compounds have mica-type structures in which two-dimensional silicate sheets are separated by monolayers of alkali metal or alkaline earth cations (7). The structure of a typical smectite, hectorite, is illustrated in Figure 1.

0097-6156/82/0192-0241 $6.00/0
© 1982 American Chemical Society

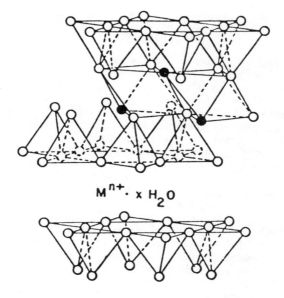

$M^{n+} \cdot x\ H_2O$

Figure 1. The hectorite structure, an idealized unit cell formula being $Na_{0.66}$-[$Li_{0.66}$; $Mg_{5.34}$]($Si_{8.00}$)O_{20}(OH,F)$_4$. Key: ○, *oxygen;* ●, *OH and occasionally fluoride. The tetrahedral sites are occupied mainly by silicon; magnesium and lithium occupy the octahedral sites.*

Unlike the micas, the interlayer regions occupied by the alkali metal and alkaline earth ions in smectites can be swelled by the adsorption of water and other polar molecules, and the interlayer ions can be replaced by ion exchange with almost any desired cation. Large differences in charge density on the silicate sheets contribute significantly to the differences in swelling and cation exchange properties of smectites and micas. The charge per unit cell for a typical smectite is $\sim$ 0.7 vs. 2.0 for mica when the unit cell is taken to contain 20 oxide ions and 4 OH groups. The relatively low charge density on the smectite sheets and the large internal surface area ($\sim$ 750 m^2/g) results in substantial separation ($\sim$ 10 Å) between charge centers. Thus a significant fraction of the exchange cations in the smectite can be replaced by a variety of large complex cations, such as those containing triphenylphosphine ligands. However, intercalation is not limited to metal complexes. Even large enzyme molecules 70 Å in diameter can be intercalated in smectites.

Since layered silicate intercalation compounds have ordered structures, they offer certain advantages over amorphorus metal oxides as solid supports. By varying the polarity of the swelling solvent, one can vary the thickness of the interlayer regions in which the catalytic reaction is taking place. The ability to control interlayer swelling offers the possibility of inducing size or shape selectivity which may not be realized for the metal complex catalysts in homogeneous solution. Cationic rhodium-phosphine complexes have been especially useful in demonstrating the versatility of layered silicate intercalation catalysts for the hydrogenation of olefins, alkynes, dienes, and prochiral α-eneamides for the hydroformylation of terminal olefins.

   Alkene and Alkyne Hydrogenations. Dirhodium acetate complex cations intercalated in hectorite have been shown to react with triphenylphosphine from methanol solution to form intercalated $Rh(PPh_3)_n^+$ species which are catalyst precursors for the hydrogenation of olefins (8):

$$\overline{Rh_2(OAc)_{4-x}^{x+}} \quad \xrightarrow[\text{(MeOH)}]{PPh_3} \quad \overline{2Rh(PPh_3)_n^+} \qquad (1)$$

wherein x = 1,2, n = 2 or 3, and the horizontal lines represent the silicate sheets.

   Table I compares the results for the hydrogenation of 1-hexene in methanol with the intercalated and homogeneous catalyst systems. Under the reaction conditions employed, the hydrogen uptake rate is lower for the intercalated catalyst than for the homogeneous catalyst. However, the intercalated catalyst greatly reduces the extent of 1-hexene to 2-hexene isomerization, relative to homogeneous solution. The ability of the intercalated catalyst to inhibit substrate isomerization has been attributed to the existence of a surface equilibrium between a monohydride and dihydride complex:

$$\overline{RhH_2(PPh_3)_n^+} \rightleftharpoons \overline{RhH(PPh_3)_n + H^+} \tag{2}$$

Schrock and Osborn have shown that the dihydride is a good hydrogenation catalyst but a poor isomerization catalyst, whereas the
monohydride is both a good hydrogenation catalyst and a good isomerization catalyst. The hydrolysis of unexchanged Na^+ ions on
the interlayer surfaces gives rise to Bronsted acidity on the
interlayer surfaces which shifts the equilibrium in eq. 2 in the
direction of the dihydride. Although hydrated Na^+ is a very weak
Bronsted acid in solution, it is sufficiently acidic in the
silicate interlayers to react with meso – tetraphenylporphyrin to
give small but detectable amounts of the diprotonated porphyrin
dication (10). Recent studies indicate that the inhibition by
the intercalated catalyst of substrate isomerization under hydrogenation conditions very much depends on the composition of the
solvating medium (11). With 0.1 wt% water in methanol no isomerization of 1-hexene is observed at 40% conversion, but with 0.5
wt% water in the reaction medium about 50% of the product is
2-hexene at 50% conversion. The sensitivity of the isomerization
reaction to water content further verifies the importance of
Bronsted surface acidity.

Table I.

Hydrogenation of 1.0 $\underline{M}$ 1-Hexene in Methanol[a]

System	PPh$_3$/Rh	% Conver.	Hydrog. Rate[b]	Product Distr. %	
				Hexane	2-Hexene
Intercalated[c]	4.0	5	16	100	–
		50	16	100	–
Homogeneous	4.0	5	200	100	–
		38	190	63	37
		66	130	65	35

[a] Initial substrate to rhodium ratio is 2000:1; temperature is
25°. [b] Hydrogen uptake rate, mL/min/mmol Rh. [c] Rhodium loading
on hectorite is 0.72 wt%.

Although the deviations from solution behavior for the hydrogenation of 1-hexene with the intercalated catalyst arise from shifts in the position of catalytically important protonic equilibria, substrate size has been found to play a dominant role in the selectivity of intercalation catalysts in alkyne hydrogenation (8). Both $RhH_2(PPh_3)_n^+$ and $RhH(PPh_3)_n$ are active for the hydrogenation of alkynes to the corresponding cis olefins. Table II shows the dependence of the relative hydrogenation rates for a series of alkynes in methanol with the intercalated and homogeneous $Rh(PPh_3)_n^+$ catalyst precursors. In methanol as the solvating medium the interlayer regions of the intercalated hectorite are about 7.7 Å thick. As the steric bulk on either side of the C≡C bond increases, the reaction rate decreases for the intercalated catalyst, relative to the homogeneous catalyst. The results of complementary experiments in which the nature of the swelling solvent is varied and the substrate size is held constant utilizing 2-decyne are shown in Table III. As the average thickness of the interlayers (Δd_{001}) is decreased from 10.0 Å in CH_2Cl_2 as the swelling solvent to 5.6 Å in benzene where there is essentially no interlayer swelling, the rate of reaction dramatically decreases for the intercalated catalyst relative to the homogeneous catalyst. These results have been attributed to transition state selectivity induced by preferred orientations of the catalyst-substrate complex on the interlayer surfaces. Figure 2A illustrates a possible orientation in which the trans P-Rh-P axis is parallel to the silicate sheets and the C≡C axis is perpendi-

Table II.

Relative Initial Rates at 25° for Alkyne Hydrogenation in Methanol with Intercalated and Homogeneous $Rh(PPh_3)_n^+$ Catalyst Precursors[a]

Alkyne	$\dfrac{\text{Intercalated Rate}}{\text{Homogeneous Rate}}$
1-hexyne	1.0
2-hexyne	0.92
2-decyne	0.48
3-hexyne	0.20
PhC≡CPh	<0.01

[a] Initial substrate concentration is 1.0 $\underline{M}$; initial substrate to rhodium ratio is 2000:1; $PPh_3/Rh = 6.0$

Table III.

Relative Initial Rates at 25° for Hydrogenation of 2-Decyne

with Intercalated and Homogeneous $Rh(PPh_3)_n^+$ Catalyst Precursors

Solvent	Intercalated Rate / Homogeneous Rate	Δd_{001} (Å)
CH_2Cl_2	0.85	10.0
MeOH	.43	7.7
$Et_2O/MeOH$ (3:1)	.24	6.7
C_6H_6	.02	5.7

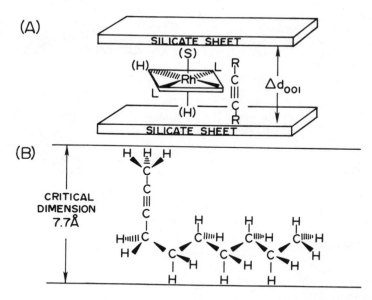

*Figure 2. Proposed orientation of the alkyne–rhodium triphenylphosphine com-
plex between the silicate sheets of hectorite, prior to hydrogen transfer (top); the
Δd_{001}, obtained by subtracting the thickness of the silicate sheet (~ 9.6 Å) from the
observed 001 X-ray reflection, is a measure of the interlayer thickness. The critical
dimension of 2-decyne (bottom) is defined as the minimum distance which must
be spanned by the molecule when the C≡C axis is perpendicular to the silicate
sheets.*

cular to the sheets. If the critical dimension for orienting the
C≡C axis at the rhodium center is less than the average interlayer thickness, then formation of the reactive intermediate will
be inhibited and reaction will be slow. For 2-decyne the critical
dimension is 7.7 Å, as illustrated in Figure 2B.

A small but detectable amount (∿ 5%) of metal complex desorbs
from the intercalated catalyst under hydrogenation conditions.
The proposed mechanism for desorption is based on the equilibrium
defined in equation 2, wherein the neutral monohydride can be lost
to solution. However, loss of rhodium through a proton dissociation mechanism can be eliminated by replacing the neutral phosphine ligands on rhodium with positively charged phosphine
ligands such as $Ph_2P(CH_2)_2^+PPh_2(CH_2Ph)$ (12).

1,3-Butadiene Hydrogenation. Rhodium complexes of the type
$Rh(diene)(dppe)^+$, where dppe = 1,2-bis(diphenylphosphino)ethane,
are catalyst precursors for overall 1,2 and 1,4 addition of hydrogen to 1,3-butadienes. In these reactions the distribution of
terminal and internal olefin products is kinetically regulated
by the reaction pathways of a common $RhH(R)(dppe)^+$ intermediate
(13). Under homogeneous reaction conditions, the thermodynamically more stable internal olefin products (1,4-addition) are
favored over the synthetically more useful terminal olefin products (1,2 addition). However, significant increases in the
yield of 1,2 addition products can be achieved by intercalation
of the catalyst precursor in hectorite. (14)

Table IV compares for a series of dienes the yields of 1,2
addition products obtained with $Rh(NBD)(dppe)^+$ as the catalyst
precursor under intercalated and homogeneous reaction conditions.
The yields of terminal olefins are consistently higher for the
intercalated catalyst. The deviation from solution yields are
larger when the intercalated catalyst is solvated with methanol
than with acetone. Methanol swells the interlayers to an average
thickness of ∿ 12 Å, whereas acetone swells the interlayers to
∿ 15 Å. Since the more constricted methanol solvated interlayers
provide the higher yields of terminal olefins, spacial factors as
well as polarization effects induced by the charged silicate
sheets may be contributing to the deviations from solution behavior. In this reaction system polarization effects may well be
more important than spacial factors in directing hydrogenation
transfer because the spacial requirements of the transition states
derived from η^1 or η^3 allyl intermediates should be very similar.

Asymmetric Hydrogenation. Rhodium complexes of the type
$Rh(diene)(diphos^*)^+$, where diphos* is a chiral bidentate diphos-
phine ligand, are catalyst precursors for the asymmetric hydrogenation of certain prochiral olefins (15). Asymmetric hydrogenation of α-acylaminoacrylates, for example, affords chiral
amino acid derivatives, some of which have medicinal utility such
as L-DOPA.

Table IV.

Hydrogenation of 1,3 Butadienes at 25°

with Rh(NBD)(dppe)$^+$ as Catalyst Precursor

	Solvent	Yield of 1,2 Addn. Products %	
		Interc. Catal.	Homo. Catal.
	Acetone	45	30
	MeOH	60	33
	Acetone	34	19
	MeOH	44	20
	Acetone	32	17
	MeOH	39	20

Rh(diene)(R-Prophos)$^+$ complexes are especially efficient homogeneous catalyst precursors for asymmetric hydrogenation: (16)

(R)-Prophos

It was of interest to us to examine the activity of such catalyst presursors when intercalated in hectorite (17). Table V provides a comparison of optical yields for asymmetric hydrogenation of three prochiral amino acid precursors with Rh(NBD)-(4-Me-(R)-Prophos)$^+$ under homogeneous and intercalated reaction conditions. The 4-methyl-(R)-prophos ligand is a derivative of (R)-Prophos in which all of the phenyl groups have been methylated in the para position. The optical yields for the intercalated catalyst are very similar to those observed for the homogeneous catalyst. Thus for 4-Me-(R)-Prophos as the ligand, the chiral recognition of the complex is retained in the intercalated state. Retention of chiral recognition in the intercalated state may not be a general property. Recently, Mozzei et al. (18) reported that the optical yields obtained for the asymmetric hydrogenation of α-acetamidoacrylic acid with chiral rhodium diammine complexes intercalated in smetites depended on the type of smectite used. Nevertheless, our results with 4-Me-(R)-Prophos indicate that the synthesis of certain amino acid derivatives such as L-DOPA, for example, would be better accomplished by utilizing an intercalated catalyst instead of a homogeneous catalyst, because of the greater efficiency in recovering and recycling the catalyst complex without loss of product optical purity.

Hydroformylation. Although cationic complexes such as Rh(diene)(PPh₃)$_2^+$ are active for olefin hydroformylation, they are not suitable for intercalation in layered silicates, because the active species formed under hydroformylation conditions are electrically neutral (19, 20). Since neutral complexes have little or no affinity for the negatively charged silicate sheets, extensive desorption of rhodium occurs during the reaction and most of the observed catalytic activity occurs in the solution phase.
    Rhodium desorption can be effectively eliminated by replacing the neutral phosphine ligands on rhodium with positively charged phosphine ligands such as Ph₂P(CH₂)$_2^+$PPh₂(CH₂Ph), abbreviated P-P$^+$. Table VI compares the results for the hydroformylation of 1-hexene in acetone with three different catalyst precursor systems containing P-P$^+$ as a ligand (20). For each of the intercalated catalysts, all of the activity occurred in the solid phase; no catalystic activity was observed for the clear filtrates. Thus,

Table V

Assymmetric Hydrogenation of Prochiral Olefins with

Rh(NBD)(4-Me-(R)-Prophos)$^{+}$ [a]

Substrate	Optical Yield (%)	
	Interc. Catalyst	Homo. Catalyst
	89.6	92.6
	78.5	72.0
	95.1	95.3

[a] Reactions were carried out at 25°, 1 atm pressure, in 95% ethanol. The chemical yields were > 98% in each case.

Table VI

Hydroformylation of 1-Hexene in Acetone[a]

Rh Precursor	P-P$^+$/Rh	Product Distribution (%)		
		n-Heptanal	2-Me-Hexanol	2-Hexene
A. Homogeneous Catalyst				
[RhCl(COD)]$_2$	4	55	22	23
[Rh(CO)$_2$Cl]$_2$	3	54	26	20
[Rh(COD)]$^+$	2	60	30	10
B. Intercalated Catalyst				
[RhCl(COD)]$_2$	4	63	23	8
[Rh(CO)$_2$Cl]$_2$	3	71	23	6
[Rh(COD)]$^+$ [b]	2	70	23	0

[a] 100°C, 600 psi CO/H$_2$ (1/1). [b] This system gave 7% of an unidentified reaction product.

the layered silicates not only provide a convenient means of immobilizing the hydroformylation catalyst, but they also provide some chemical advantages over the homogeneous catalysts. The yields of the synthetically more valuable normal chain aldehyde are consistently higher for the intercalated catalysts. Also, the extent of the 1-hexene isomerization to 2-hexene is lower for the intercalated catalyst than for the homogeneous catalyst. Apparently, the restricted interlayers of the intercalated catalyst favors the formation of the sterically less demanding α-alkyl intermediate. Similar steric factors may also be affecting the isomerization pathway.

    Enzyme Intercalation. As noted earlier the intercalation of molecular catalysts in layered silicates is not limited to metal complexes. Large enzyme molecules can also be intercalated at pH values below their isoelectric points. Because the large internal surface area of smectite, very large enzyme loadings can be anticipated. For hexagonal close packing of glucose oxidase (M.W. ≃ 160,000), for example, the anticipated loading is 2.3 g enzyme per g of silicate. In practice, loadings up to 1 g enzyme/g silicate can be achieved (21). In comparison, typical loadings for enzymes immobilized by conventional methods on metal oxides are in the range 0.1 - 5 wt%.

The specific activity and longevity of glucose oxidase intercalated in hectorite is dependent in part on the extent of surface
coverage.   As illustrated in Figure 3, the enzyme activity decays
by two pathways: a fast pathway which is loading dependent, and
a slow pathway which is loading independent.   The fast decomposition pathway can be almost completely eliminated by incorporating
in the interlayer regions alkylammonium ions which may be acting
as hydrogen bonding disruptors.   Thus the fast decomposition pathways appears to be due to conformational denaturation of the
enzyme through hydrogen bonding with the silicate oxygens.   The
slower decomposition pathway may be due to protein hydrolysis or
loss of FAD cofactor.

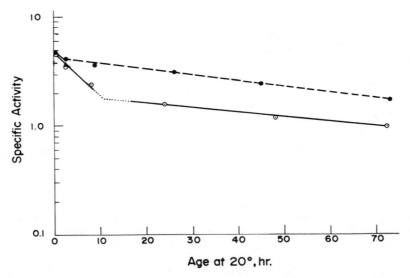

*Figure 3.   Specific activity of glucose oxidase intercalated in a smectite layered
silicate versus time of aging at 20°C. Loading is 20 g of enzyme/g of silicate. The
dashed line shows the specific activity in the presence of tetrabutylammonium ion.*

Acknowledgements

I wish to acknowledge the contributions of R. Raythatha,
J.G.S. Lee, L. Halloran, J. Hoffman, H.M. Chang, F. Farzaneh,
W.H. Quayle, and G. Garwood to various aspects of this work.   I
also wish to thank my colleague Professor M.M. Mortland for many
useful discussions.   Partial support of this work by the National
Science Foundation is gratefully acknowledged.

Literature Cited

1. Whitehurst, D.D. Chemtech, 1980, 44.
2. Gates, B.C.; Lieto, J. Chemtech, 1980, 195.
3. Grubbs, R.H. Chemtech, 1977, 512.
4. Hartley, F.R.; Vezey, P.N. Adv. Organomet. Chem., 1977, 15, 189.
5. Yermakov, Yu.I. Catal. Rev.-Sci. Eng., 1976, 13, 77.
6. Bailar, J.C. Jr. Catal. Rev.-Sci. Eng., 1974, 10, 17.
7. Grim, R.E. "Clay Mineralogy", 2nd ed., McGraw-Hill, New York, 1968, pp. 77-92.
8. Pinnavaia, T.J.; Raythatha, R.; Lee, J.G.S.; Halloran, L.J.; Hoffman, J.F. J Amer. Chem. Soc., 1979, 101, 6891.
9. Schrock, R.R.; Osborn, J.A. J. Amer. Chem. Soc., 1976, 98, 2134.
10. Cady, S.S.; Pinnavaia, T.J., Inorg. Chem., 1978, 17, 1501.
11. Raythatha, R.; Pinnavaia, T.J., unpublished results.
12. Quayle, W.H.; Pinnavaia, T.J. Inorg. Chem., 1979, 18, 2840.
13. Schrock, R.R.; Osborn, J.A. J. Amer. Chem. Soc., 1976, 98, 4450.
14. Raythatha, R.; Pinnavaia, T.J. J. Organomet. Chem., in press.
15. Kagan, H.B.; Dang, T.P. J. Amer. Chem. Soc., 1972, 94, 6429.
16. Fryzuk, M.D.; Bosnich, B. J. Amer. Chem. Soc., 1978, 100, 5491.
17. Chang, H.M.; Pinnavaia, T.J., unpublished results.
18. Mozzei, M.; Marconi, W.; Riocci, M. J. Molec. Catal., 1980, 9, 381.
19. Crabtree, R.H.; Felkin, H. J. Molec. Catal., 1979, 5, 75.
20. Farzaneh F.; Pinnavaia, T.J., unpublished results.
21. Garwood, G.; Mortland, M.M.; Pinnavaia, T.J., unpublished results.

RECEIVED November 4, 1981.

Selectivity Aspects of the Fischer–Tropsch Synthesis with Supported Iron Clusters

FRANÇOIS HUGUES, BERNARD BESSON, PAUL BUSSIERE, JEAN-ALAIN DALMON, MICHEL LECONTE, and JEAN-MARIE BASSET

I.R.C. C.N.R.S. 2 av. A. Einstein, 69626 Villeurbanne Cédex, France

YVES CHAUVIN and DOMINIQUE COMMEREUC

I.F.P. 2 av. de Bois-Préault 92000 Rueil-Malmaison, France

The catalysts derived from supported iron clusters exhibit in Fischer-Tropsch synthesis a high selectivity for propylene. Those catalysts are also selective for the stoechiometric homologation of ethylene to propylene and of propylene to n and iso butenes. The results are explained on the basis of a new mode of C–C bond formation which implies α – olefin coordination to surface methylene fragments or methylene insertion into a metal alkyl bond.

The mechanism of carbon–carbon bond formation in Fischer-Tropsch synthesis (1) has not yet been fully understood at the moment (2) (3). Three types of mechanisms have been proposed: (i) insertion of CO into a metal–alkyl bond to produce a metal-acyl species which undergoes further steps of hydrogenation(2c); (ii) insertion of a methylene fragment in a metal alkyl bond(2b); (iii) hydroxy–methylene condensation between two hydroxy-carbenes. We propose here a new mechanism of carbon–carbon bond formation in Fischer-Tropsch synthesis which is based on the recent discovery of a highly selective catalyst (3e) derived from molecular iron clusters (5). The catalyst which is selective for propylene in Fischer-Tropsch synthesis is also selective for ethylene homologation to propylene which suggests for Fischer-Tropsch a mechanism derived from the mechanism of olefin homologation recently proposed by Schrock (6a) and verified by others (6b).

Chemisorption of $Fe_3(CO)_{12}$ on a magnesia support (96 m^2/g) previously dehydroxylated at $150°C$ under vacuum (10^{-4} Torr) for 16 hours, (magnesia 150), leads to the formation of the anionic supported clusters $HFe_3(CO)_{11}^-$ and $Fe_3(CO)_{12}$ (ads) according to the following reactions (7):

$$Fe_3(CO)_{12} + Mg - OH \longrightarrow HFe_3(CO)_{11}^- \quad Mg^+ + CO_2 \quad \text{(a)}$$

$$Fe_3(CO)_{12} + Mg - O - Mg \longrightarrow Fe_3(CO)_{12} \text{ (ads)} \qquad \text{(b)}$$

Reaction (a) will occur mainly on a fully hydroxylated support whereas equilibrium (b) will occur on a fully dehydroxylated support (7) (8). Thermal decomposition of the adsorbed clusters under vacuum (10^{-4} Torr) for 16 hours at 130°C leads, inter alia (9), to the formation of very small particles of zerovalent iron. These very small iron particles exhibit a super paramagnetic behaviour as determined by Mössbauer spectroscopy (9) ferromagnetic resonance (10) and magnetic measurements (12). The average particle size deduced from the magnetic measurements was found to be 14 Å which corresponds to ca. 130 Fe atoms which is much larger than the nuclearity of the starting cluster (11). These very small particles supported on magnesia exhibit interesting selectivities when they are contacted either with CO + H_2, or with C_2H_4 or with C_3H_6 as indicated in the following examples.

In a typical example $Fe_3(CO)_{12}$ (0.026 g ; 0.052 m.mole) was chemisorbed in a sealed tube on a magnesia$_{(150)}$. The supported cluster was thermally decomposed as previously. The resulting catalyst contained 1.8% wght Fe/MgO.

Introduction of CO + H_2 (760 Torr) in a molar ratio 2 : 1 in the glass equipment was followed by a stepwise increase of temperature from 25 up to 200°C. Analysis of the gas phase gave the results represented on Figure 1a. At 176°C the conversion of CO to hydrocarbons is close to 1 % with mainly propylene (32%), methane (26,1 %) ethylene (9,2 %), 1-butene (7,3 %), cis-2-butene (3,6 %), trans-2-butene (5,5 %), isobutene (1 %) and C_5 hydrocarbons (7 %). All the paraffins except methane are present in much smaller amount than olefins. Figure (1b) represents typical results obtained in Fischer-Tropsch synthesis in a dynamic reactor using a catalyst derived from $Fe_3(CO)_{12}/Al_2O_3$ (3e).

The high selectivities for propylene which can be as high as 45 % (12) and the low selectivities for ethylene suggest that ethylene could be a primary product in Fischer-Tropsch which could undergo a secondary reaction leading selectivity to propylene. It was therefore logical to study the behaviour of ethylene on such catalysts. In another experiment $Fe_3(CO)_{12}$ (0.100 g ; 0.20 m.mole) was chemisorbed in a sealed tube on a magnesia$_{(150)}$ and then thermally decomposed as previously to give a catalyst containing 2 % wgth Fe/MgO. Introduction of C_2H_4 into this catalyst was followed by a thermal treatment at low temperature to avoid secondary reactions and high conversions. At 170°C, Figure 1c, ethylene is converted (about 3 %) to ethane (2 %) (self-hydrogenation) and to C_1 and C_3-C_4 products (1 %). These C_1 and C_3-C_4 products are propylene (70 %), CH_4 (5.9 %), 1-butene (11.3 %), cis-2-butene (4,5 %), trans-2-butene (5,7 %) and isobutene (1 %). Since high selectivity for propylene can be reached on the same catalyst and at the same temperature either from a mixture of CO + H_2 or from C_2H_4 alone, some elementary steps leading to propylene in both cases are likely to be the same : ethylene would be a primary product formed from CO + H_2 which would undergo a secondary reaction leading selectivity to propylene (13).

TABLE I

COMPARATIVE ACTIVITY OF VARIOUS

IRON BASED CATALYSTS

Catalyst	% Fe Wt	T°C	% Conv.	Selectivity to HC	Selectivity to olefins
$Fe_3(CO)_{12}/Al_2O_3$	0.82	270	3.3	100	57
*$Fe(CO)_5/Al_2O_3$	1.85	260	3.3	100	43
*$Fe(CO)_5/MgO$	0.50	265	1.4	100	60.3
$Fe(NO_3)_3/Al_2O_3$	8.1	270	19.4	62.6	38

* Mainly as $(HFe_3(CO)_{11})^-$. Flow reactor; amount of catalyst : 40 g. . selectivity and conversion are taken after 5 hours on stream.

$$\text{Conversion} = 100 \times \frac{\sum_{n=1}^{n=5} n\ (C_nH_{2n+2}) + \sum_{m=2}^{m=5} m(C_mH_{2m}) + CO_2}{CO\ \text{input}}$$

$$\begin{array}{c}\text{Selectivity to}\\ \text{HC}\end{array} = 100 \times \frac{\sum_1^5 n\ C_nH_{2n+2} + \sum_2^5 m\ C_mH_{2m}}{\sum_1^5 n\ C_nH_{2n+2} + \sum_2^5 m\ C_mH_{2m} + CO_2}$$

$$\begin{array}{c}\text{Selectivity to}\\ \text{olefins}\end{array} = 100 \times \frac{\sum_2^5 m\ C_mH_{2m}}{\sum_1^5 n\ C_nH_{2n+2} + \sum_2^5 m\ C_mH_{2m}}$$

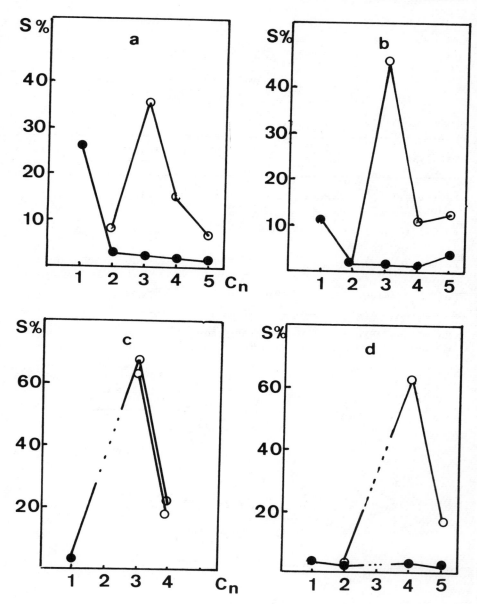

Figure 1.   Selectivities in the reactions $CO + H_2$ (a–b) or C_2H_4 (c) or C_3H_6 (d) with catalysts Fe/MgO (a,c,d) or Fe/Al_2O_3 (b). Temperatures: a, 176°C; b, 270°C; c, 170°C; d, 140°C. In c and d products larger than C_5 have been neglected. In c C_2H_4 in excess and C_2H_6 produced by self-hydrogenation of C_2H_4 is not represented. Key: ○, olefin; ●, paraffin.

Bath reactor. Amount of catalyst 400 mg, reaction time ca. 10 h. The catalysts are thermally and irreversibly decarbonylated at 150°C before catalytic run.

Since butenes were also produced from CO + H_2 or C_2H_4 on the same Fe/MgO catalyst it was logical to study the behaviour of propylene on such catalyst. In a third experiment $Fe_3(CO)_{12}$ (40 mg ; 0.08 m.mole) was chemisorbed on a magnesia$_{150}$ (1.1. g) and thermally decomposed under vacuum as previously described. C_3H_6 (140 Torr) was introduced into this supported catalyst which was heated stepwise from 25 up to 200°C. At 140°C propylene was converted to propane (0.3 %) (self-ydrogenation) and to a mixture of C_1, C_2, C_4, C_5, mainly olefinic, hydrocarbons (0.1 %). In the C_1, C_2, C_4, C_5 fraction the selectivity for butenes was 65 % (CH_4 : 5.9 %, C_2H_4 : 5.9 %, C_4H_8 : 65 %, C_5H_{10} : 17 %) which indicates that homologation of propylene to butenes occurs via a "C_1" surface fragment (2b). At 140°C the butene fraction contains 1-butene (79 %), trans-2-butene (6 %), cis-2-butene (12 %) and isobutene (3 %). At 168°C the butene fraction contains 1-butene (15 %), cis-2-butene (32,6 %), trans-2-butene (44,9 %) and isobutene (9,1 %) ; the pentene fraction contains 90 % linear pentene and 10 % of isopentenes (fig. 1d).

The above results indicate that small iron particles, having sizes close to 14 Å, exhibit in Fischer-Tropsch synthesis a rather high selectivity for propylene and a low selectivity for methane. Even higher selectivities have been observed with $Fe_3(CO)_{12}/Al_2O_3$ (3e) (45 %) or with Co clusters encapsulated within the pores (11 Å) of "A type" zeolites (100 %) (14). Such high selectivites have probably a mechanistical origin with respect to the mode of C-C bond formation. Selective formation of propylene from CO + H_2 or from C_2H_4 as well as selective formation of butenes from propylene on the same catalyst suggest the following mechanism for propagation.

Formation of CH_4 from C_2H_4 (or from C_3H_6) can be accounted for by homolytic cleavage of C_2H_4 (and C_3H_6) into surface carbene species most likely methylene, which can be further dehydrogenated to carbyne like and surface carbon fragments (15). It is not unreasonable to assume that during Fischer-Tropsch experiment, CO is dissociated (16) to surface carbon (17) and "Fe^{2+} oxo species" (18). The surface carbon would undergo the reverse of reaction (1) that is hydrogenation to methylene and coupling of methylene to give ethylene (19).

Propagation involves coordination of the α-olefin to the surface carbene giving rise to a metallo-cyclobutane transition state followed by β-H transfer. Similar reaction has been observed recently by Pettit (20) who selectively obtained propylene from the reaction of ethylene with an octacarbonyl-μ-methylene-diiron complex.

The next propagation step involves propylene coordination to the surface carbene with formation of n-butene reaction (3) or isobutene reaction (4) . The high selectivity for n-olefin, in our experiments as well as in conventional Fischer-Tropsch catalysts, must be accounted for by a selective coordination and (or) reaction of the   olefin (21) according to reaction (3) which is probably due to the electrophilic character of the surface

$$C_2H_4 \ + \ n\,Fe \ \longrightarrow \ \underset{Fe \ - \ Fe}{\overset{CH_2}{\diagup \ \diagdown}} \ \overset{+H}{\longrightarrow} \ \underset{Fe}{\overset{CH_3}{|}} \ \overset{+H}{\longrightarrow} \ CH_4 \ \ + \ n\,Fe \qquad (1)$$

$$-H \ \downarrow$$

$$\underset{Fe \ - \ Fe \ - \ Fe}{\overset{CH}{\diagup \ | \ \diagdown}} \ \overset{-H}{\longrightarrow} \ \underset{Fe \ - \ Fe \ - \ Fe \ - \ Fe}{\overset{C}{\diagup \ | \ \diagdown}}$$

$$\underset{Fe \ - \ Fe}{\overset{CH_2}{\diagup \ \diagdown}} \ + \ C_2H_4 \ \longrightarrow \ \underset{Fe \ - \ Fe}{\diagup \diagdown} \ \longrightarrow \ C_3H_6 \ \ + \ \ n\,Fe \qquad (2)$$

$$\underset{Fe \ - \ Fe}{\overset{CH_2}{\diagup \ \diagdown}} \ + \ C_3H_6 \ \longrightarrow \ \underset{Fe \ - \ Fe}{\diagup \diagdown} \ \longrightarrow \ n\text{-}C_4H_8 \qquad (3)$$

$$\underset{Fe \ - \ Fe}{\overset{CH_2}{\diagup \ \diagdown}} \ + \ C_3H_6 \ \longrightarrow \ \underset{Fe \ - \ Fe}{\diagup \diagdown} \ \longrightarrow \ i\text{-}C_4H_8 \qquad (4)$$

$$\underset{Fe \ - \ Fe}{\overset{CH_2}{\diagup \ \diagdown}} \ + \ R\text{-}CH{=}CH_2 \ \longrightarrow \ \underset{Fe \ - \ Fe}{\overset{R}{\diagup \diagdown}} \ \longrightarrow \ R\text{-}CH_2\text{-}CH{=}CH_2 \qquad (5)$$

$$\underset{Fe \ - \ Fe}{\overset{CH_2}{\diagup \ \diagdown}} \ + \ R\text{-}CH{=}CH_2 \ \longrightarrow \ \underset{Fe \ - \ Fe}{\overset{R}{\diagup \diagdown}} \ \longrightarrow \ R\text{-}C(CH_3){=}CH_2 \qquad (6)$$

$$\underset{Fe \ - \ Fe \ - \ Fe}{\overset{CH_2}{\diagup} \quad \overset{CH_2}{|}{\nearrow}^{R}} \ \longrightarrow \ \underset{Fe}{\overset{CH_2}{|}\overset{CH_2\text{-}R}{}} \ \longrightarrow \ R\text{-}CH{=}CH_2 \qquad (7)$$

Possible mechanisms for C-C bond formation in Fischer-Tropsch.

carbene. This electrophilic character of surface CH_x species has been shown to occur on metal surfaces by work-function measurements (22) as we l as with "carbidic iron clusters" which were found to be carbocationic in character (17a). Such electropositive carbene would be the reason for reaction (3) to occur rather than reaction (4) which should be favored for steric reasons.

The high selectivity for α-olefins may be due to the selective β-H transfer from the C_2 carbon of the metallo-cycle to the most substituted carbon of the metallo-cyclobutane. Such selectivity in the β-hydrogen transfer was observed when ethylene or propylene was reacted with $TaCp(CHCMe_3)Cl_2$ (23). It is impossible to decide whether or not the metallo-cyclobutane involve a single Fe atom, two iron atoms as suggested by Pettit's experiments (19) or an "ensemble" of many iron atoms. However thermal decomposition of platinacyclobutanes (24) or tungsta-cyclobutanes (26) lead to a β-hydrogen transfer leading to the corresponding olefins (16).

Mechanistically it is logical to observe high selectivity for propylene if we assume that coupling of methylene to ethylene as well as ethylene coordination to surface carbene are fast reactions. Propylene for steric hindrance would react more slowly than ethylene with surface carbene reaction (3) whereas reaction (4) would be less favored for electronic reasons. It is difficult at this point to speculate why the selectivity for propylene is associated with small iron particles. One possibility is that the small iron particles displace the equilibrium olefin$_{(ads)}$ $\rightleftharpoons$ olefin$_{(gas)}$ and prevent thus further steps of propagation via the olefin + carbene mechanism ; besides these small Fe particles would have small hydrogenation properties which thus avoid methane formation from the carbene and saturated hydrocarbon formation from the olefin.

In conclusion, although our results do not rule out the mechanism of carbene insertion into a metal-alkyl bond (2b), the possibility of making C - C bonds in Fischer-Tropsch via a carbene-olefin mechanism should be considered as an alternative path. Further studies are in progress to decide between both types of mechanisms.

LITERATURE CITED

(1)   Fischer F., and Tropsch, H., Brenstoff. Chem. 7, 97 (1926).

(2)   a. Pichler, H., in Advances in Catalysis, Frankenburg, W.G., Komarewsky, V.I., and Rideal E.K., Eds., 4, 271 Academic Press, New York, (1952).
b. Biloen, P., Helle, J.N., and Sachtler, W.M.H., J. Catal. 58, 95 (1979)
c. Henrici-Olive, G., and Olive, S., Angew. Chem. Int. Ed., Engl., 15, 136 (1976).
d. Storch, H.H., Golumbic, N., and Anderson, R.B., The Fischer-Tropsch and related synthesis, Wiley, New-York (1951).

(3)   Usually typical heterogeneous Fischer-Tropsch catalysts

give a broad range of hydrocarbon distributions. It is only recently that selective Fischer-Tropsch catalysts have been reported ; some of them include new catalysts derived from molecular clusters either in solution or supported on inorganic oxides. See for example :

a. Muetterties, E.L., Bull. Soc. Chim. Belg. 84, 859 (1975).

b. Pruett, R.L., Ann. N.Y. Acad. Sc., 295, 239 (1977).

c. Ichikawa, M., J. Chem. Soc. Chem. Comm., 11 and 26 (1976).

d. Smith, A.K., Theolier, A., Basset, J.M., Ugo, R., Commereuc, D., and Chauvin, Y., J. Amer. Chem. Soc., 100, 2590 (1978).

e. Commereuc, D., Chauvin, Y., Hugues, F., Basset, J.M., and Olivier, D., J. Chem. Soc., Comm., 154 (1980).

f. Blanchard, M., Vanhove, D., Petit, F., and Mortreux, H., J. Chem. Soc., Chem. Comm., 908 (1980).

g. Kugler, E.L., A.C.S. meeting Petrol. divis., San Francisco, 564 (19).

(4)   In the mechanism proposed by Biloen et al. (2d) it is assumed that a CH_3 fragment "jumps" on top of a $CH_{2_{ads}}$ fragment to form a $CH_3 - CH_2$ (ads) species. This could be formally interpreted as a cis-migration of an alkyl ligand, Such cis-migration was demonstrated in only very few cases with free carbenes : CH_2 was inserted into the Ni - R bond of NiR_2 (bpy) to afford $R - CH_2 - CH_2 - R$ see Yamamoto, T., J.C.S. Chem. Comm., 617 (1978). The reverse reaction was observed by McLain, S.J., Sancho, J., and Schrock, R.R., J. Amer. Chem. Soc., 101, 5451 (1979) ; metallo-cyclopentane may lead to metallo-cyclobutane+carbene by ring contraction. The opposite path which involves insertion of a carbene in a metallo-cyclobutane is not unreasonable.

(5)   The analogy between molecular clusters and small metal-particles and (or) surfaces was put forward recently. See for example : Muetterties, E.L., Rhodin, T.N., Band, E., Brucker, C.F., and Pretzer, W.R., Chem. Rev., 79, 91 (1979) ; Basset, J.M., and Ugo, R. in Aspects of Homogeneous Catalysis, Ugo, R., Edition Reidel, 3, 137 (1977).

(6)   a. McLain, S.J., Wood, C.D., and Schrock, R.R., J. Amer, Chem. Soc., 101, 4558 (1979).

b. Johnson, T.H., and Cheng., S.S., J. Amer Chem. Soc., 101, 5277 (1979).

(7)   a. Hugues, F., Smith, A.K., Ben Taarit, Y., Basset, J.M., Commereuc, D., and Chauvin, Y., J.C.S. Chem. Comm., 68 (1980).

b. Hugues, F., Besson, B., Primet, M., and Basset, J.M., to be published.

(8)   On a partially dehydroxylated support both species will be present. Thermal decomposition of $Fe_3(CO)_{12}$ supported on alumina has also been studied by Brenner, A., J.C.S. Chem. Comm., 251 (1979) ; Brenner, A., and Hucul, D.A., Inorg. Chem., 18, 2836 (1979).

(9)   The Mössbauer spectrum taken at 298 K exhibits a single peak at 0.32 mm/s with respect to sodium nitroprusside. The occurence of a single line for metallic iron instead of a six line spectrum usually observed means that iron is present in very small super-paramagnetic particles. See for example : Dumesic, S.A., Tøpse, H., Khammouna, S., and Boudart, M., J. Catal., 37, 503 (1975). On a magnesia support which is not fully dehydroxylated, Mössbauer spectroscopy also indicate the formation of Fe^{2+} (doublet at 1.52 mm/s with respect to sodium nitroprusside).

(10)   The FMR spectra, taken at varying temperature (77 up to 473 K) gave an anisotropic original with a g_{300K} value which is shifted with respect to that of bulk iron (2.062 compared with 2.12). The decrease of the linewidth with increasing temperature is characteristic of a ferromagnetic compound. The decrease of the magnetization with increasing temperature indicates a superparamagnetic behaviour of the iron particle. Derouane, E.G., Simoens, A.J., Colin, C., Martin, G.A., Dalmon, J.A., and Vedrine, J.C., J. Catal., 52, 50 (1978). Hugues, F., Bussière, P., Basset, J.M., Commereuc, D., Chauvin, Y., Bonneviot, L., and Olivier, D., Preprints VII. Int. Cong. Catal., Tokyo, July 3rd 1980, paper A.51.

(11)   It was possible to measure accurately the average metal particle size from the magnetization curve taken at 4.2 K with magnetic fields ranging from 0 up to 70 k. Oe (supraconductive coil).

(12)   With small particles of Co encapsulated in A type zeolite and obtained by Cd metal vapor reduction of Co^{2+}, a selectivity for propylene from syn-gas as high as 100 % was recently observed : Frenkel, D., and Gates, B.C., J. Amer. Chem. Soc., 102, 2478 (1980).

(13)   Radioactive ethylene was found to be incorporated in the propagation chain products in Fe based Fischer-Tropsch catalysts. However the catalysts used exhibited a poor selectivity. See for example : Hall, W.K., Kokes, R.J., and Emmet, P.H., J. Amer. Chem. Soc., 82, 1027 (1960) ; Timmer, J.T., and Emmet, P.H., J. Amer. Chem. Soc., 75 5177 (1953). Radioactive ethanol, propanol and isopropanol were also shown to be incorporated in the growing chain. But, the most important radioactivity was found respectively in the C_2 fraction (C_2H_4 + C_2H_6), C_3 fraction (C_3H_6 + C_3H_8), and C_3 fraction (C_3H_6 + C_3H_8) which indicates that non oxygenated species (such as olefins) might be responsible for this incorporation.

(14)   Although it is assumed in ref. (12) that the selectivity for propylene is due to the shape-selective A-type zeolite, we believe that selectivity is mainly due to particle size effect since non porous aluminas with small particles of Fe(15 Å) leads also to high selectivity see also ref. (3e). The higher selectivity observed in ref. (12) with Co-clus-

ters might be explained by the sharp distribution of low
particle size obtained with zeolithic support (11 Å). In
our case, magnetic measurements indicated a slightly broader distribution with particle sizes ranging from 6 up to
20 Å, which might explain the relatively smaller selectivity of our catalyst. For the shape selectivity effect versus particle size effect in Fischer-Tropsch synthesis. See
also : Vanhove, D., Makambo, P. and Blanchard, M., J. Chem.
Soc. Comm., 605 (1979), and Nije, H., Jacobs, P.A., and
Uytterhoeven, J.M., J. Chem. Soc. Chem. Comm., 1095 (1979).

(15)   C - C bond scission occurs for ethylene chemisorption above
300 K on Fe(100) and Fe(111) crystal surfaces. CO decomposition lead to the same sequence of surface structure as
C_2H_4, which are mainly due to surface carbon Yoshida, K.,
and Somorjai, C.A., Surf. Sc., 75, 45 (1978) and references
there in.

(16)   On Fe, Co, Ni and Ru metal particles, CO is dissociatively
chemisorbed above ca. 423 K into surface carbon, which is
probably triply bridged, and "metal-oxo" species. See for
example : Martin, G.A., Primet, M. and Dalmon, J.A., J.
Catal., 53, 321 (1978) ; Rabo, J.A., Risch, A.P., and
Poulma, M.L., J. catal., 53, 295 (1978) ; Wentrcek, P.R.,
Wood, B.J., and Wise H., J. Catal., 43, 363 (1976) ; Low,
G.G., and Bell, A.T., J. Catal., 57, 397 (1979) ; McCarty,
J.J., and Wise, H., J. Catal., 57, 406 (1979). The reverse
of reaction (1) leading from dissociated CO to surface carbene and to ethylene is therefore a reasonable path under
H_2 atmosphere.

(17)   The reactivity of surface carbon relevant to Fischer-
Tropsch synthesis begins to be understood from the recent
works on iron clusters containing coordinatively unsaturated "carbidic" carbon or η^2-CH ligands :
a. Bradley, J.S., Ansell, G.B., and Hill, E.W., J. Amer
Chem. Soc., 101, 7417 (1979)
b. Beno, M.A., Williams, J.M., Tachikawa, M., and Muetterties, E.L., J. Amer. Chem. Soc., in press (1980).

(18)   Such phenomenon also occurs during the transformation of
$Fe_3(CO)_{12}$ into small iron particles as determined by Mös-
bauer spectroscopy and magnetic measurements.

(19)   Coupling of carbene to form olefin has been shown to occur
with $(CO)_5$ W = C(ϕ)$_2$ which gives tetraphenyl ethylene :
Casey, C.P., and Burkhardt, T.J., J. Amer. Chem. Soc., 95,
5833 (1973) ; ibidem., 96, 7808 (1974). See also, Brady,
R.C. and Pettit, R., J. Amer. Chem. Soc., 102, 6181 (1980).
Masters, C., J. Amer. Chem. Soc., 101, 1633 (1979).

(20)   Summer, C.E., Riley, J.P., Davis, R.E., and Pettit, R., J.
Amer. Chem. Soc., 102, 1754 (1980).

(21)   Readsorption and secondary reactions of the intiailly produced α-olefins is an important pathway in Fischer-Tropsch
reactions on Fe single crystals : Dwyer, D.J., and Somorjai,
G.A., J. Catal., 56, 249, (1979). Schulz, H., and Achtsnit,

H., Proc. 5th Ibero-American Symposium on Catalysis, Lisbon, Protugal (1976), also Schulz, H., private communication.

(22) Although there are no data available on Fe, dissociative chemisorption of C_2H_4 on Platinum single crystal surfaces (210), (110) and (533) produces a decrease of work function which means that CH_x fragments arising from such dissociation are electrophilic in character : van Strien, A.J., and Nieuwenhuys, B.E., Surf. Sc., 80, 226 (1979). Bonzel, H.P., and Krebs, H.J., Surf. Sc., 91, 499 (1980).

(23) McLain, S.J. Wood, C.D., and Schrock, R.R., J. Amer. Chem. Soc., 101, 4558 (1979).

(24) Johnson, T.H., and Cheng, S.S., J. Amer. Chem. Soc., 101, 5277 (1979).

(25) Adam, G.J., Davies, S.G., Ford, K.A., Ephritikine, M. Todd, P.T. and Green, M.L.H., J. Mol. Catal., 8, 15 (1980).

(26) Photochemical activation of tungstacyclobutanes lead to metathesis like products : Ephritikine, M., and Green, M.L.H., J.C.S. Chem. Comm., 926 (1976). Thermal decomposition leads to homologation.

RECEIVED November 4, 1981.

Reactivity of Catalysts Derived from Organometallics Directly Deposited on Supports

T. J. THOMAS, DENNIS A. HUCUL, and ALAN BRENNER

Wayne State University, Department of Chemistry, Detroit, MI 48202

Static and reactive characterization of organometallics directly deposited on supports delineate five parameters which are important in controlling catalytic activity: coordinative unsaturation, oxidation state, dispersion, immobilization, and cluster size. The means of measuring and controlling these experimental parameters is described and the catalysts are contrasted to more traditional heterogeneous and homogeneous catalysts. Unlike immobilized homogeneous catalysts, these catalysts strongly interact with the support and generally do not retain their molecular character. Numerous activity data from model reactions (ethylene hydrogenation, ethane hydrogenolysis, and methanation) are given. In a number of cases the directly deposited organometallics have a much higher catalytic activity than their homogeneous counterparts, and sometimes also possess significantly higher dispersions and activity than traditional (salt derived) heterogeneous catalysts. A simple structure-activity relationship allows the predictions of the optimal pretreatment of a supported organometallic and when the resulting catalyst is likely to be significantly more active than a traditional heterogeneous catalyst.

During the last several years our research group has been involved in the development of a new class of heterogeneous catalysts: organometallics directly deposited on high surface area refractory supports such as alumina, silica, and molecular sieves. These materials physically lie at the frontier between traditional homogeneous and heterogeneous catalysts (note that the metal is not insulated from the support by a chain of ligands and these are not immobilized homogeneous catalysts) and in fact can combine the better features of both types of catalysts, Table I.

0097-6156/82/0192-0267 $6.00/0

Table I
Advantages of Organometallics Directly
Deposited on Refractory Supports

1. Many catalyst precursors
2. Unusual catalyst configurations (such as clusters)
3. Easier characterization
4. Immobilization of coordinatively unsaturated sites.
5. High thermal and chemical stability.

Over the last few years a number of papers have been published
dealing with the characterization (especially by infrared
spectroscopy) of supported organometallics (especially carbonyl
complexes) (1). There have also been scattered reports indicating
that these catalysts can be prepared in higher dispersions (2)
than their traditional analogs (made by aqueous impregnation with
metal salts followed by calcination and reduction) and can have
improved activity for several reactions including the
hydrogenation of olefins (3,4), metathesis (5,6), methanation
(7,8), and Fischer–Tropsch synthesis (9). In this report static
and reactive characterization techniques are combined to achieve a
systematic understanding of the surface chemistry of these new
catalysts and to derive a simple structure–activity relationship
which is invaluable for the development of improved catalysts.

Experimental Section

Catalysts were prepared by physically dispersing a carbonyl
complex on γ–alumina (Conoco Catapal SB, usually calcined at 500
$^\circ$C) by impregnation from pentane solution or sublimation of the
solid carbonyl. The catalysts were activated and partially
characterized by temperature programmed decomposition (TPDE).
Briefly, TPDE involves raising the temperature at a linear rate of
about 5 $^\circ$C/min as He is swept through a glass reactor and the
evolution of gases (primarily CO and H_2) is continuously monitored
with a pair of thermal conductivity detectors. Other gases formed
during TPDE (primarily CH_4 and CO_2) are analyzed separately after
TPDE by backflushing through a trap of silica gel which was held
at –196 $^\circ$C during the run. Details of the rigorously air free
catalyst preparation, the high purity reaction system, and TPDE
technique have been previously published (10,11).
Dispersion measurements were usually done at 25 $^\circ$C. A very
accurate pressure transducer was used which allows the measurement
of about 0.001 cm^3 of adsorbed gas. Details of the chemisorption
methodology have been published (12).
All activity measurements were done with a flow system
immediately after catalyst activation and without removing the

catalyst or reactor from the reaction line. Flows were controlled and monitored with an electronic mass flow controller (Brooks Instrument). The effluent from a reactor was analyzed at roughly 1 min intervals using a motor driven gas sampling valve (Carle). Standard methods of gas chromatographic analysis were used, with the peak integrations being done by a Spectrophysics System I integrator.

Activity measurements are expressed as a formal turnover frequency, N_f. N_f is the number of molecules reacting per unit time per metal atom on the catalyst. Note that N_f does not correct for the dispersion of a metal, and in fact $N_f = D \cdot N$, where N is the normal turnover frequency and D is the fractional dispersion of the catalyst. N_f and N are seen to be complimentary concepts. N_f is more useful for measuring the true efficiency of a catalyst since artificaly high activities are not generated by a catalyst with a very low dispersion.

Synthetic Methodology

For a variety of reasons largely related to experimental expediency (such as ease of availability, simple stoichiometry, and the small adsorption of CO(g) on a support), these studies have specifically focused on supported transition metal carbonyl complexes. However, it is felt that carbonyls are merely models for low-valent organometallics and it is likely that the observed patterns of surface chemistry and activity have general validity. The method of catalyst synthesis is radically different from that for a traditional heterogeneous catalyst, as indicated by Figure 1. Whereas traditional methodology involves impregnation with an aqueous solution of a high valent salt and requires a high temperature reduction, the carbonyl route starts with a zero valent complex and inert solvent (or no solvent at all) and often requires only mild thermal activation. As suggested by Figure 1, except for the more noble group 8 metals many elements are difficult to reduce when supported, so the traditional route of synthesis can confine a catalyst to only the high valent states. This restriction need not operate with supported organometallics. This in turn suggests that there might be a strong dichotomy in the nature of supported carbonyls, with complexes of difficult to reduce metals yielding very different catalysts than their traditional analogs.

Static Characterization

In this phase of the study emphasis has been placed on several properties which can be directly related to catalytic activity: stoichiometry, oxidation state, and dispersion. Since most carbonyl complexes are coordinatively saturated, it is clear that ligands must dissociate to develop active sites. Further, since the adsorption of CO(g) is quite small on the supports and CO is a rather stable molecule, it follows that the development of coordinative unsaturation should correlate with the evolution of CO(g) during activaton. However, it has also been shown that during activation incipient zero valent metal formed by the decomposition of a complex can undergo a redox reaction with hydroxyl groups which are on the surface of most supports, equation 1 (13).

$$M(CO)_j + n(\sigma\text{-OH}) \xrightarrow{\Delta} (\sigma\text{-O}^-)_n M^{n+} + (n/2)H_2 + jCO \qquad (1)$$

Again, it is important to note that $H_2(g)$ is not adsorbed on a support so the evolution of H_2 during catalyst synthesis is a very simple measure of a dramatic change in the nature of the catalyst from a low valent material to something resembling a supported metal oxide. (Although H_2 evolution is the main reaction causing oxidation, other reactions can also modestly contribute (13). There is good agreement between the oxidation number as determined by gas evolutions and as independently measured by chemical titration (13)).

In order to simultaneously monitor CO and H_2 evolutions during thermal activation, the technique of temperature programmed decomposition (TPDE) has been developed. This technique is fast, simple, inexpensive, gives reproducible results, can be made highly quantitative ($\pm 1\%$), and is extremely sensitive (<1 µmole of complex). Figures 2 and 3 illustrate a salient feature of the stoichiometry of supported complexes. Decomposition of an unsupported complex (either in bulk or in solution) usually occurs in a narrow temperature range to yield a low surface area metallic mirror (and perhaps other products) of low activity. However, decomposition on a support starts at lower temperatures and proceeds to higher temperatures, yielding a broad range of unique subcarbonyl species.

A study of the oxidation of supported complexes has been recently published and is summarized in Table II (13). It is immediately clear that decomposition at temperatures high enough to effect complete decarbonylation also results in the oxidation of the initially zero valent complex. The means of controlling the oxidation state of the product catalyst has been carefully studied and will be reported in detail separately. Activating at a temperature just below the onset of H_2 evolution will yield a fairly decomposed subcarbonyl catalyst which is still presumedly zero valent. It is also known that pretreatment of alumina at high temperatures reduces the concentration of hydroxyl groups (14). Activation at 1000 °C leaves the alumina about 0.6% hydroxylated, compared to 28% when activated at 500 °C. The surface area is also reduced to 125 m^2/g (from 203 m^2/g for a 500 °C activation) and some phase changes may have occurred, but it is clear that collapse to low surface area α-Al_2O_3 has not happened. Therefore, conditioning the support near 1000 °C will nearly completely inhibit reaction (1) and lead to the formation of primarily zero valent material upon TPDE to 600 °C.

The dispersion of supported carbonyls is a function of many

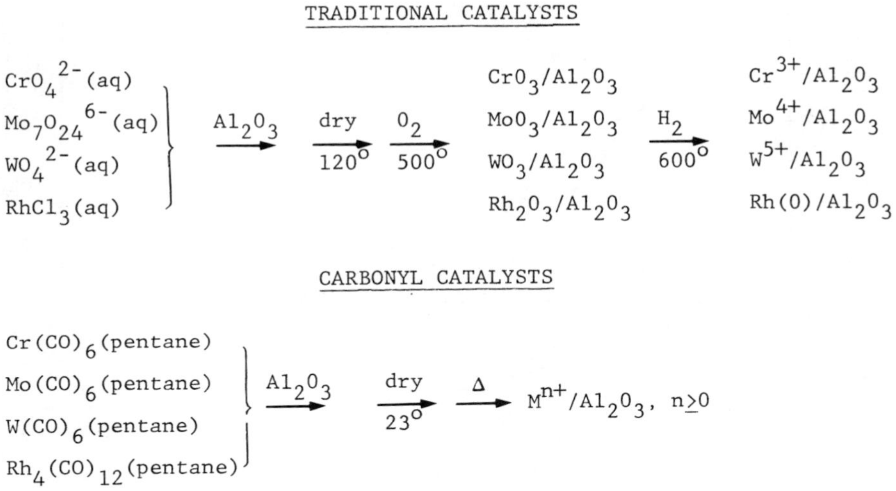

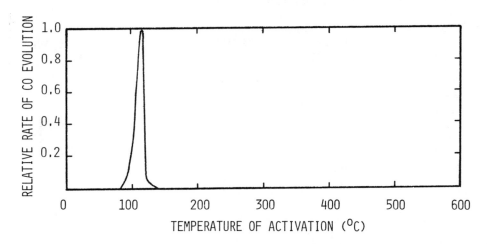

TRADITIONAL CATALYSTS

$$CrO_4^{2-}(aq)$$
$$Mo_7O_{24}^{6-}(aq)$$
$$WO_4^{2-}(aq)$$
$$RhCl_3(aq)$$

$$\xrightarrow{Al_2O_3} \quad \xrightarrow[120^o]{dry} \quad \xrightarrow[500^o]{O_2}$$

$$CrO_3/Al_2O_3$$
$$MoO_3/Al_2O_3$$
$$WO_3/Al_2O_3$$
$$Rh_2O_3/Al_2O_3$$

$$\xrightarrow[600^o]{H_2}$$

$$Cr^{3+}/Al_2O_3$$
$$Mo^{4+}/Al_2O_3$$
$$W^{5+}/Al_2O_3$$
$$Rh(0)/Al_2O_3$$

CARBONYL CATALYSTS

$$Cr(CO)_6(pentane)$$
$$Mo(CO)_6(pentane)$$
$$W(CO)_6(pentane)$$
$$Rh_4(CO)_{12}(pentane)$$

$$\xrightarrow{Al_2O_3} \quad \xrightarrow[23^o]{dry} \quad \xrightarrow{\Delta} \quad M^{n+}/Al_2O_3, \ n \geq 0$$

Figure 1. Catalyst syntheses.

Figure 2. TPDE of unsupported $Fe_3(CO)_{12}$ (12).

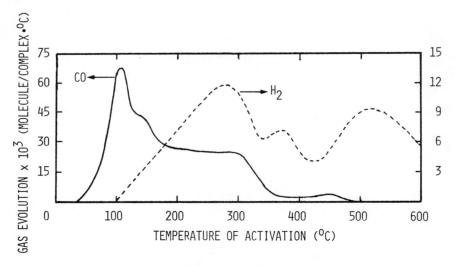

Figure 3.   TPDE of $Fe_3(CO)_{12}/Al_2O_3$ (12).

Table II
Oxidation of Catalysts During TPDE in Flowing He to 600 °C

Complex	Temperature (°C) at Which O.N $\cong$ 0.5	Average O.N. After TPDE (per Metal Atom)
$V(CO)_6$	440	2.5
$Cr(CO)_6$	170	4.5
$Mo(CO)_6$	290	4.6
$W(CO)_6$	220	5.5
$Mn_2(CO)_{10}$	160	1.4
$Re_2(CO)_{10}$	200	5.4
$Fe_3(CO)_{12}$	230	2.4
$Ru_3(CO)_{12}$	260	4.0
$Os_3(CO)_{12}$	270	3.6
$Co_4(CO)_{12}$	380	2.2
$Rh_4(CO)_{12}$	400	2.0
$Ir_4(CO)_{12}$	410	1.8
$Ni(CO)_4$	320	1.6

variables, especially the temperature of activation, exposure to gases (particulary those that will lead to irreversible oxidation of a catalyst), and loading. A number of carbonyl catalysts have been prepared (variable pretreatment, but usually 200 °C in He) which have substantially higher dispersions than a traditional catalyst (generally reduced at 400 °C in flowing H_2) of similar loading. Representative data is shown in Table III (current work under more standard conditions is giving even higher dispersions in some cases (15)).

Reactive Characterization

Reactive characterization involves the use of simple test reactions to determine the patterns of activity of catalysts. For this study ethylene hydrogenation, ethane hydrogenolysis, and methanation have been chosen. Each of these model reactions tests a certain reactive functionality (simple olefin hydrogenation, C–C bond cleavage, and CO reduction, respectively), is simple to run, and primarily yields a single product. Also, there is substantial data in the literature for the activity of conventional catalysts.

Combining activity and TPDE data quickly leads to a simple theory for the designed synthesis of optimal catalysts. As shown in Figure 4, a TPDE chromatogram usually divides the surface chemistry of a supported complex into three distinct regions. In the α region there is only slight loss of CO, so the catalysts are presumedly coordinatively saturated and therefore should be of very low activity. In the β region, the complexes have lost considerable CO (potentially developing coordinative unsaturation) but have had only slight H_2 evolution, indicating that the catalyst is still close to zero valent. The γ region is defined as the region in which there is essentially complete evolution of CO(g). Normally it would be expected that activation in this regime would yield the most active catalyst. However, TPDE shows that complete decarbonylation is usually accompanied by the evolution of H_2. Hence, these catalysts are also substantially oxidized and therefore are expected to have low activity for the types of reactions being considered here. Thus, one arrives at the following formula for catalyst synthesis on most supports:

> Catalysts of difficult to reduce metals (such as V, Cr, Mo, W, Mn, Fe, Co, and Ni) should be most active after activation in the β region since this maximizes coordinative unsaturation but leaves a catalyst low valent.

> Catalysts of easily reducible metals (such as Ru, Os, Rh, and Ir) can be active both after activation in the β region and after activation in the γ region followed by reduction. The last treatment should leave a catalyst both completely decarbonylated and zero valent.

Table III
Enhanced Dispersion* of Carbonyl Catalysts

Metal or Complex	Loading (%M)	% Dispersion	
		Carbonyl	$(\frac{Carbonyl}{Salt})$
$Cr(CO)_6$	0.9	20	20
$Mo(CO)_6$	0.9	90	100
$W(CO)_6$	0.1	46	100
$Re_2(CO)_{10}$	0.2	46	100
$Fe(CO)_5$	0.4	16	30
$Ru_3(CO)_{12}$	0.1	172	5
$Os_3(CO)_{12}$	0.1	13	16
$Co_2(CO)_8$	0.1	4	7
$Ni(CO)_4$	0.2	16	4

* % dispersion = $100(CO/M)$. In some cases the adsorption stoichiometry is not 1 CO:1 M, but this will not effect the comparison of carbonyl and salt derived catalysts.

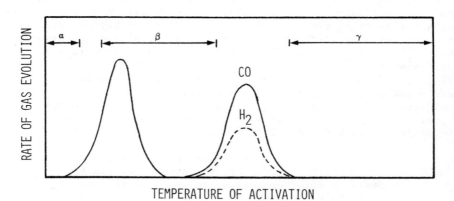

Figure 4.   *Primary regions of surface composition during the thermal activation of a supported carbonyl complex.*

<u>Hydrogenation</u> of <u>Ethylene</u>. This test reaction has been run under a variety of activation conditions. Catalysts derived from $Cr(CO)_6$, $Mo(CO)_6$, $W(CO)_6$, $Ru_3(CO)_{12}$, $Os_3(CO)_{12}$, and the Fe carbonyls have been found to be at least 10-fold more active than their traditional counterparts. The dichotomy between the more difficult to reduce metals and those easier to reduce is beautifully exemplified by the data in Tables IV and V. It is seen that catalysts derived from the more difficult to reduce metals show better activity after activation in the β region, whereas catalysts derived from more noble metals are more active after a high temperature reduction. It might also be noted that these catalysts are orders of magnitude more active than immobilized carbonyl complexes (16).

As already noted, TPDE on a dehydroxylated alumina should afford a route to completely decarbonylated but still low valent catalysts of difficult to reduce metals (17,18). As expected, the activities of $Cr(CO)_6$, $Mo(CO)_6$, and $W(CO)_6$ after TPDE to 600 °C are extremely high (N_f at 0 °C is about 1, 27, and 1 s^{-1}, respectively). Especially for Mo and W these are by far the most active hydrogenation catalysts of these metals ever reported (excepting evaporated metal films of low surface area). On the other hand, when supported on a more conventional alumina (pretreated at 500 °C), TPDE to 600 °C results in catalysts of very low activity because the average oxidation state is about 5.

Table VI illustrates still another important property of supports vis-a-vis homogeneous carbonyl complexes; the ability to immobilize coordinatively unsaturated sites. It is noteworthy that in solution $Fe(CO)_5$ maintained a slight activity only in the presence of continued irradiation, whereas all measurements on the supported catalysts were made in the dark after photoactivation.

Table IV
Activity for the Hydrogenation of Ethylene

| | N_f (s^{-1}) | | |
| | Activated | Activated | (H_2/He) |
Catalyst	200 °C, He	600 °C, H_2	Activity
$Cr(CO)_6$	0.04	0.006	0.15
$Mo(CO)_6$	0.05	0.03	0.6
$W(CO)_6$	0.016	0.0007	0.04
$Mn_2(CO)_{10}$	0.00009	0.00008	0.9
$Fe_3(CO)_{12}$	0.013	0.0009	0.07

T = 0°C, H_2/C_2H_4 = 4, P = 1 atm.

Table V
Activity for the Hydrogenation of Ethylene

	N_f (s^{-1})		
Catalyst	Activated 200 °C, He	Activated 600 °C, H_2	(H_2/He) Activity
$Re_2(CO)_{10}$	0.13	7.3	56
$Ru_3(CO)_{12}$	1.8	225	125
$Os_3(CO)_{12}$	0.16	11	69
$Rh_4(CO)_{12}$	8	140	18
$Ir_4(CO)_{12}$	0.057	7.5	132

$T = 0°C$, $H_2/C_2H_4 = 4$, $P = 1$ atm.

Table VI
Activity* of Photoactivated Catalysts
for Monoolefin Hydrogenation

Complex	Homogeneous Catalyst	Heterogeneous Catalyst
$Cr(CO)_6$	$<10^{-5}$ ([19])	0.2
$Fe(CO)_5$	$2x10^{-4}$# ([20])	0.1

* N_f (s^{-1}) at 25 °C.
\# Requires continuous irradiation.

Hydrogenolysis of Ethane. Table VII summarizes those
catalysts which show improved activity compared to a reduced salt.
Both types of catalysts were activated at 400 °C in flowing H_2.
Again, a strong dichotomy is evident. With the exception of Os
(which shows a higher dispersion as a carbonyl derived catalyst),
only catalysts of difficult to reduce metals show improved

Table VII
Enhanced Activity of Carbonyl Derived
Catalysts for the Hydrogenolysis of Ethane

Complex	N_f (s^{-1}) at 350 $^{\circ}$C	(Carbonyl/Traditional*)
$V(CO)_6$	4×10^{-4}	15
$Mo(CO)_6$	7×10^{-2}	1600
$Mn_2(CO)_{10}$	2×10^{-2}	500
$Fe(CO)_5$	4×10^{-3}	31
$Os_3(CO)_{12}$	4×10^{-1}	92
$Co_2(CO)_8$	2×10^{-1}	40
$Ni(CO)_4$	5×10^{-1}	1700

$P = 1$ atm, $H_2/C_2H_6 = 2/1$.
* Salt derived catalyst.

activity. In the case of the Mo catalyst, the $Mo(CO)_6$ was
supported on dehydroxylated alumina since TPDE on a standard
alumina shows that activation at 400 $^{\circ}$C will leave the Mo highly
oxidized. Consistent with this, the activity of such a catalyst
is very similar to that of a traditional Mo catalyst.

There has been much interest in the possible use of carbonyl
cluster complexes to generate discrete ensembles of supported
metal atoms (1,16,21). These materials might be expected to show
unusual activities and selectivities for structure sensitive
reactions. However, it appears unlikely that structural integrity
is maintained at the high temperatures required for many of the
structure sensitive reactions. In this respect, results comparing
Ru carbonyls to a traditional Ru catalyst are illuminating. The
carbonyl derived catalysts are only about 1/20th as active as a
traditional catalyst (all loadings were 0.1% Ru) for the
hydrogenolysis of ethane. It is known that CO and H_2
chemisorption on traditional Ru catalysts generally give very good
agreement for the dispersion of a catalyst, the ratio of
CO(ads)/H(ads) being close to unity. However, $Ru(CO)_5$ and
$Ru_3(CO)_{12}$ gave ratios of 45 and 19, respectively. This suggests
that H_2 chemisorption (which being dissociative requires two
surface bonds) might itself be a structure sensitive reaction,
whereas CO chemisorption is not. Further, it is expected that H_2
chemisorption will be inhibited on very small particles.
(Although both bonds can certainly be to the same metal atom, it
is expected that the multiplicity of sites and surface migration
available on a metal crystallite will facilitate adsorption of H_2.

Consistent with this, H_2-D_2 exchange is usually many orders of magnitude faster on metal surfaces than on molecular complexes of the corresponding metals.) Similarly, since hydrogenolysis is believed to require multiple sites, it is possible that a catalyst containing a higher proportion of very small metal ensembles might be less active. The anomolous CO/H chemisorption ratios for the carbonyl derived catalysts are consistent with this explanation and suggest that this ratio might be an interesting probe of highly dispersed supported metals (22).

Methanation. Table VIII shows those carbonyl catalysts which when activated at 250 °C were found to be more active than a reduced oxide. Again, with the exception of Os the list is limited to the difficult to reduce metals. As in the case of ethylene hydrogenation, after activation at 500 °C in H_2 a mutually exclusive group is formed, consisting mostly of noble metals.

Table VIII
Enhanced Activity of Fresh* Carbonyl Catalysts for Methanation

Complex	N_f (s^{-1})	(Carbonyl/Redox[#])
$V(CO)_6$	5×10^{-1}	8
$Cr(CO)_6$	1×10^{-6}	3
$Mo(CO)_6$	2×10^{-3}	629
$W(CO)_6$	1×10^{-3}	632
$Mn_2(CO)_{10}$	7×10^{-8}	5
$Os_3(CO)_{12}$	6×10^{-5}	12

T = 250 °C, $H_2/CO = 3$, P = 1 atm, loading = 1.5% metal.
* Catalysts activated at 250 °C in flowing He.
# Redox is carbonyl catalyst oxidized and reduced at 500 °C.

Acknowledgement

Support of this research by DOE is gratefully acknowledged.

Literature Cited

1. For recent reviews see Smith, A. K.; Basset, J. M. J. Molec. Catal. 1977, 2, 229 and Brown, T. L. J. Molec. Catal. 1981, 12, 41.
2. Brenner, A. J. Chem. Soc., Chem. Commun. 1979, 251.
3. Brenner, A. J. Molec. Catal. 1979, 5, 157.
4. Brenner, A. "Relations Between Homogeneous and Heterogeneous Catalysis", Centre National Recherche Scientifique, Paris, 1978, p 195.
5. Brenner, A.; Burwell, R. L., Jr. J. Catal. 1978, 52, 364.
6. Smith, J.; Howe, R. F.; Whan, D. A. J. Catal. 1974, 34, 191.
7. Brenner, A.; Hucul, D. A. "Proc. Int. Conf. Chem. Uses Molybdenum, 3rd", Climax Molybdenum Company, Ann Arbor, 1979, p 194.
8. Bowman, R. G.; Burwell, R. L., Jr. J. Catal. 1980, 63, 463.
9. Commereuc, D; Chauvin, Y.; Hughes, F.; Basset, J. M.; Oliver, D. J. Chem. Soc., Chem. Commun. 1980, 154.
10. Brenner, A.; Hucul, D. A.; Hardwick, S. J. Inorg. Chem. 1979, 18, 1478.
11. Brenner, A.; Hucul, D. A. Prepr. Div. Pet. Chem., Am. Chem. Soc. 1977, 22, 1221.
12. Brenner, A.; Hucul, D. A. Inorg. Chem. 1979, 18, 2836.
13. Hucul, D. A.; Brenner, A. J. Phys. Chem. 1981, 85, 496 and references therein.
14. Peri, J. B. J. Phys. Chem. 1965, 69, 211.
15. Sudhakar, C.; Yesodharan, E. P.; Cichowlas, A.; Majer, M.; Brenner, A. Prepr. Div. Pet. Chem., Am. Chem. Soc. 1982, 27, in press.
16. Gates, B. C.; Lieto, J. Chemtech 1980, 10, 248.
17. Brenner, A.; Burwell, R. L., Jr. J. Catal. 1978, 52, 353.
18. Brenner, A.; Hucul, D. A. J. Catal. 1980, 61, 216.
19. Wrighton, M.; Schroeder, M. A. J. Am. Chem. Soc. 1973, 95, 5764.
20 Schroeder, M. A.; Wrighton, M. S. J. Am. Chem. Soc. 1976, 98, 551.
21. Muetterties, E. L.; Rhodin, T. N.; Band, E.; Brucker, C. F. Chem. Rev. 1979, 79, 91.
22. This group is currently exploring the use of CO/H chemisorption ratios, H_2-D_2 exchange rates, and isotopic patterns of ethylene deuterogenation as probes of the nature of supported metals.

RECEIVED November 4, 1981.

Silacrowns, a New Class of Immobilizable Phase Transfer Catalysts

BARRY ARKLES, WILLIAM R. PETERSON, JR., and KEVIN KING

Petrarch Systems Research Laboratories, Bristol, PA 19007

Immobilized phase transfer catalysts can be expected to demonstrate the same advantages as other immobilized catalysts. The reactions are clean, the products are uncontaminated by catalysts, the catalyst is reuseable. The desireable properties of phase transfer catalysts that must be maintained include their ability to facilitate certain organic syntheses, behave as ionophores, solubilize metal salts and act as complexing agents. Polymer bound phase transfer catalysts, both onium salt[1,2,3,4] and crown ether[5,6] have been reported. The polymer bound phase transfer catalysts appear to require two special conditions for optimum product turnover: a relatively long "spacer" group between the polymer and the catalytic center and a swollen polymer substrate. It has been recently reported that the use of silica gel for immobilization of onium salts reduces the importance of "spacer groups" for catalytic activity although they do modify the adsorptive capacity of the silica.[7] Crown ethers have also been recently immobilized on silica.[8,9] The system demonstrates an adsorptive capability for metal ions that may be useful in metal ion chromatography.

All silica immobilized phase transfer catalysts previously reported involve two or more steps for the immobilization. Problems with preparations of this type include the difficulty in obtaining maximum functionality on the substrate and residual substrate bond intermediates which may interfere in final applications. The purpose of this work was to prepare well-characterized functionalized phase transfer catalysts that could be immobilized on siliceous substrates in a single step. As will be shown the preparation of functionalized onium catalysts proceeds readily. The route to facile immobilization of crown ether was not so direct. Avenues for high yield chemistry employing accessible or economic intermediates were not available. A new class of crown ethers which are readily functionalized during synthesis was developed. We have designated them "sila-crowns". This report concentrates upon the properties and characterization of these new phase transfer catalysts.

0097-6156/82/0192-0281 $6.00/0
© 1982 American Chemical Society

Since 1967 when C. Pedersen discovered the class of
compounds known as crown ethers, literally thousands of
applications have been developed in which their ability to
complex metal ions, solvate inorganic and organic salts in
polar and non-polar solvents and facilitate anionic reactions
have been exploited.[10] The compounds are cyclic polyethylene
oxides. Two obstacles have prevented their wider utilization,
particularly in commercial processes. Current synthetic
methods are extremely costly. The materials have generally
high levels of toxicity. Both these factors coupled with the
difficulty in removing the crown ethers by processes other
than distillation have hindered wider applications.

A class of compounds with complexation properties re-
markably similar to the crown ethers, is indicated by the
following general structure $R^1R^2Si(OCH_2CH_2)_n\ddot{O}$. A specific
example is dimethylsila-14-crown-5.

The name indicates the substituents on the silicon, the
number of members in the ring, and the number of oxygens.
This compound may be compared to 15-crown-5. Although there
is one less member in the ring for the silacrown, the longer
silicon-oxygen bonds result in an O-Si-O unit that is 75% of
the length of an $O-CH_2-CH_2-O$ unit. Summation of bond lengths
indicate an overall réduction in macrocyle circumference of
4.5% when compared to 15-crown-5. This simplistic comparison
does not take into account the puckered multidentate structure
the crown ethers assume in cation complexes. Under these
conditions the differences in structure would be expected to
be further mitigated. X-ray structural analysis which would
provide a more definitive basis for comparison has not yet
been performed.

Although cyclic polyethyleneoxysilanes have been previously reported,[11] the ring structures had less members and
the diameters were clearly smaller than lithium ions. Cyclic
siloxanes have been evaluated as complexing agents. The
materials are weak ionophores with stability constants far
lower than crown ethers.[12,13] Efforts to employ the cyclic
siloxanes to facilitate anionic polymerizations analogous to
crown ethers have given negative results.[14] The difference in
reactivity has been attributed to the lower electron density

of the oxygen in siloxanes. Nevertheless, the work may be interpreted to suggest the replacement of a single O-Si-O unit for an O-CH$_2$CH$_2$-O unit in a crown ether would not eliminate its ability to form cation complexes.

Results and Discussion

The silacrowns are readily prepared by transesterification of alkoxysilanes with polyethylene glycols. A typical reaction is

$$R^1R^2Si(OEt)_2 + HO(CH_2CH_2O)_nH \longrightarrow$$

$$R^1R^2\overline{Si(OCH_2CH_2)_n}O + 2EtOH$$

The conditions of transesterification must be selected to promote cyclization in preference to polymerization. The reaction may be catalyzed by a variety of materials, including methylsulfonic acid, toluenesulfonic acid and sodium, but titanates were generally preferred. A wide range of organic groups (R^{1}R^2) can be readily substituted to alter the solubility, phase partition and reactivity of the silacrowns. The reactants are combined and approximately 80-95% of the alcohol is slowly distilled from the reaction mixture. If the silacrown being prepared contains a moiety which does not have great thermal stability, such as a vinyl group, it is useful to add a higher boiling solvent such as toluene. The product is removed from the reaction mixture by distillation. It appears that there is some molecular rearrangement during the course of distillation in the presence of transesterification catalysts that results in the preferential removal of the more volatile silacrowns from the reaction mixture. The direct interaction of chloro, amino, and acyloxsilanes with polyethylene glycols can also lead to the desired products but in significantly lower yield. The silacrowns are generally colorless, odorless, liquids of moderate viscosity. Sila-14-crown-5, sila-17-crown-6 and sila-20-crown-7 structures have been prepared. Substituents on the silicon include methyl, vinyl, phenyl and methoxy groups. The compounds are tabulated below:

Compound	M.W.	b.p.
dimethylsila-8-crown-3*	162.3	90°/50
dimethylsila-11-crown-4*	206.3	96°/9
dimethylsila-14-crown-5	250.4	125-130°/0.5
dimethylsila-17-crown-6	294.4	168-170°/0.3
dimethylsila-20-crown-7	338.5	240-244°/0.2
vinylmethylsila-14-crown-5	252.4	129-131°/0.5
vinylmethylsila-17-crown-6	306.4	169-172°/0.3
methoxymethylsila-17-crown-6	310.4	170-173°/0.3
phenylmethylsila-14-crown-5	312.5	180-185°/0.1-0.15

*reported in reference 11

Stability and metal ion salt solubilities of the sila-crowns have not been quantitatively evaluated. The sila-17-crown-6 materials offer simple qualitative evidence of complex formation. Potassium permanganate is mixed with chlorobenzene. The salt rapidly settles and no coloration of the chlorobenzene is observed. The addition of 1-2% of the silacrown produces the characteristic deep purple color of solvated potassium permanganate. After 1 hour vinylsilacrown solutions turn brown and a fine percipitate is observed, presumbly due to silacrown promoted oxidation of its own vinyl group.

The phase transfer catalytic properties of the silacrowns were investigated in a number of systems.

The substitution reaction of cyanide with benzyl bromide (Table 1) was evaluated with and without silacrown promoted catalysis and compared with 18-crown-6 and decamethylcyclopentasiloxane (D_5). Reaction conditions and times were not optimized. The catalytic activity of the sila-17-crown-6 appeared to be equivalent to 18-crown-6. Dodecamethylcyclopentasiloxane did not demonstrate catalytic activity. The specificity of the sila-14-crown-5 for sodium ions and not potassium ions provides evidence for complex formation analogous to the crown ethers.

In order to survey anion activation, substitution reactions of halogens, pseudohalogens and organic anions were evaluated under mild conditions. The majority of the reactions were run by simply mixing a twice molar excess of the salt with the substrate in acetonitrile containing 0.1-0.2M silacrown and agitating overnight. Displacements by cyanide acetate and iodide proceed smoothly. Higher temperatures are required for fluoride. The results are summarized in Table II.

The solid/liquid phase transfer analysis of potassium cyanide in a series of substitution reactions are indicated in Table III. Again, the reactivity of the silacrowns appear comparable to crown ethers.

The first silacrowns prepared for immobilization contained vinyl functionality. Attempts were made to introduce support reactivity by hydrosilylating the compounds with trichlorosilane and methyldimethoxysilane. Although the hydrosilylations proceed smoothly, within 1-15 minuties the materials underwent rapid secondary reactions to form glassy solids or viscous liquids.

Silacrowns which may be readily immobilized on siliceous supports are the methoxysilacrowns. Like other members of the series the compounds are prepared by transesterification. In this case the starting materials are trimethoxysilanes. The methoxysilacrowns behave similarly to the other silacrowns in solid/liquid phase transfer catalysis. The catalytic properties of these compounds were translated to solid supports by

TABLE I

REACTIONS OF MCN WITH BENZYL BROMIDE

CONDITIONS	REACTANTS	CATALYST	TIME	YIELD
Solid/Liquid	KCN	---	4	0%
Solid/Liquid	KCN	---	48	54%
Solid/Liquid	NaCN	---	4	0%
Liquid/Liquid	KCN	17-6	16	100%
Liquid/Liquid	KCN	17-6	16	100%
Solid/Liquid	KCN	18-6*	6	100%
Solid/Liquid	KCN	D_5**	16	20%
Solid/Liquid	NaCN	14-5	16	100%
Solid/Liquid	KCN	14-5	4	3%

Reactions at room temperature in acetonitrile

*Literature Values[10]

**Decamethylcyclopentasiloxane

TABLE II

SILA-17-CROWN-6 CATALYZED

REACTIONS OF BENZYL BROMIDE + KX

REACTANT	PRODUCT	YIELD
KCN	Benzyl Cyanide	100%
KOAc	Benzyl Acetate	100%
KF	Benzyl Fluoride	5%
KF	Benzyl Flouride at reflux 48 hours	55%

Reaction after 16 hours at ambient temperature in acetonitrile with 0.13M silacrown

TABLE III

SILACROWN SOLID/LIQUID PHASE TRANSFER

CATALYSIS OF POTASSIUM CYANIDE SUBSTITUTIONS

REACTANT	CATALYST	TIME	YIELD
Octyl Bromide	17-6	48	63%
Hexyl Bromide	18-6*	40 at reflux	100%
Benzyl Bromide	17-6	16	100%
Benzyl Chloride	17-6	16	100%
Allyl Bromide	14-5	16	0%
Benzyl Chloride	---	48	29%
Benzyl Chloride	---*	75	25%
Benzyl Chloride	18-6*	1	99%
Allyl Bromide	17-6	16	74%**
Allyl Bromide	---	16	0%

Reactions at room temperature in acetonitrile

* Literature Value[10]

** mixtures of allyl cyanide and crotononitrile

incorporating them into a refluxing mixture of toluene and controlled pore glass. The immobilized silacrown may be depicted:

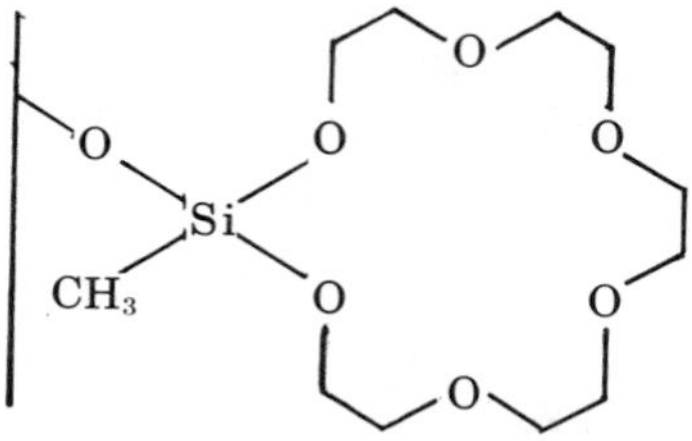

The immobilized silacrown was added to a two phase mixture containing concentrated aqueous potassium cyanide and substrate dissolved in acetonitrile. The mixture was stirred at 600-1000 rpm. Results are shown in Table IV. The immobilized silacrown catalyzed cyanide displacement reactions in the three cases. The conversion of benzyl chloride to benzyl cyanide proceeded to 100% conversion, similar to the soluble silacrown. The conversion of benzyl chloride to benzyl cyanide proceeded further than the soluble silacrown. There is insufficient data to determine whether this is a general phenomenon. It has been pointed out by other workers[7] that silica provides an adsorptive surface that can provide assistance in phase transfer. The reaction of potassium cyanide with allyl bromide under liquid/liquid phase transfer conditions produced a mixture of allyl cyanide and crotononitrile. This may be compared to the cataysis exhibited by another new phase transfer catalyst, immobilized trimethoxysilyloctyltributylammonium bromide, which produced only allyl cyanide.

While this initial report clearly indicates the phase transfer catalytic properties of the silacrowns in both soluble and immobilized forms, much information is required to define their catalytic parameters and synthetic limitations. Current information regarding optimum concentrations, temperatures and times for conversions, determination of stability constants and structural conformation is incomplete. Long term hydrolytic stability in particular, under basic conditions may be a serious limiting factor.

Experimental

Silane intermediates were obtained from Petrarch Systems Fine Chemicals Division. Pentaethyleneglycol was obtained from Fairfield. Porous glass was obtained from Electronucleonics.

Vinylmethylsila-14-Crown-5. A 250ml single neck flask equipped with a magnetic stirrer and heating mantle was charged with 0.5mole (93ml) of vinylmethyldiethoxysilane, 0.5mole(86ml) of tetraethylene glycol and 0.5ml of tetrabutyltitanate. The

TABLE IV

IMMOBILIZED PHASE TRANSFER CATALYST
PROMOTED CYANIDE SUBSTITUTION

CATALYST	REACTANT	TIME	PRODUCT	YIELD
Ⓢ $- (CH_2)_8 N^+ Bu_3 Br^-$	allyl bromide(55%)	16	allyl cyanide	45%
Ⓢ- sila-17-6	allyl bromide(0%)	16	allyl cyanide crotononitrile	45% 55%
Ⓢ -sila-17-6	benzyl bromide(0%)	25	benzyl cyanide	100%
Ⓢ -sila-17-6	benzyl chloride(3%)	16	benzyl cyanide	97%

Ⓢ - indicates support bound

mixture was stirred at 50-60° for 16 hours with a cold finger distillation head in place. The pot temperature was increased to 85-100° and about 50ml of ethanol was removed. The mixture was then distilled under vacuum. The fraction boiling at 129-131° at 0.5mm was collected. Approximately 62g of vinylmethyl-sila-14-crown-5 was isolated. The compound was identified by infrared and organic mass spectroscopy. As expected the compound did not exhibit a molecular ion, but exhibited $(M-CH_3)+$ at 247 and $(M-CH=CH_2)+$ at 235.

Vinylmethylsila-17-Crown-6. Under the same conditions described above 37.4ml of vinylmethyldiethoxysilane, 46.6g of pentaethylene glycol, 0.2ml of tetraisopropyltitanate and 25ml of toluene were charged into a 250ml flask. Approximately 20ml of ethanol was removed at atmospheric pressure. The product fraction was collected at 169-172° at 0.3mm. The yield was 36g. The analysis was performed as above.

Dimethylsila-17-Crown-6 and Dimethylsila-20-Crown-7. Under conditions similar to those described in example 1 148.3g of dimethyldimethoxysilane was combined with 300g of a mixture of polyethyleneglycols with an average molecular weight of 300. 230g of dimethylsila-17-crown-6, b.p. 169-170° at 0.3mm and 45g of dimethylsila-20-crown-7, b.p., 240-244° at 0.2mm were obtained.

The remaining silacrowns were prepared similarly.

Immobilization of Methoxymethylsila-17-Crown-6

Controlled pore glass (80-120mesh, 226A, $99m^2/g$) was treated with 10-15% HCl overnight to induce silanol formation, washed with water and dried free of bulk water. A single neck flash was charged with 50ml of a 2% solution of methoxymethyl-sila-17-crown-6 and 10g of porous glass. The mixture was re-fluxed overnight. The treated beads were washed with toluene and dried.

8-Bromooctyltrimethoxysilane. A 3 neck 1 liter flask equipped with magnetic stirrer, addition funnel and condensor was charged with 400ml of trimethylorthoformate and warmed to 30-35°. Over the course of three hours 327g of 8-bromooctyl-trichlorosilane was added. The mixture was distilled. The fraction boiling at 127-130°/2mm was identified as 8-bromooctyl-trimethoxysilane, 93% yield.

N-(8-trimethoxysilyloctyl)tributylammonium Bromide. Bromo-octyl trimethoxysilane, 31.3g(53.1ml) of methanol and 23.8ml of tributylamine were combined in a 250ml single neck flask and refluxed for 16 hours. The product was retained in 50% methanol solution.

Immobilized N(8-trimethoxysilyloctyl)tributylammonium
Bromide. 50mls of a 5% solution of the name compound was placed
in a 150ml beaker. The solution was warmed to 35° and 10g of
the pretreated porous glass described above was added. The
mixture was stirred manually. The supernatant was decanted.
The porous glass was washed twice with methanol and dried overnight at 50-60°.

Solid/Liquid Phase Transfer Experiments

The general procedure for the experiments was to combine
0.05M of organic reactant with 0.10M of inorganic reactant
(neat or saturated aqueous solution), 25ml of acetonitrile and
1ml of silacrown. For comparative purposes control and
literature examples of 18-crown-6 are reported. Unless otherwise noted the reactions were run at ambient temperature.
Product conversion was determined by gas chromatography.

Liquid/Liquid Phase Transfer Experiments

A concentrated aqueous solution of potassium cyanide was
prepared containing 1g of KCN in 2ml of solution. 0.05M of
organic reactant was combined with 0.1M of aqueous KCN and 2g
of silacrown treated porous glass. The reaction mixtures
were stirred at 600-1000 rpm with a magnetic stirrer. Product
conversion was determined by gas chromatography.

Conclusions

A new class of compounds, macrocyclic polyethylenoxysilanes,
called silacrowns have been prepared which demonstrate phase
transfer catalytic properties. An alkoxy functional silacrown
has been immobilized in a single-step reaction on a siliceous
support. The immobilized silacrown also demonstrates phase
transfer catalytic properties. A functionalized onium phase
transfer catalyst was also prepared that reacts directly with
a siliceous support and is catalytically active.

LITERATURE CITED

1. S. L. Regen, J. Am. Chem. Soc. 97, 5695 (1975)
2. S. L. Regen, J. Am. Chem. Soc. 98, 6720 (1976)
3. S. L. Regen, J. Org. Chem. 42, 875 (1977)
4. M. Tomoi, W. Ford, J. Am. Chem. Soc. 103, 3821 and 3829 (1981)
5. M. Cinquini, S. Collons, H. Molinari, F. Montanari and F. Tundo, J. Chem. Soc. Commun. 394, (1976)
6. M. Tomoi, O. Abe, M. Ikeda, K. Kihara, H. Kakiuchi, Tetraedron Lett., 3031 (1978)
7. P. Tundo, P. Ventarello, J. Am. Chem. Soc., 101, 5505 (1979)
8. T. Waddell, D. Leyden, D. Hercules in "Silylated Surfaces" ed. by D. Leyden and W. Collins, Gordon and Breach, N.Y. (1980)
9. T. Waddell, D. Leyden, J. Org. Chem. 46, 2105 (1981)
10. R. Izatt, J. Christensen "Synthetic Multidentate Macrocylic Compounds" Academic Press, N.Y. (1978)
11. R. Krieble, C. Burkhard, J. Am. Chem. Soc. 69, 2689 (1947)
12. C. D. Olliff, G. Pickering, K. Rutt, J. Inorg. Nucl. Chem. 42, 288 (1980)
13. C. Olliff, G. Pickering, K. Rutt, J. Inorg. Nucl. Chem. 42, 1201 (1980)
14. Yu Yuzhelevskii, V. Pchelintsev, N. Fedoseeva, Vysokomol Soedin Ser. B 18(II) 873, (1975) Chem. Ab. 86: 73181v

RECEIVED November 17, 1981.

INDEX

INDEX

Jacket design by Martha Sewall.
Production by Deborah Corson.

Elements typeset by Service Composition Co., Baltimore, MD.
Printed and bound by The Maple Press Co., York, PA.